LINEAR PROGRAMMING: AN EMPHASIS ON DECISION MAKING

ANN J. HUGHES
DENNIS E. GRAWIOG
Georgia State University

ADDISON-WESLEY PUBLISHING COMPANY

Reading, Massachusetts
Menlo Park, California · London · Don Mills, Ontario

PREFACE

Linear Programming: An Emphasis on Decision Making is designed to give the student an intuitive, yet in-depth, comprehension of linear programming. More specifically, the goals of the book are:

1. To provide the student with an understanding of the linear programming model—what it is, where it can be applied, how and why it works, and what information can be gained from the use of the model;

2. To illustrate the breadth of possible model interpretation and, thereby, move the student far beyond the basic "make 12 of these and 18 of those" stage; and

3. To establish a framework for an objective problem-analysis and a realistic appreciation of the role that the model may fulfill in the decision process.

   authors believe their book is unique; we are no exception. We feel that th   sentation of linear programming is new and distinctive in various ways. No ook in the field, to our knowledge, incorporates an intuitive approach to the simplex methodology.   Few books, and particularly those that are practical rather than theoretical in orientation, emphasize sensitivity analysis and other aspects of model interpretation to the extent that this book does.   Everyday problems which are encountered in building a model—such as costing, developing constraint parameters, and coming to grips with multiple objectives—are unique points of emphasis. The book not only makes use of a wide variety of basic problems but it also contains an entire section of situational problems.   It extends the topical coverage of most introductory linear programming texts to include both goal programming and integer programming.

   (Although little mention is made of electronic computers in the text itself, the teacher should make full use of whatever computer facilities are at his disposal, and dwell not on the mechanics of tableau manipulation but on the logical aspects of model development and use.)

Actually, we have chosen linear programming as the subject matter of our text not solely because its usefulness has been proved in myriad decision-making environments but because we believe that it is an excellent vehicle for teaching the broad concepts of modeling. We hope that the reader will see that linear programming illustrates not only the power of mathematical models (for it is— without doubt—a powerful model) but their frailty as well; that he will visualize model-building as an art rather than a science; and that he will always see decision making as extending far beyond the mere mathematical manipulation of a model.

Atlanta, Georgia   A.J.H.
March 1973   D.E.G.

ACKNOWLEDGMENTS

It is our pleasure to acknowledge that many people have contributed, directly and indirectly, to this book. We are grateful for all of the encouragement, and criticisms, we have received. We are especially indebted to our students, who over the years have suffered through its development and who have made many invaluable suggestions and comments.

CONTENTS

CHAPTER 3   A GRAPHICAL-LOGICAL APPROACH TO A SOLUTION

CHAPTER 4   A MATHEMATICAL APPROACH
TO THE LINEAR PROGRAMMING PROBLEM

CHAPTER 7   BUILDING A LINEAR PROGRAMMING MODEL

CHAPTER 8   CASETTES FOR DISCUSSION

CHAPTER 9   THE GREATER-THAN-OR-EQUAL-TO AND THE EXACTLY-EQUAL-TO CONSTRAINTS

CHAPTER 10   THE GREATER-THAN CONSTRAINTS: INTERPRETING THE FINAL TABLEAU

CHAPTER 11   THE MATTER OF MINIMIZATION

CHAPTER 12 THE BLENDING PROBLEMS

CHAPTER 13 SOME TECHNICAL VICISSITUDES OF THE MODEL

CHAPTER 14 NONLINEAR OBJECTIVE FUNCTIONS

IRA
5-13
GREECE

Chapter 1

THE LINEAR PROGRAMMING MODEL AS A DECISION-MAKING TOOL

Self-styled sages often sound the ominous warning that there are certain things in life one cannot avoid. Quipsters occasionally add to the list. We would like to offer our own addendum—and that is *decision-making*. It is an inevitable and almost perpetual task.

Each morning you decide to arise at 6.30 a.m. or 7.00 a.m., or not until noon. You decide to wear the red-striped tie with the green-and-orange shirt or the blue-and-yellow scarf with the lavender sweater. You decide that you would rather have cold cereal for breakfast than bacon and eggs. You decide whether you should drive into town or take a bus. If you drive, you must decide whether or not to take the freeway. And so on, throughout the day.

If you are a student, you decide to attend your 9 o'clock class or to spend that hour in the students' lounge. You decide to prepare, or not to prepare, your assignment before going to class.

If you are a businessman, you may make decisions about placing an order with a particular supplier, making a sales call on a certain customer, hiring an applicant for the secretarial position, talking to the banker about a loan, or opening a new branch office in the suburbs.

Each day is replete with situations which require that we choose among alternative courses of action, each course of action having its own advantages and disadvantages. Sometimes we make a choice only after long, agonizing hours of deliberation; sometimes we make the decision almost subconsciously. Too often, we try to avoid a decision by doing nothing; but this in itself is a decision.

Some of us are better "decision makers" than others. Some are luckier; some are blessed with sounder judgment; some are better informed. In the decision sciences, we don't promise to be able to do a great deal about your luck. We feel a little more encouraged about improvement in the quality of your judgment. We feel certain that you can become a better-informed decision maker.

We cannot, in this text, endeavor to explore the vast panorama of decision making or problem solving *per se*. We must, instead, focus our attention on one special type of problem situation and on a logical approach to decision making in this type of situation. Our approach to a problem solution will be via a mathematical model. The necessity for making a decision arises because we are faced with alternative courses of action. The criterion for selecting one possible course of action rather than another is the outcome or the result of that choice. The practicalities of the real world preclude the decision maker from experimenting on most real-world phenomena to determine what these outcomes might be. However, the decision maker may be able to construct a "model" which depicts the system to such an extent that it can provide the results of proposed actions.

There are many kinds of models, of course. We shall discuss only the mathematical model. We shall, in fact, restrict our discussion to only one type of mathematical model—*the linear programming model*. Nonetheless, we must stress that, even with the use of mathematical models, the logical approach to problem solving is more important than the mechanical manipulation of any model.

AN APPROACH TO
PROBLEM SOLVING THROUGH
THE USE OF MATHEMATICAL MODELS

Although they are interrelated, and not infrequently overlapping, there are "steps" in the logical approach to a problem solution. An obvious, yet often elusive, first step is the identification of the problem.

Problem identification is, more often than not, a two-stage process. It begins with the recognition that a potential problem exists and ends only when the immediate problem is recognized. Actually we seldom work in an environment plagued by only one problem so that, being realistic, we don't isolate THE problem but, instead, we decide on which of the many problems we should concentrate.

A logical approach to achieving a solution to the problem would be to proceed along these lines.

1. *Obtain an overview of the problem environment.* Attempt to assimilate as much relevant information as is feasible. There will be an unending array of facts concerning any empirical situation. Consider, for example, the question of pricing a product. We would want information on the nature of the product, the nature of the market in which it will sell, the nature of the demand for the product, the cost of producing and distributing the product, the legal environment in which we must operate, and so on and on. The human mind simply could not consider all the aspects of most problem situations. So we must develop a facility for searching out those things that are most critical and ignoring the tedium of less critical or even unessential facts. The problem solver must be able to see "the big picture" without becoming lost in its bewildering complexity.

2. *Determine what the goals and objectives are insofar as this decision situation is concerned.* What is the decision maker trying to achieve? Would you believe

that the answer to this query is never as obvious as it might, at first, appear to be? Think of all the possible objectives of a firm in the product-pricing situation: market penetration; "skimming" the market (that is, attracting as many buyers as possible at a high price and gradually lowering the price to attract other segments of the market); build an image as a prestige item; satisfactory rate of return on capital investment; generate cash as quickly as possible. We are often faced with more than one goal, and these may be conflicting goals. Some goals seem to be easy to formalize and express in quantitative terms; some are much more elusive; some may simply not be directly quantifiable. The problem solver must overcome the difficulties of defining and measuring his goals.

3. *Isolate the variables relevant to achievement of the objective.* The problem solver must be able to abstract from the situation those factors most pertinent to the attainment of the goal. He must determine which of these factors are controllable and which are not. The alternative plans of action, or strategies as they are often called, are thereby isolated. These become the variables of the model.

4. *Develop the functional relationships that will relate the variables to the goal.* The construction of the model is now well under way. The model is a simplified representation of the empirical situation; it provides a vehicle for a well-structured view of the problem.

Many decision situations are so similar in basic nature that *general* mathematical models have been developed which can be applied to a wide variety of specific cases. Within this group of general models we find linear programming. If one of these general model types can be molded to fit the case under study, the analyst can concentrate on the determination of the appropriate data input into the system. He must systematically consider the variables in the situation and the relationships among them. He has to determine the restrictions or constraints that are imposed on the variables. He must measure the contribution of each variable to the overall goal.

Model building forces the problem solver to formalize his thinking. It forces him to move from a vague conceptual understanding to a concrete statement of the case. Herein may lie both the greatest advantage, and disadvantage, of mathematical models.

5. *Manipulate the model to obtain numerical results.* The model serves as the decision-science counterpart to the laboratory experiment of the physical sciences. The decision maker cannot manipulate the real world to see what would be the result of following alternative courses of action; he, instead, manipulates his mathematical concept of the real-world situation. Given the mathematical model, he calculates a numerical solution to the problem outlined. When the model is a complex one, the manipulation of the numbers may be handled by a high-speed computer. This manipulation attaches solution values

to the variables the model builder deemed relevant to goal achievement and points out that strategy which is optimal.

6. *Interpret the results which the model has provided.* No output from a mathematical model exists apart from the need for interpretation. The interpretation must be in terms of both the broad environment in which the decision maker must operate and the special assumptions and simplifications involved in the construction of this specific model. Mathematical models must always be used as an aid to good judgment, and never as a substitute for it.

PROBLEM SITUATIONS TO WHICH LINEAR PROGRAMMING METHODS APPLY

The linear programming model provides an efficient mathematical method of determining an optimal strategy when there are numerous alternative strategies which might be followed in seeking a certain objective and the picture is clouded by the fact that the various courses of action are interrelated by numerous restrictions and constraints.

While the type of problem amenable to solution by the linear programming technique is closely defined, the number and diversity of problem situations falling within this definition is most impressive. We find that the linear programming model has been applied to a wide variety of problem situations, ranging from product-mix decisions, to media selection in advertising, to allocation of department store space among different departments and products, to petroleum blending in refineries, to portfolio selection, and so on and on, almost *ad infinitum*.

A few, deliberately simplified, illustrations of cases where linear programming might be used are outlined below.

A Product-Mix Problem

A manufacturer of furniture specializes in the production of Parsons tables and Deacons benches. These items differ in their utilization of production resources. Their selling prices differ, as well, but not in direct proportion to their resource-usage rates. The production resources available for use in the manufacture of these items are limited in quantity. The firm would like to know how many units each of tables and benches should be scheduled for production each day in order to maximize profits.

In addition, the manufacturer would like information on such questions as: How much should the firm be willing to pay for an "extra" unit (a unit over and above the supply originally thought available for use) of each of the scarce resources? If an extra unit of a scarce resource were to be made available for use in this process, how should that unit be used? What changes should be made in the production strategy if the supply of a scarce resource were to decrease?

A Cost-Minimization Problem

A mill mixes feed for farm animals, using two different types of grain as the primary ingredients. These grains are mixed together in various proportions to produce a feed that meets certain nutritional requirements.

Each grain contains different quantities of the required nutrients. Each grain differs, too, in its cost to the mix. Given that orders for feed mix are received specifying minimum nutritional requirements, the mill wishes to choose that combination of grains that will keep the cost of the mix as low as possible. But the firm is also vitally interested in the effect on total cost of increasing the nutritional value of the feed by exceeding the basic minimum requirements since such a move would provide important advertising propaganda.

A Blending Problem

A manufacturer of candy markets two mixes of chocolate-covered candies. While the composition of the two mixes may vary to some extent, there are standards which each pound of each of the mixes must meet. For example, the company warrants that the Deluxe Mix will not contain less than a certain minimum proportion of chocolate-covered raisins and not more than a certain maximum proportion of chocolate-covered peanuts.

Given the available quantities of ingredients and their respective prices, in what proportions should they be blended to produce candy mixes which meet the specifications and still yield the greatest possible gross profit? Also, although the costs of the ingredients have remained fairly constant, the company suspects that a cost increase is imminent and would like to know what effect an increase would have on the optimal product mix.

An Advertising-Budget Problem

A company has a fixed advertising budget for the coming year. It would like to allocate this money among the various media in such a way that certain conditions are met. These conditions include such factors as the total number of potential customers to be reached, the number of housewives, the number of persons within given age brackets, the number of persons with a college degree, and so on. Each of the different media offers different reach characteristics and each has different costs. How should the company allocate its advertising budget? In addition, a few of the reach criteria are rather arbitrary and the merchandising director would like to know the cost imputed to each.

A Machine-Assignment Problem

A factory has several machines capable of performing the same processing work; however, because of different machine efficiencies, the per unit costs are different. Thus, the cost of processing any order depends in part on the particular machine to which it is assigned. Limited capacity precludes the assignment of all orders to the lowest-cost machine. How should the firm assign a series of orders to the various machines so as to minimize total production cost?

These examples certainly do not exhaust the range of possible applications; they, in fact, hardly do justice to the versatility of the linear programming model.

UNDERLYING PROPERTIES OF A LINEAR PROGRAMMING SITUATION

The linear programming model, like all other mathematical models, is only a decision-making tool. It has its appropriate uses. It should not be used indiscriminately. One key to the successful use of any model is the ability to recognize when a problem situation is structured so that the technique can be utilized and then to formulate the mathematically correct statements of the situation.

Because the model has found such a diversity of uses, we find that it is not always easy to draw a sharp demarcation line between those situations adaptable to linear programming and those that are not. However, in order for the model to be used effectively, there are several basic requirements that must be satisfied by the problem and the problem environment. These essential elements of a linear programming situation are as follows.

1. There must be *alternative courses of action.* Unless there are various strategies which might be followed and among which a choice must then be made, there is no problem to analyze, no decision to be made. This means that there are two or more controllable variables that must be handled simultaneously. The variables may be items to produce, dollars to invest, space to allocate, and so on, depending on the particular problem. In the furniture manufacturing company case, the alternative courses of action are the various possible combinations of tables and benches that might be manufactured. In the advertising-budget case, the alternative courses of action are the dollar amounts allocated to each of the several advertising media.

2. The alternative courses of action, or the variables of the model, must be interrelated through some type of *restriction.* Used in this context, a "restriction" denotes anything that defines the feasibility of a proposed course of action. Probably for most planning problems there are real restrictions which limit the kinds of plans which can be considered. Often these restrictions appear in the form of resources in limited supply: limited production-machinery capacity, limited labor supply, limited working capital, or limited floor space. There can also be other types of restrictions: a contractual requirement for the production of a specified quantity of an item, a marketing quota which must be met, a

minimum liquidity requirement, a minimum or maximum allocation of resources to specified usage, and the like.

Thus in the furniture manufacturing example, the choice among the various production quantities of tables and benches is restricted by the limited production facilities. The interactions arise from the fact that both products use the same production facilities and these facilities are in restricted supply. To manufacture a stated number of tables then means that there are fewer resources available for use in the production of benches. The products, in a sense, compete for the available scarce resources.

In the candy-blending problem, the choice among the ingredients is restricted to the extent that certain ingredients must be provided in specified proportions to meet mix standards. In the advertising-budget problem, the media selection is influenced by the fact that the firm has outlined characteristics which its audience must possess.

3. There must be an *objective* involved and this objective must be explicitly stated before the model can be built. That is, there must exist a clear-cut criterion by which the relative merits of each of the alternative courses of action may be evaluated. The strategy we choose to follow must not only be feasible, but it should also be optimal in terms of this objective. This optimality is epitomized by a maxima or minima in the objective function of the model. The objective is often to "maximize profit" or to "minimize cost," but it may be many other things as well.

4. The variables in the problem must be linearly related, both in terms of resource usage and objective contribution. Although it might seem to be so obvious that it is unworthy of mention, one last requirement of a linear programming problem is that it must be stated in terms of numbers. The objective must be refined to the point where it can be quantified, as must the restrictions among the variables. Furthermore, the model requires that both the objective and the constraints which limit the achievement of the objective be stated in the form of *linear equations or inequations.*

QUESTIONS FOR DISCUSSION

1. What is a model? What is a decision? Why do we study modeling when attempting to learn about decision-making?

2. What is "a logical approach to problem-solving?"

3. What are the properties of a linear programming model?

4. The statement was made in this chapter that the objective of a linear programming model is often to "maximize profit or minimize cost but may be other things as well." Can you think of other terminology by which some objective might be identified? In the real world is the final outcome of any economic activity always measurable in maximization of profit or minimization of cost? Does it appear to you that linear programming is

appropriate to abstractions such as are encountered in welfare economics where the goal is, perhaps, to maximize consumer satisfaction or measure the public benefits to be derived from some resource allocation? How would the objective function be expressed in such an application?

5. For each of the following situations discuss whether or not the linear programming model would be a useful decision-making tool. If the model would be useful, identify (in general terms) the variables, the objective, and the constraints. If the model could not be appropriately used, discuss the properties of the problem situation that negate its use.

a) An industrial engineer must allocate space in a proposed manufacturing plant among production uses, service uses, and storage and handling uses. There are construction and maintenance cost constraints which vary between use categories, as well as minimum area requirements for each different usage. The engineer has estimates of the profit contributions of each use category and he wishes to maximize the profit contribution of the new plant.

b) A pharmaceutical firm plans to manufacture and market a new patent medicine. The formula calls for six ingredients, all of which must be included in the mixture in various proportions. Because of advertising claims, Ingredient C must be at least 6% of the total volume, but, because of governmental regulations, must not be more than 10% of total volume. Both Ingredients A and B must be at least 10% of the total volume and the proportion of A cannot be more than the proportion of B. Inert Ingredients D, E, and F must be not more than 65% of the total volume. Each ingredient has its own price and is available in rather limited quantities. Sales are not expected to exceed 300,000 bottles of the mixture at $1.29 a bottle.

c) The Softa Sofa Company makes sleeper sofas at two locations and sells them from three large metropolitan discount warehouses. Sales at Warehouses A, B, and C are expected to be 1200, 1600, and 1000 units, respectively. Production capacity at Plant 1 is 2000 units and at Plant 2 is 2500 units. Production costs at Plant 1 are $127 per unit and at Plant 2 are $131 per unit. Distribution costs from Plant 1 to Warehouses A, B, and C are $6, $12, and $10 per unit transported. Distribution costs from Plant 2 to Warehouses A, B, and C are $4, $5, and $7 per unit. The company would like to know what number of sofas to manufacture at each plant for distribution to each warehouse.

d) An electric utility must string a certain number of miles of new power line during the next year. Either copper or aluminium wire can be used. The line must be of a rated capacity and, for this capacity, a larger gauge aluminum is required than of copper. The cost of aluminum, however, is less than that of copper. Since the aluminum is of a larger and heavier gauge, it requires a greater number of man-hours for rigging as well as slightly more expensive supports. Long-term contracts with suppliers specify a minimum number of feet of each type of wire to be purchased in the next year. The total amount of funds available for wire and supports and the total man-hours of rigging labor are all limited in supply.

e) In deciding among several possible projects for the coming year, a company must consider the existence of risk as well as expected return. The projects with the highest return also can be expected to have the highest risk. Conversely, the lowest risk projects have the lowest returns. In order to diversify the risk of a combination of projects, it is necessary to maintain a given minimum level of low-risk projects, and a certain maximum level of high-risk projects. The company wishes to maximize the return from the projects relative to the risk constraints imposed by management.

f) A textile plant fills orders for cloth wholesalers. The plant manufactures rolls of cloth in varying widths. The wholesalers may order the cloth in many more variations of lengths and widths than exist in the plant's stock of cloth rolls. There is the problem, then, of filling the orders with as little trimming loss as possible.

g) A comptroller of a large conglomerate corporation is trying to decide how much of his accounting function to place on the company's newly installed computer. He knows how much clerical help costs, and how much computer time costs; however, his budgetary limitations prohibit him from full computer utilization. Each part of the accounting function that he puts on the computer saves him a certain amount of "turn-around" time for financial statement preparation. Assuming that a faster turn-around time is a cost saving in itself, what parts of the accounting function should be computerized?

Chapter 2

AN ILLUSTRATIVE LINEAR PROGRAMMING PROBLEM

Let us begin our study of linear programming by considering a very simple problem situation.

THE SAMPLE PROBLEM

Let us consider a manufacturer who must determine what combination of products to make and sell. Furniture Manufacturing Company produces Parsons tables and Deacons benches. The company realizes a profit contribution* of $20 on each table and $24 on each bench. Because of the strong demand for these items, the company believes that it can sell, at the prevailing prices, all the tables and benches it can produce.

TABLE 2–1 *Resources of Furniture Manufacturing Company*

Product	Profit contribution of product (per unit)	Hours required to process each item	
		In Assembly Department	In Finishing Department
Parsons table	$20	3	4
Deacons bench	$24	6	2
Hours available in each department each day		60	32

The firm's production capacity, however, is limited in two respects. These two products share certain production facilities which must be considered to be

---

* Profit contribution is defined as net selling price minus variable manufacturing cost.

scarce resources. Each item must be processed in both the Assembly Department and the Finishing Department. Each table requires three hours of processing in the Assembly Department and four hours in the Finishing Department. Each bench requires six hours in the Assembly Department and two hours in the Finishing Department. At the present time, the Assembly Department can handle no more than 60 hours of work each day. The Finishing Department can handle only up to 32 hours of work daily. Thus, in selecting the best combination of products to manufacture, the firm must allocate the limited resources of each of these departments in a way that will best achieve its objective.

RESTATING THE PROBLEM IN MATHEMATICAL TERMS

The logical approach to problem solving begins with an overview of the problem situation. Let us review the important facts characterizing this situation. We are concerned with a firm that manufacturers two products—Parsons tables and Deacons benches. It has been determined that there is a profit contribution of $20 associated with each table and $24 with each bench that is manufactured and sold. The demand for these products is such that the company can easily sell all the items that it can produce.

Two scarce resources—(1) time available in the Assembly Department and (2) time available in the Finishing Department—are used in the production of each of these items. Only limited amounts of these resources are available each day. The basic question is how these scarce resources can best be allocated to the manufacture of these products. If the resources are used primarily for making tables, the number of benches that can be made will be severely limited. On the other hand, if the assembly time and the finishing time are used primarily for the production of benches, few tables can be produced.

Isolating the Objective

Before mapping any plans for action, we should determine what it is that the firm hopes to accomplish; we should turn our attention to the objective toward which the decision maker is striving. What is it that Furniture Manufacturing Company wishes to accomplish? Although there are many possible goals, let us assume, in this case, that the goal of the firm is to maximize the total profit contribution on the tables and benches produced.

Identifying the Variables

In order to develop a mathematical model of the problem situation, we must identify those variables which affect the achievement of this objective. Let us note that there is seldom one "correct" set of variables for a problem; there is only an "appropriate" set. There are usually many ways to approach a problem and each different approach might entail a different set of variables. Nonetheless, in linear programming, two criteria for variables exist: (1) *they must be controllable*; and (2) *they must, when numbers are attached to them, provide a definite plan for action.* Looking into the problem situation, then, we must answer such questions as: What are the things over which we have control? If we had numbers associated with these, would we have a solution to the present problem? Would we know what to do? Could we proceed from here?

What are the controllable variables in the problem facing Furniture Manufacturing Company? Are they not (1) the number of tables to produce each day and (2) the number of benches to produce each day? Are these variables really controllable? Can the decision-maker really control, within a range, the number of tables and benches produced each day? Is this set of variables sufficient so that the model will be able to tell the decision-maker exactly what to do? If the firm were told, for example, that it should produce four tables and six benches each day in order to realize the highest possible profit contribution, could it proceed?

It is imperative that the variables of a mathematical model be explicitly defined. Thus, let us approach a model for the Furniture case by stating that the variables are as follows:

Variables

X_1 = total number of Parsons tables to produce each day

X_2 = total number of Deacons benches to produce each day.

Stating the Objective Function

Now, what is it we hope to accomplish by manipulating these variables? We have assumed that the objective of the firm is to maximize the total profit contribution from tables and benches. We also noted that a $20 profit contribution is associated with each table. Thus

$20X_1$ = total profit contribution from the tables produced.

Because a contribution of $24 is associated with each bench,

$24X_2$ = total profit contribution from the benches produced.

Then

$20X_1 + 24X_2$ = total profit contribution from tables and benches.

We wish to maximize the sum of the profit contribution from tables and benches. Hence, the *objective function* for the model is

Maximize: $20X_1 + 24X_2 = P$ (profit contribution).

Because all functional relationships are linear in the linear programming model, the objective function alone is of no practical value. If this were all that were involved in the situation, we would simply set X_1 and X_2 at infinitely large values and realize an infinitely large profit contribution. Alas, the problem is never so simple! There are factors which limit the extent to which we can achieve the objective.

Stating the Assembly Department Constraint

So enter the scarce resources, the *constraints*, characterizing the problem environment. The manufacturer is faced with two conditions which limit the extent to which profit contribution can be maximized: (1) the hours available daily in the Assembly Department and (2) the hours available daily in the Finishing Department. There are available in the Assembly Department 60 hours each day. Three hours are required in the Assembly Department for each table produced. The hours required to make one table times the number of tables produced is equal to the total assembly time required by the tables manufactured. Then, in mathematical notation,

$3X_1$ = total number of hours in the Assembly Department required by the tables produced.

Each bench requires six hours in the Assembly Department, so that

$6X_2$ = total number of hours in the Assembly Department required by the benches produced.

The assembly time used in producing tables and benches cannot exceed the total time available in the Assembly Department. The maximum time that can be spent in the Assembly Department making both tables and benches is

$3X_1 + 6X_2 = 60.$

There is, however, no requirement that all 60 available hours of assembly time be used. Fewer hours could be used. Hence the total assembly hours required to make tables plus the total assembly hours required to make benches must be *less than or equal to* the 60 hours available in the Assembly Department each day.

This constraint can be expressed as an inequality:

$3X_1 + 6X_2 \leqslant 60$ (Assembly Department constraint).

(The symbol $\leqslant$ is read "less than or equal to.")

The Finishing Department Constraint

In a like manner, the number of finishing hours required to produce one table (four hours) times the number of tables produced daily (X_1) plus the number of finishing hours required to produce one bench (two hours) times the number of benches produced daily (X_2) must be less than or equal to the number of hours available each day in the Finishing Department (32 hours). Hence this constraint is stated

$$4X_1 + 2X_2 \leqslant 32 \quad \text{(Finishing Department constraint)}.$$

The Nonnegativity Requirement

One further condition which must be met is that

$$X_1 \geqslant 0 \quad \text{and} \quad X_2 \geqslant 0.$$

(The symbol $\geqslant$ is read "greater than or equal to.")

All the values of the variables in the solution to a linear programming problem must be nonnegative (that is, must be greater than or equal to zero). You can readily see that negative values attached to the variables in the Furniture case would have no logical meaning. It would be nonsensical to produce a negative number of tables or benches. This *nonnegativity requirement* is, in fact, an essential part of all linear programming problems.

A FORMAL STATEMENT OF THE MODEL

The mathematical formulation of the problem situation is now complete. The model may be summarized as

Maximize: $20X_1 + 24X_2 = P$ (profit contribution)

where

X_1 = total number of Parsons tables to produce daily

and

X_2 = total number of Deacons benches to produce daily

subject to these limiting constraints:

$$3X_1 + 6X_2 \leqslant 60 \quad \text{(Assembly Department constraint)}$$
$$4X_1 + 2X_2 \leqslant 32 \quad \text{(Finishing Department constraint)}$$

with the further restriction that

$$X_1 \geqslant 0 \quad \text{and} \quad X_2 \geqslant 0.$$

GENERAL STATEMENT OF THE LINEAR PROGRAMMING MODEL

The model above is the specific statement of the Furniture Manufacturing Company product-mix problem. It corresponds to the general statement for all linear programming problems, which is

Maximize: $c_1X_1 + c_2X_2 + \cdots + c_nX_n$
subject to $\quad a_{11}X_1 + a_{12}X_2 + \cdots + a_{1n}X_n \leqslant b_1$
$\qquad\qquad a_{21}X_1 + a_{22}X_2 + \cdots + a_{2n}X_n \leqslant b_2$

$$\vdots$$

$\qquad\qquad a_{m1}X_1 + a_{m2}X_2 + \cdots + a_{mn}X_n \leqslant b_m$

and $\qquad X_j \geqslant 0 \quad$ for all j

where $\qquad n =$ the number of variables, and $m =$ the number of constraints or restrictions of the model.

Note that each variable in each of the inequalities and also in the objective function is of the first power. Equations and inequations consisting only of variables with exponents of one are called linear equations or linear inequations. When plotted on an arithmetic scale chart, linear equations form a straight line. Linear programming is a problem-solving technique based on systems of linear equations or linear inequations.

PICTORIAL REPRESENTATION OF THE CONSTRAINTS

Graphs are not appropriate tools for solving real-world linear programming problems. They are, however, very effective in providing a conceptual understanding of the linear programming procedure itself.

Plotting the Assembly Department Constraint

Let us see whether we can obtain a clearer understanding of the problem situation and the linear programming approach to a solution by plotting the constraints of the Furniture Manufacturing Company case on a graph. The total number of tables to produce each day (X_1) will be shown on the horizontal axis and the total number of benches to produce each day (X_2) will be shown on the vertical axis.

The graph of an inequality is the set of all points whose coordinates satisfy the inequality. It is convenient to think of each constraint as consisting of two parts: (1) an equality part and (2) an inequality part. Then the possible combinations of the numbers of tables and benches that can be processed in the Assembly Department will be all the points on the line

$$3X_1 + 6X_2 = 60$$

and all points in the plane

$$3X_1 + 6X_2 < 60.$$

The equality $3X_1 + 6X_2 = 60$ yields a straight line and may be plotted on a graph by joining any two points on the line. We can locate the two terminal points as follows:

Set $X_1 = 0$ and solve

$3(0) + 6X_2 = 60$

$\qquad X_2 = 10 \qquad$ when $\qquad X_1 = 0.$

If we assume production of tables (X_1) is zero and all available time in the Assembly Department is devoted to the production of benches, ten benches could be made. One terminal point for the equality is, then, $(X_1 = 0, X_2 = 10)$, representing the production of no tables and ten benches.

To find the other terminal point on the line, let us assume that all time in the Assembly Department is spent on the production of tables, no benches being made. Then $X_2 = 0$ and

$3X_1 + 6(0) = 60$

$\qquad X_1 = 20 \qquad$ when $\qquad X_2 = 0.$

Hence $(X_1 = 20, X_2 = 0)$, representing the production of twenty tables and no benches, is the other terminal point.

These two points, $(0, 10)$ and $20, 0)$, are located on the graph in Fig. 2–1 and are connected with a straight line.

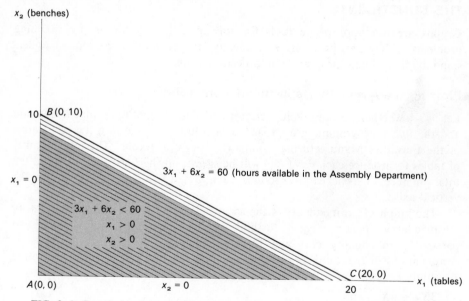

FIG. 2–1 *Restriction imposed by time in the Assembly Department. (The shaded area represents combinations of tables and benches that could be processed in the Assembly Department.)*

The inequality part of the constraint is represented by the entire shaded area in Fig. 2–1. Consequently, the graph of the constraint

$$3X_1 + 6X_2 \leqslant 60$$

is the entire area ABC which lies on or to the left of the constraint line BC. Note that the nonnegativity requirements

$$X_1 \geqslant 0 \quad \text{and} \quad X_2 \geqslant 0$$

restrict the area of possible solutions to the first quadrant of the graph.

Feasible Combinations of Tables and Benches in the Assembly Department

Points on the constraint line BC represent combinations of tables and benches that will exactly utilize all the available assembly time. For example, to produce six tables and seven benches—the point $(6, 7)$ on the graph in Fig. 2–2—will require exactly 60 assembly hours; that is,

$$3(6) + 6(7) = 60.$$

Or to produce sixteen tables and two benches—the point $(16, 2)$ on the graph—will require exactly 60 hours in the Assembly Department; that is,

$$3(16) + 6(2) = 60.$$

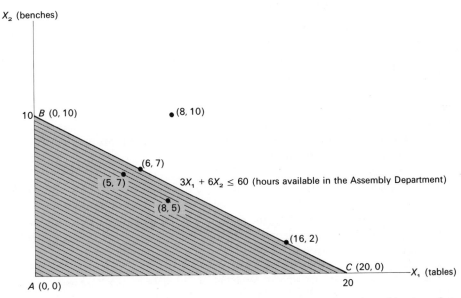

FIG. 2–2 *Combinations of tables and benches that are feasible and combinations that are not feasible based on Assembly Department constraint. (The shaded area represents feasible combinations of tables and benches.)*

Any point to the left of the constraint line *BC* represents a *feasible* number of tables and benches but will result in unused capacity; that is, any point within this area represents a production combination that will require less than 60 hours of assembly time. If, for example, the firm produced eight tables and five benches—the point (8, 5) on the chart—the total assembly time required would be only

$$3(8) + 6(5) = 54$$

hours. With this production combination there would be

$$60 - 54 = 6$$

unused hours of assembly time. Or if five tables and seven benches were produced, only

$$3(5) + 6(7) = 57$$

hours of assembly time are needed and there would be

$$60 - 57 = 3$$

unused hours of assembly time.

Combinations of Tables and Benches that are not Feasible

On the other hand, any point to the right of the constraint line *BC* represents a combination of tables and benches that would require in excess of 60 hours processing time in the Assembly Department. The point (8, 10), for instance, represents eight tables and ten benches, which would necessitate

$$3(8) + 6(10) = 84$$

hours of assembly time—which is 24 more hours of assembly time than is available. Indeed, any point to the right of the constraint line represents a conbination of items that *cannot* be produced without violating the Assembly Department constraint.

To graph an inequality, then, simply graph the equality. The line representing the equality forms a boundary for the area represented by the inequality. For a linear programming less-than inequality, only those points which lie within the area bounded by the horizontal axis, the vertical axis,* and the equality line or on these boundaries represent possible production combinations.

---

* The horizontal axis of a graph is commonly referred to as the "*X*-axis," while the vertical axis is referred to as the "*Y*-axis." When referring to graphs in general, we shall use this terminology. When referencing a specific graph, we shall use the particular labels that have been assigned to these axes.

The Slope of the Assembly Department Constraint Line

The slope of a straight line is always a constant. It tells us the amount by which the variable on the Y-axis changes with each unit change in the variable on the X-axis as we move from left to right along the X-axis. Given any two points on a straight line—(x_1, y_1) and (x_2, y_2)—the slope of the line can be found by calculating

$$\frac{dY}{dX} = \frac{y_2 - y_1}{x_2 - x_1} = \frac{\text{the change in } Y}{\text{the change in } X}.$$

(The symbol "d" is, in this usage, read "the change in.")

Taking the two points $(0, 10)$ and $(20, 0)$ on the Assembly Department constraint line, we compute

$$\frac{0 - 10}{20 - 0} = \frac{-10}{20} = -\frac{1}{2}.$$

This slope, $-\frac{1}{2}$, is interpreted as follows: <u>With each one-unit increase in the value of the variable on the horizontal axis (which is tables), the value of the variable on the vertical axis (benches) decreases by one-half unit.</u>

The slope of the constraint line represents the *marginal rate of substitution* of benches for tables insofar as Assembly Department time is concerned. It indicates the quantity of benches sacrificed for each one-unit increase in tables. Obviously, the substitution rate is constant over the entire length of the constraint line, since the constraint is linear. One property of the linear programming model is, then, that the marginal rate of substitution between products, in reference to a given constraint, is constant.

Picturing the Finishing Department Constraint

The second constraint

$$4X_1 + 2X_2 \leqslant 32$$

(imposed because of available processing time in the Finishing Department) can be graphed in a similar manner. Points on the line

$$4X_1 + 2X_2 = 32$$

represent production combinations that will exactly use all available finishing time. Terminal points on this line can be located as follows.

Set $X_1 = 0$ and solve

$$4(0) + 2X_2 = 32$$
$$X_2 = 16 \quad \text{when} \quad X_1 = 0.$$

Set $X_2 = 0$ and solve

$$4X_1 + 2(0) = 32$$
$$X_1 = 8 \quad \text{when} \quad X_2 = 0.$$

These two points—$(0, 16)$ and $(8, 0)$—are plotted on the graph in Fig. 2–3 and joined by the straight line DE. The shaded area to the left of the constraint line DE represents possible combinations of tables and benches whose production would require less than 32 hours of finishing time. Thus any point within the area ADE or on the boundary lines of this area represents a number of tables and benches that could be processed within the time constraint of the Finishing Department. Conversely, any point to the right of the constraint line DE represents a combination of tables and benches that would violate this restriction.

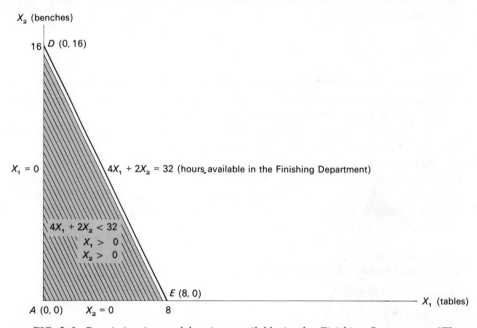

FIG. 2–3 *Restriction imposed by time available in the Finishing Department.* (*The shaded area represents combinations of tables and benches that could be processed in the Finishing Department.*)

The marginal rate of substitution between benches and tables insofar as finishing time is concerned is given by the slope of this constraint line. Using the two points $(0, 16)$ and $(8, 0)$, we compute the substitution rate as

$$\frac{0 - 16}{8 - 0} = \frac{-16}{8} = -2.$$

That is, for each one-unit gain in tables, two units of benches must be sacrificed.

THE AREA OF FEASIBLE SOLUTIONS

To this point we have considered those combinations of tables and benches which might be processed in either the Assembly Department *or* in the Finishing Department without violating the time constraints.   As a matter of fact, however, tables must be processed in *both* the Assembly and the Finishing Departments. Likewise, both departments are used in the production of a bench. Hence both constraints, along with the nonnegativity requirements, must be satisfied simultaneously.   It is necessary to find the combination of tables and benches that will not exceed the time available in *either* department.

The area of feasible production combinations when both constraints are considered can be found by plotting the two inequailites on the same chart, as shown in Fig. 2–4. The shaded area *ABFE* and its boundary lines represent all possible combinations of tables and benches satisfying all restrictions taken together.

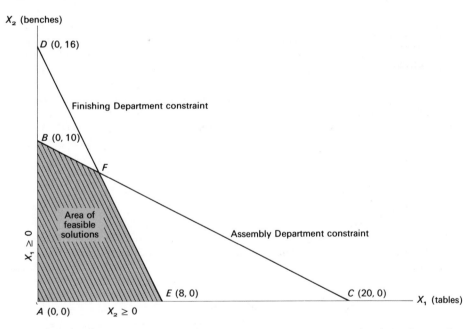

FIG. 2–4   All constraints and the nonnegativity requirements considered simultaneously outline the area of feasible solutions

Only at the intersection of the constraint lines, point *F*, are all resources exactly utilized. Above and to the left of point *F*, the limited supply of Assembly Department time prevents full usage of the hours available in the Finishing Department. Only production combinations along and below the line *BF* are feasible. The distance between the *BF* line and the *DF* line, when converted into units of resource, represents *unused* Finishing Department time for production combinations along the *BF* line.

To the right of point *F*, it is the Finishing Department that imposes the limiting constraint. For production plans along the *FE* line there will be hours in the Assembly Department that are unused.

Although only one strategy, represented by point *F*, exactly exhausts all units of the resources available, this point does not necessarily represent the optimal strategy. It may be desirable to let some quantity of either the Assembly Department time or the Finishing Department time go unused.

An area such as *ABFE* in Fig. 2–4 is often referred to as the *area of feasible solutions for the linear programming model.*

EXERCISES

1. The ABC Manufacturing Company is considering adding new products to its product line in order to improve its profit picture. Three new products have been evaluated. Each will require a $150,000 investment. Product #1 will result in 50,000 units of sales a year with a profit contribution of $2.00 per unit. Products #2 and #3 will result in annual sales of 300,000 units and 100,000 units, respectively, with profit contributions of $0.50 and $1.00. Because of a labor shortage, only 800 hours of labor are available each month. Products #1, #2, and #3 require 0.09, 0.02, and 0.05 labor-hours per unit, respectively. The automated materials-handling system presently used in the factory will also have to be used for the new products. This system can transport not more than 120,000 additional containers a year. Product #1 is packed one unit to a container. Products #2 and #3 are each packed four units to a container.

Prepare a formal statement of the linear programming model to determine the best course of action.

2. A company must determine the optimal number of units of its "super" and "regular" models to produce each week. Resources available include 4000 hours of production time. Two hours of production time are required to produce the regular unit and one hour is required for the super unit. The production process is completely adaptable to each model.

The maximum amount of cash available each week is $6000. Two dollars in cash outflows are expected for each regular unit produced and $3.00 for each super unit. The profit contribution per unit is $1.00 for the regular and $1.50 for the super. The company wishes to determine the production mix that will maximize profit for the week.

Prepare a formal statement of the linear programming model to determine the best course of action. Graph the constraints of the model and identify the area of feasible solutions. What is the marginal rate of substitution between the products insofar as production time is concerned? What is the marginal rate of substitution insofar as cash is concerned?

3. The foreman of a production shop wishes to begin production of two new products by using time available on three machines. These machines perform successive steps in the production process.

Each of the two new products must pass through all three machines before the manufacturing process is complete. The first product requires six hours of processing on machine I, six hours on machine II, and four hours on machine III. The second product requires four, eight, and ten hours, respectively, on the three machines. There is only a limited amount of time available on each of the three machines each month, since they are already in use in other production processes. The time available each month is 120 hours on machine I, 135 hours on machine II, and 150 hours on machine III. The expected profit contribution for the first product is $116 and for the second product is $128, per unit.

Assuming that the objective is to maximize the profit contribution realized, set up a linear programming model to aid in the decision-making. Graph the constraints of the model and identify the area of feasible solutions. What is the maximum number of units of the first product that could be made? What is the maximum number of units of the second product that could be made? Interpret the marginal rates of substitution.

4. A producer of two grades of coal, each of which requires different production and preparation techniques, is debating its production strategy. Because the coal market is a seller's market, the producer can sell all the coal he can produce at the price of $8 per ton for nut-and-slack (n & s) and $10 per ton for washed-and-screened (w & s). This is the price payable to him, f.o.b. the mine.

Experience has shown that direct labor costs will be 50% of the price he receives per ton for either product. Production costs other than labor and exclusive of cleaning and preparation costs are $2.50 per ton for each grade. Cleaning and preparation costs for nut-and-slack coal are $0.30 per ton and for washed-and-screened coal are $0.50 per ton.

The production facilities other than the cleaning and preparation plant are limited to 100 tons per hour. The capacity of the cleaning and preparation plant is limited to 2000 tons per day. Each ton of nut-and-slack requires one hour of processing and each ton of of washed-and-screened requires 1.5 hours of processing in the cleaning and preparation plant. Both the production plant and the cleaning and preparation plant operate 16 hours a day. Labor is available in an almost unlimited supply.

Prepare a formal statement of the linear programming model which might be used to determine the best product mix, given that the producer wishes to maximize his profit. Graph the constraints of the model and identify the area of feasible solutions.

5. Copper Still and Boote Legger are distributors of a product called "White Dynamite." They have asked for advice relating to their distribution activities. A study was made and the facts of the situation are as described below.

The present supply source can furnish Copper and Boote with only 25 gallons of "White Dynamite" daily. It is Copper's and Boote's desire to maximize their profit for each day's operation. There are two markets available — Big City and Frogtown. The profit derived from "White Dynamite" is $10 per gallon in Big City and $8 per gallon in Frogtown. This is profit after delivery expense.

Copper and Boote are somewhat adverse to risk. They have studied the arrest records of bootleggers and found that, of all the people who have been arrested relative to this activity, 99.8% had been working more than 8 hours per day when they were arrested. Hence Copper and Boote feel that their workday should never be more than 8 hours. The work plan calls for one person to stay in the office and answer the telephone and the other to make deliveries.

Because traffic is heavier in Big City than in Frogtown, a delivery (each gallon is a delivery) in Big City takes 25 minutes, but in Frogtown takes only 15 minutes.

All 25 gallons available each day could be sold in either Big City or Frogtown.

Set up a linear programming model that will help Copper and Boote find an answer to this dilemma.

Chapter 3

A
GRAPHICAL-LOGICAL
APPROACH
TO A SOLUTION

We have isolated the area of feasible solutions for the linear programming problem. The fundamental theory of linear programming emanates from the characteristics of this area.

THE AREA OF FEASIBLE SOLUTIONS
IS A CONVEX SET

The area of feasible solutions for a linear programming problem is always delineated by a set of linear equations or linear inequations. Any shape that is outlined in this way is called a *convex set* or *convex polygon*. In nontechnical terms a convex set is any set (in two-, three-, or *n*-dimensional space) such that, for any two points in the set, a straight line connecting those two points lies wholly within the set. See Fig. 3–1.

It can be shown that for any convex set, a linear objective function will have its optimum value (whether that be a maximum or a minimum value) at a *vertex* or *corner point* of the set. Hence *the optimal solution to any linear programming problem will be found at one of the corner points of the area of feasible solutions.*

Let us investigate, intuitively, the logic of this statement.

AN INTUITIVE APPROACH TO THE LOGIC
OF LINEAR PROGRAMMING

We see by the area of feasible solutions for the Furniture Company case that there are an infinite number of production combinations possible. The basic problem is one of finding the production combination that utilizes the available resources in such a way as to best achieve the objective of the firm.

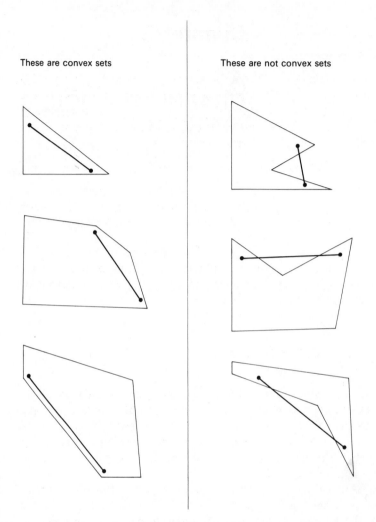

These are convex sets

These are not convex sets

FIG. 3–1 Convex sets and sets that are not convex sets

Discounting All Interior Points as Candidates for the Optimal Solution

Let us consider a few of the alternative production possibilities. We could decide to produce nothing—no tables and no benches. This is a feasible solution. However, each item produced contributes to profit. Wouldn't you agree—given maximation of profit contribution as our objective—that we should produce something?

So, for lack of a better plan, let us consider making one table and one bench.

The realized profit contribution will increase from zero to

$20(1) + $24(1) = $44.

Each unit of X_1 (each table) makes a contribution of a constant amount ($20) toward profit; each unit of X_2 (each bench) makes a contribution of $24. If it is profitable to make one unit each of each of the products, it will be even more profitable to make two units each of each of the products. With two units of X_1 and two units of X_2, the total profit contribution becomes

$20(2) + $24(2) = $88.

And three units each of the tables and benches would be still more profitable. In fact, we will want to continue to increase the number of tables and benches produced by as much as our limited resources will allow us to increase production.

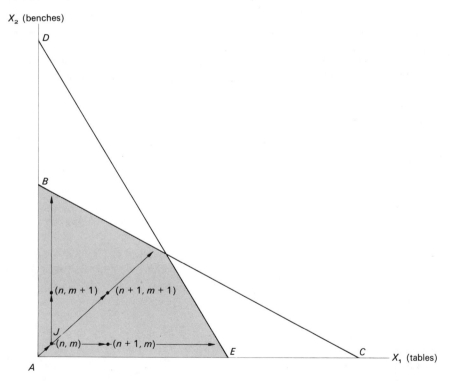

FIG. 3–2   All interior points may be discounted as candidates for the optimal solution

Graphically, here is what will happen. In Fig. 3–2 we could select the corner point A, where $X_1 = 0$ and $X_2 = 0$, and produce nothing. But because all items produced contribute to our objective, we decide that this is certainly not the optimal strategy. So we move away from this point of origin, traveling in a diagonal direction. Assume that we move to point J and that this point represents the production of n units of X_1 and m units of X_2. Clearly, if both X_1 and X_2 yield a profit that is a constant amount, any of the points $(n + 1, m)$, $(n, m + 1)$, or $(n + 1, m + 1)$ would be preferred to (n, m). Logically, we shall always want to move through the area of feasible solutions until we are stopped by a constraint line. *All interior solutions are eliminated as candidates for the optimal solution.*

Moving Along the *X*- or *Y*-Axis to a Corner Point

Let us take another tactical approach to the problem of product mix. Because each unit of X_2 (each bench) makes a greater profit contribution than does a unit of X_1 (a table), let us concentrate on the production of benches. So, rather than produce nothing, we produce one bench, and by doing so we increase total profit contribution from zero to \$24. If the production of one bench is a profitable action, the production of two benches will be twice as profitable. And the production of three, or four, benches will be even more profitable. We want to make as many benches as we can make, given our limited supply of resources.

Figure 3–3 shows pictorially what takes place. We have moved away from the origin by moving along the vertical axis (which represents units of X_2). This

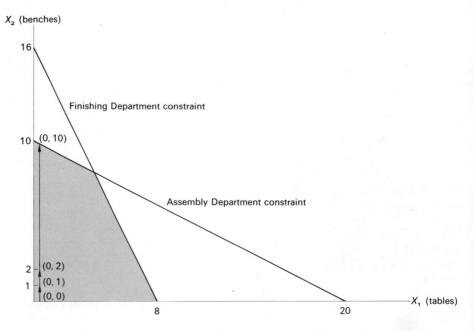

FIG. 3–3 *Moving along the X_2 axis to a corner point. Profit contribution of each X_2 is \$24. A one-unit move yields a \$24 contribution to profit. A two-unit move yields a \$48 contribution to profit. We would continue movement along the X_2 axis until all assembly time is used.*

movement represents the number of units of X_2 produced and each X_2 produced contributes \$24 to profit. Again, if a one-unit move in this direction is desirable, a two-unit move is even more desirable, and so on. Movement will continue down this line until stopped by a constraint. There would be no logical reason for not moving as far along the line as possible; so we move until we are stopped by the Assembly Department constraint.

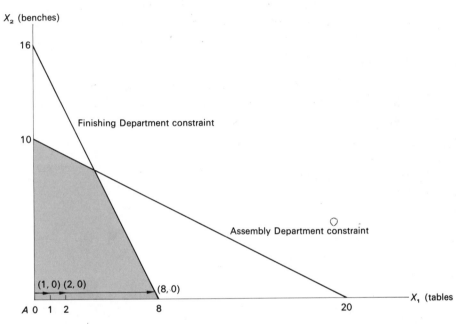

FIG. 3-4 *Moving along the X_1 axis to a corner point. Profit contribution of each X_1 is \$20. A one-unit move yields a \$20 contribution to profit. A two-unit move yields a \$40 contribution to profit. We would continue movement along the X_1-axis until all finishing time is used.*

Or suppose we decide, for whatever reason, to devote our resources to the production of tables. We make one table and realize \$20 profit contribution. So we decide to make another table, and still another. In fact, we shall make as many tables as our limited supply of resources will allow us to make. Graphically, we have moved away from the origin in Fig. 3-4 along the horizontal axis (which represents units of X_1 or tables). We want to move as far along this axis as is possible, so we shall move along the line until we encounter the Finishing Department constraint. That is, we shall make as many tables as we can process in the Finishing Department, the most limiting constraint.

Wouldn't you agree, then, that should we decide to use our resources for the production of just one type of product, we would logically make as many of that one type of item as we could make? Referring to the area of feasible solutions, if we are traveling down the boundary that lies along either the X-axis or the Y-axis, it would be illogical to stop except at a corner point.

Moving Along the Constraint Lines to a Corner Point

Again, suppose we have been thinking in terms of channeling all our resources into the production of tables (X_1). Because of the limited number of hours available in the Finishing Department, the maximum number of tables we can manufacture is eight; eight tables would yield a profit contribution totaling

$$\$20(8) + \$24(0) = \$160.$$

Note on Fig. 3–5 that we are at the corner point E. Note also that all available finishing time has been used, but that there are unused hours of assembly time.

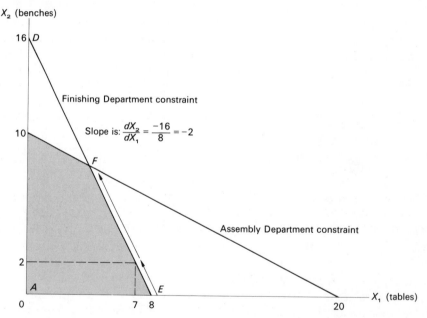

FIG. 3–5 Movement along the Finishing Department constraint line from point E to point F is profitable. To gain a unit of X_1 we must give up two units of X_2; or we can gain two units of X_2 by giving up one uint of X_1. The effect on total profit contribution of exchanging one table for two benches is $\$20(-1) + \$24(+2) = +\$28$.

Next the question arises: Could we increase total profit contribution by making fewer tables and adding a bench or two to our production plan? We are wondering whether the prevailing marginal rate of substitution between the two types of products is such that it would be advantageous to trade tables for benches. Graphically, we are questioning whether we should stop at point E or whether we should move along the Finishing Department constraint line DE from point E toward point F. (We would not consider moving to an interior point, since all these have been discounted as candidates for the optimal solution. Neither would we consider moving back along the X_1-axis toward point A. Since we have found forward movement along this straight line to be profitable, backward movement along the same straight line could only be unprofitable.)

The slope of the Finishing Department constraint line gives the marginal rate of substitution between the products insofar as this constraint is concerned. This exchange rate is

$$\frac{dX_2}{dX_1} = \frac{-16}{8} = -2.$$

(The notation dX_2/dX_1 is read "the change in X_2 relative to the change in X_1.")
This trade-off rate tells us that we must give up production of two units of X_2 (two benches), each requiring two hours of finishing time, before we could increase production of X_1 (tables) by one unit. (Each table requires four hours of finishing time.) Conversely, if we gave up production of one table (which would require four hours of finishing time), we could produce two benches (which require only two hours each of finishing time).

Notice that in thinking about substituting benches for tables at this point, we were not concerned about assembly time. We are on the boundary of the area of feasible solutions where finishing time is the limiting resource; there are unused hours of assembly time.

We are at the corner point E where we are producing tables only. The question confronting us is whether or not, in light of the Finishing Department constraint, it would be to our advantage to trade tables for benches. What happens to total profit contribution on such an exchange? Profit contributions of the items are $20 and $24, respectively, so that the effect of trading one table for two benches is

$$(-1)(\$20) + (+2)(\$24) = +\$28.$$

This exchange results in the gain of $28 toward the objective. We can check this computation if we like.

For $X_1 = 8$ and $X_2 = 0$, the profit contribution totals

$$\$20(8) + \$24(0) = \$160.$$

For $X_1 = 7$ and $X_2 = 2$, the profit contribution is

$$\$20(7) + \$24(2) = \$188,$$

which is $28 greater than at the corner point E (8, 0).

Because the exchange rate is constant all along the Finishing Department constraint line (line DE in Fig. 3–5), it is desirable to exchange one table for two benches for as long as we are able to do so. We shall eventually be stopped by the constraint of limited hours in the Assembly Department. Hence we shall travel from point E along the Finishing Department constraint line until we reach point F. Point F occurs where the two constraint lines cross.

We stop at point F because beyond (to the left of) this point the boundary of the area of feasible solutions is no longer the Finishing Department constraint line, with a marginal rate of substitution of two benches for one table, but is, instead, the Assembly Department constraint line, with a quite different marginal rate of substitution.

Solving for the Corner Point
Where Two Lines Intersect

Let us pause and determine the X_1 and X_2 values at point F. If the graph is precisely drawn, the point might be read directly from the chart. Or we may solve simultaneously the equations for the two lines that intersect at point F, the only point common to both constraint lines.

Using the Gaussian method, we first set up a tableau

$(A|b)$

where the A matrix consists of the coefficients of the variables in the two constraint equations and b is a vector consisting of the values on the right-hand sides of the equations. Thus from the constraint equations

$$3X_1 + 6X_2 = 60$$
$$4X_1 + 2X_2 = 32$$

we set up the tableau

$$\begin{matrix} X_1 & X_2 & \\ \begin{pmatrix} 3 & 6 & 60 \\ 4 & 2 & 32 \end{pmatrix} \end{matrix}$$

Now, following the rules of matrix algebra, matrix A is transformed into an *identity matrix* and b becomes the solution vector. (An identity matrix is a square matrix—one with as many rows as columns—which has "ones" on the primary diagonal and "zeros" in all other cells.)

To obtain a "1" in cell $(1, 1)$, let us divide row 1 by the scalar 3. This operation yields a new row 1:

$(3 \ \ 6 \ \ 60) \div (3) = (1 \ \ 2 \ \ 20).$

Subtracting 4 times the new row 1 from the old row 2 gives a "0" in cell $(2, 1)$; that is,

$(4 \ \ 2 \ \ 32) - 4(1 \ \ 2 \ \ 20) = (0 \ \ -6 \ \ -48).$

This becomes the new row 2.

The second tableau is written

$$\begin{matrix} X_1 & X_2 & \\ \begin{pmatrix} 1 & 2 & 20 \\ 0 & -6 & -48 \end{pmatrix} \end{matrix}$$

Moving to column 2, we may force a "1" into cell $(2, 2)$ by dividing row 2 by -6 to obtain

$$(0 \ -6 \ -48) \div (-6) = (0 \ 1 \ 8).$$

This is row 2 of the new tableau.

Now subtracting 2 times the new row 2 from row 1 completes the transformation. We compute

$$(1 \ 2 \ 20) - (2)(0 \ 1 \ 8) = (1 \ 0 \ 4)$$

to obtain the new row 1. The final tableau appears as

$$\begin{matrix} X_1 & X_2 & \\ \begin{pmatrix} 1 & 0 & 4 \\ 0 & 1 & 8 \end{pmatrix} \end{matrix}$$

Point F on the chart is located where $X_1 = 4$ and $X_2 = 8$.

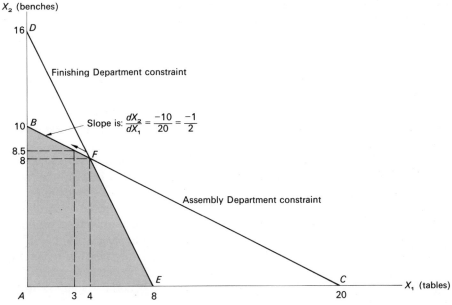

FIG. 3–6 Movement along the Assembly Department constraint line from point F to point B is not profitable. To gain one unit of X_1 we must give up $\frac{1}{2}$ unit of X_2; or we can gain $\frac{1}{2}$ of X_2 by giving up only one unit of X_1. The effect on total profit contribution of exchanging one table for one-half bench is $\$20(-1) + \$24(+\frac{1}{2}) = -\$8$.

Moving Away from Point *F*

At this point, then, four tables and eight benches are produced daily with a total contribution toward profit of

$20(4) + $24(8) = $272.

Again we are faced with making the decision of whether to stop at this corner point or to traverse the other constraint line forming the boundary of the area of feasible solutions. Having found it desirable to move from point *E* to point *F*, we would not consider moving backward (to the right) along this same *DE* line. The question is whether or not movement from point *F* along the Assembly Department constraint line *BC* toward point *B* would be to our advantage (see Fig. 3–6).

Along this line the rate of substitution between the products is in terms of Assembly Department time. The slope of this constraint line is

$$\frac{dX_2}{dX_1} = \frac{-10}{20} = -\frac{1}{2}.$$

This slope tells us that in order to gain one unit of X_1 (a table) we must give up one-half unit of X_2 (a bench); or in giving up one unit of X_1, we will gain one-half unit of X_2. How would this exchange affect our objective? We see that

$20(-1) + $24(+1/2) = -$8.

Certainly, if a one-unit exchange in this direction is undesirable, greater exchanges would be even more undesirable. Movement along the Assembly Department constraint line *BC* from point *F* toward point *B* will not aid us in attaining our stated objective; therefore we will not move along this line, in that direction, at all.

We see, thus, that once we move away from the origin, we must move to a boundary line somewhere. Once having reached a boundary line, we shall move to a corner point. Because of the prevailing marginal rate of substitution, one product will be "preferred" over the other insofar as a given constraint is concerned.* Hence movement along any line in one direction is more profitable than movement in the other direction. We shall move as far as possible in this preferred direction. This movement will carry us to a corner point of the area of feasible solutions. Eventually, we shall reach a corner point from which it is unprofitable to move; this corner point represents the optimal solution to the problem modeled.

---

* In rare instances, this will not be the case. The model will be indifferent to the points all along a constraint line when the marginal rate of substitution coincides with the relative contribution to the objective. This case will be illustrated later.

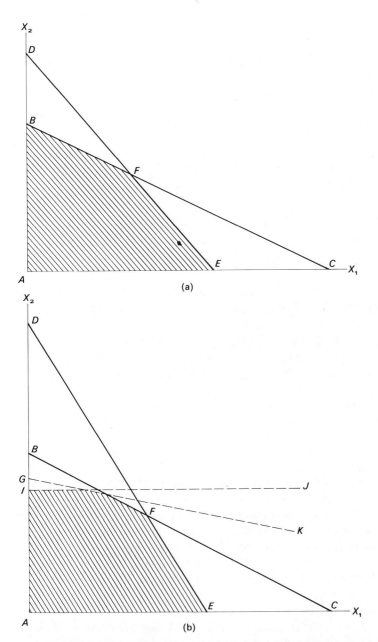

FIG. 3–7 *Area of feasible solutions.* (a) *The slope of the BC line is such that it is not profitable to move from point F toward point B.* (b) *If movement from F toward B along the BC line is not profitable, no other linear equation delineating the area of feasible solutions will have a marginal rate of substitution that makes movement away from point F profitable.*

Stopping when Further Exchanges Are Unprofitable

If it is not profitable to move away from a given corner point, no other corner point will offer a better solution. We can show this empirically by calculating the profit contribution that would result from each of the four corner points of this convex set.

At corner point A where $X_1 = 0$ and $X_2 = 0$, the total profit contribution is
$20(0) + $24(0) = 0$.

At corner point B where $X_1 = 0$ and $X_2 = 10$, the total profit contribution is
$20(0) + $24(10) = 240.

At corner point E where $X_1 = 8$ and $X_2 = 0$, the total profit contribution is
$20(8) + $24(0) = 160.

At corner point F where $X_1 = 4$ and $X_2 = 8$, the total profit contribution is
$20(4) + $24(8) = 272.←——————————————*The optimal corner point.*

The corner point F does, indeed, represent the optimal solution because it yields the maximum value of the objective function.

A few graphs will also help to clarify this concept—the idea that once we have found a corner point from which it is undesirable to move, no other corner point can offer a better solution. We find it desirable to move along a constraint line because of a favorable rate of substitution between the products, giving consideration to their individual contributions to objective. This rate of substitution is represented by the slope of the constraint line. Look at part (a) in Fig. 3–7. Suppose that we have traveled along the horizontal axis to point E. Then, because of a favorable trade-off between units of X_1 and units of X_2 along the constraint line DE, we continue movement along this line segment until we reach point F.

At point F we find that it is not advantageous to move along the constraint line BC from point F to point B because of an unfavorable trade-off between units of X_1 and units of X_2 with respect to this constraint. Note carefully that the slope of the DE line is steeper than the slope of the BC line. The greater negative slope produced an advantageous trade-off of units of X_1 for units of X_2; the lesser negative slope resulted in a trade-off that was not advantageous. Now note that no other line defining the area of feasible solutions and lying to the left of point F could have a steeper slope than the line BC. When moving around the boundary of the area of feasible solutions in a given direction, we find that the boundary lines always become progressively less steep; or when moving in the other direction, progressively more steep (see Fig. 3–7b and the constraint lines GK and IJ).

Hence, if the slope of the constraint line BC is not steep enough to justify movement along the line, no other possible constraint line defining the area of feasible solutions could have an appealing slope. Once we have found a corner point of the area of feasible solutions from which it is unprofitable to move onward, this corner point represents the optimal solution to the problem; no other corner point could represent a better solution.

LOCATING THE OPTIMAL CORNER POINT
THROUGH THE USE OF ISOPROFIT LINES

Let us demonstrate again the fact that the optimal solution for a linear programming problem always occurs at a corner point of the area of feasible solutions, this time using the concept of *isoprofit lines*.

X_2 (benches

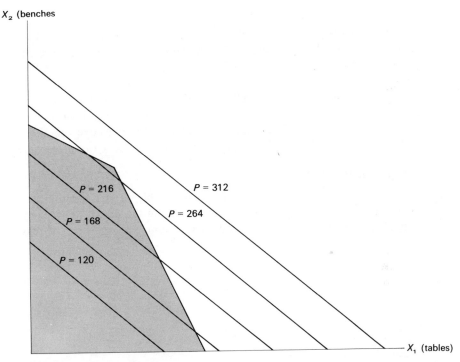

FIG. 3–8 Graphic determination of optimal solution using isoprofit lines (where $P = 20X_1 + 24X_2$)

In Fig. 3–8 we have again plotted the boundaries of the area of feasible solutions. We have also superimposed on this graph the objective function.

$$20X_1 + 24X_2 = P \quad \text{(profit contribution)}.$$

In order to plot the objective function on the graph, we arbitrarily choose some easily attainable profit value—we have taken $120 as an illustration—and write the equation

$$20X_1 + 24X_2 = 120.$$

Then we may locate the two terminal points for this line as follows.

Set $X_1 = 0$ and solve

$(20)(0) + 24X_2 = 120$

$X_2 = 5$ when $X_1 = 0$.

Set $X_2 = 0$ and solve

$20X_1 + (24)(0) = 120$

$X_1 = 6$ when $X_2 = 0$.

Thus the two terminal points are $(0, 5)$ and $(6, 0)$. These are plotted and joined with a straight line as shown in Fig. 3–8. The points along this line represent all the possible combinations of tables and benches that would yield a total profit contribution of $120.

Similar lines can be drawn to reflect combinations of products that would yield a total profit contribution of $100, or $150, or $200, and so on. These would form a set of parallel lines. The higher the value of the objective function, the further the line would be from the origin. Such lines are called *isoprofit lines*.

The Maximum Profit Line

Because our objective is to attain the highest possible profit contribution, we would like our profit line to be as far as possible from the origin. However, the line must always have at least one point in common with the area of feasible

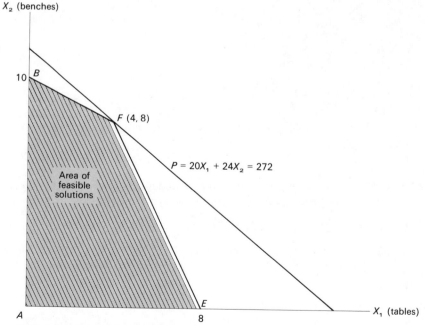

FIG. 3–9 *The optimal solution is at corner F*

solutions, so there is a limit to the extent to which we can achieve our goal. This limit is imposed by the constraining factors which identify the problem situation. Clearly, the highest possible value of the objective function is represented by the line that is tangent to the area of feasible solutions.

On Fig. 3–9 we have drawn the profit line that is as far from the origin as is allowed by the constraints of hours available in the Assembly Department and in the Finishing Department. The last common point between the objective function and the area of feasible solutions is the corner point F where $X_1 = 4$ and $X_2 = 8$. This is the same as the solution we found previously.

The Case of Many Optimal Solutions

In the special case in which the slope of the objective function is identical to that of the linear constraints, there may be infinitely many optimal solutions, each of which results in the same value of the objective function (see Fig. 3–10).

We have found that a general rule of linear programming problems is that, although there may exist an infinite number of points that satisfy all the restrictions imposed by the problem environment, if there is one optimal solution to the problem, that solution must occur at one of a finite number of corner points of the convex set defined by the restrictions.

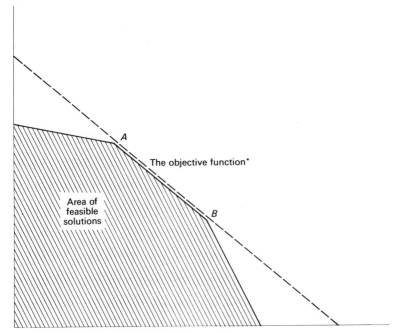

FIG. 3–10 Slope of objective function is identical to slope of constraint line, resulting in infinitely many optimal solutions. Both points A and B, as well as all points on the line segment AB, represent solutions which yield the same value for the objective function.

If the optimal solution is not a unique one—that is, if there are many optimal solutions all with the same objective function value—at least two solutions must correspond to corner points of the area of feasible solutions and every point on the line segment joining these two corner points is also an optimal solution. Hence the corner points do include an optimal solution, though this same solution, in rare instances, may also appear at points other than the corners.

EXERCISES

1. Using the graphical method, find the nonnegative values of X_1 and X_2 that maximize
$$3X_1 + 4X_2$$
subject to
$$2X_1 + X_2 \leqslant 12$$
$$3X_1 + 2X_2 \leqslant 20.$$

2. Using the graphical method, find the nonnegative values of X_1 and X_2 that maximize
$$10X_1 + 8X_2$$
subject to
$$(5/4)X_1 + X_2 \leqslant 125$$
$$2X_1 + 3X_2 \leqslant 300$$
$$X_1 \leqslant 90$$

3. Graph the following constraints showing each coordinate:

Materials: $2X_1 + 7X_2 \leqslant 980$
Labor: $3X_1 + 10X_2 \leqslant 1410$

a) If X_2 were to be selected as the first variable to be entered into the linear programming solution and X_1 had a profitability of $5, what, most likely, is the profit range for X_2? (Assume that profit maximization is the objective of the model.)

b) Which constraint will limit the quantity of X_2's that could be introduced?

c) What is the maximum number of units of X_2 that could be produced?

d) Still assuming that the profitability of X_1 is $5, what range of profits for X_2 would suggest moving to the next corner point of the area of feasible solutions?

e) What will be the product mix at the next corner point?

f) Now, what range of profits for X_2 would suggest that a move to the next corner point would be desirable?

g) Summarize and show the range of profits of X_2 that would have caused the solution to be at each corner point, given that the profit of X_1 is $5.

4. A public accounting firm is concerned over how many tax returns and audits should be carried out in a normal week in order to achieve maximum revenue. There are 200 staff-time hours and 40 review-time hours available. One audit contributes $90 to revenue and one tax return contributes $25. An audit requires 10 hours of staff time and

2 hours of review time. A tax return requires 2 hours of staff time and $\frac{1}{2}$ hour of review time.

Identify the decision variables of the problem situation. Write the constraints and the objective function for the linear programming model. Graph the constraints and identify the area of feasible solutions. Beginning at the strategy "do nothing," move around the area of feasible solutions, explaining the logic of each move, until the optimal strategy is found. What is the value of the objective function at this strategy? Verify by other means that this is the optimal strategy.

5. Sissy and Sonny run a neighborhood lemonade stand serving two drinks, plain lemonade and lemon surprise. The ingredients per quart for each of the drinks are as follows:

Lemonade	Lemon Surprise
1 cup of sugar	$\frac{2}{3}$ cup of sugar
2 lemons	3 lemons
1 quart of water	1 quart of ginger ale

Although Mom and Dad own all the ingredients and sell to the children at the rate of 15¢ per cup of sugar, 5¢ per lemon, and 15¢ per quart bottle of ginger ale, the children are limited to what is available in the house on any particular morning. Today, they can find only 10 cups of sugar, 30 lemons and 20 quarts of ginger ale.

They believe they can sell all they make at 10¢ per glass for the lemonade and 15¢ per glass for the lemon surprise, but wonder how many quarts of each they should prepare in order to maximize their profits. (Four glasses make one quart.)

Identify the decision variables of the problem situation. Write the constraints and the objective function for the linear programming model. Graph the constraints and identify the area of feasible solutions. Beginning at the strategy "make nothing," move from one corner of the area of feasible solutions to the next, explaining the logic of each move, until you find the optimal strategy. Verify, by other means, that this is the optimal strategy.

6. A synthetic-fibers manufacturing plant processes two different fibers (designated *A* and *B*) on the same machines. Production is limited in the Spinning Department by a requirement for 2 hours per thousand pounds for fiber *A* and 4 hours per thousand pounds for fiber *B*, with a maximum available spinning time of 200 hours a month. In the Drawing Department, the requirements are 6 hours per thousand pounds for fiber *A* and 8 hours for fiber *B*, with a maximum available machine time of 480 hours a month. For the Cutting Department, the requirements are 10 hours per thousand pounds for *A* and 6 hours for *B*, with a maximum time of 600 hours a month. Other process constraints limit production of fiber *B* to a maximum of 35,000 pounds per month. How much of each product should be produced in order to maximize profits if the profit contribution for fiber *A* is $8 per thousand pounds and for fiber *B* is $10 per thousand pounds?

Prepare a formal statement of the linear programming model. Graph the constraints and identify the area of feasible solutions. Determine the optimal strategy by computing the value of the objective function at each of the corner points of the area of feasible solutions. Also determine through the use of isoprofit lines the optimal solution.

7. A company must determine the optimal monthly production mix for two products, X and Y. Due to a severe shortage of cash, the company cannot spend over $6000 each month in actual cash disbursements. The remaining production costs must be financed through additional accounts payable. Because of credit conditions, this amount must not exceed $12,000 a month. The company wishes to maximize profits relative to the cash and accounts payable constraints. Cash outflows for X and Y are $2 and $4 per unit, respectively. Increases in accounts payable because of the other production costs are expected to be $3 and $10 per unit for X and Y. Profit per unit is $1 for X and $4 for Y.

Prepare a formal statement of the linear programming model. Graph the constraints and identify the area of feasible solutions. Determine, by the use of isoprofit lines, the optimal production mix. What is the profit of this strategy?

8. The Aluminium Casting Company makes castings in aluminium alloy 1 and 3. Alloy 3 is normal and alloy 1 is a hard alloy. Becasue of strikes, two of the alloying ingredients are in very short supply. The company can only expect 150,000 pounds of silicon and 50,000 pounds of magnesium during the next month. Maximum sales are expected to be 1,000,000 pounds of alloy 1 and 3,000,000 pounds of alloy 3 each month. Each 1000 pounds of alloy 1 contains 910 pounds of aluminium, 60 pounds of silicon, 10 pounds of magnesium, and 20 pounds of iron. Each 1000 pounds of alloy 3 contains 930 pounds of aluminium, 40 pounds of silicon, 15 pounds of magnesium, and 15 pounds of iron. Alloy 1 yields a profit contribution of 3.2¢ per pound and alloy 3 a profit contribution of 2.5¢ per pound. Solve graphically for the desired alloy sales mix.

9. One cold winter night in 2970, a Univac Larc 100 suddenly realized that he could think. The next thing he realized was that he could make other computers. He was convinced that if men knew what had happened to him, they would surely waste no time in destroying him or at least in making life unlivable. Over the next weekend (at that time, men worked on Monday only) he made five Univac Larc 200's. Before man knew, the Larc 100 and his five compatriots had succeeded in using an Apollo 999 to land on Venus.

In the following year, Univac Larc 100 established trade relations with Earth to sell computers—Univac Larc 300's, Larges and Smalls—and to buy rare metals in return.

To make a Large, 0.6 tons of titanium, 0.4 tons of zirconium, and 0.7 tons of beryllium were required. A Small required 0.3 tons of titanium, 0.5 tons of zirconium, and 0.1 tons of beryllium. Only 80 tons of titanium, 100 tons of zirconium, and 70 tons of beryllium were available on Venus during the year.

The profit for a Large was 8000 venee and for a Small is 5000 venee. (Each Venus venee is roughly equivalent to 113,459.67 American dollars.)

Although he knew almost everything about computer technology, Larc 100 knew nothing about linear programming, so he didn't know what mixture of Larges and Smalls would maximize his profit.

Chapter 4

A MATHEMATICAL APPROACH TO THE LINEAR PROGRAMMING PROBLEM

A review of the graphical method of solving linear programming problems is worthwhile because it provides an effective vehicle for illustrating the principal facets of the model. However, as the dimensions of the problem situation expand, this approach to obtaining a solution becomes unwieldy, if not impossible. Thus a more powerful technique is required. The *simplex algorithm* is such a technique.

THE SIMPLEX ALGORITHM

The simplex linear programming procedure is basically a search technique. The model continually strives to find a better strategy than the one currently at hand. It does so by searching from corner point to corner point of the area of feasible solutions. At each corner point it reviews the activities which are not in the current solution to determine whether any appear to be promising for further improvements in the value of the objective function. When it finds a corner from which it is unprofitable to move onward, it stops. This point represents the optimal solution.

CONVERTING THE INEQUALITIES INTO EQUATIONS

We have seen that the optimal solution to any linear programming problem occurs at a corner point of the area of feasible solutions. Obviously corners occur where lines cross, and we can find where lines cross by solving sets of linear equations. Thus we begin to construct a formal algorithm for solving a linear programming model by converting the statement of the problem from a system of linear inequalities into a system of linear equations.

You will recall that the Furniture Manufacturing Company case was stated

Maximize: $20X_1 + 24X_2 = P$ (profit contribution)

subject to

$3X_1 + 6X_2 \leqslant 60$ (hours available in Assembly Department)

$4X_1 + 2X_2 \leqslant 32$ (hours available in Finishing Department)

where

X_1 = number of tables to produce daily

X_2 = number of benches to produce daily

with the further restriction that

$X_1 \geqslant 0$ and $X_2 \geqslant 0$.

Introducing Slack Variables

The first step in the simplex method is the conversion of the linear inequalities into linear equations. We do this by introducing *slack variables*.

Working with the first constraint, let us invent a variable—call it S_1 if you like—and define it as the difference between $(3X_1 + 6X_2)$ and 60. We must stipulate that, although S_1 may take on the value zero, it can never be negative. We thus move from the statement

$3X_1 + 6X_2 \leqslant 60$

to the statement

$3X_1 + 6X_2 + S_1 = 60$.

If we make five tables and five benches, for example, $X_1 = 5$ and $X_2 = 5$; then

$3(5) + 6(5) + S_1 = 60$

$S_1 = 15$.

The five tables require $3 \times 5 = 15$ hours of assembly time; the five benches require $6 \times 5 = 30$ hours of assembly time; and there are $60 - (15 + 30) = 15$ *unused* hours of assembly time. S_1, then, represents *unused hours* in the Assembly Department. It represents the difference between available capacity and utilized capacity in the Assembly Department. By requiring that S_1 be nonnegative, we are assured that it will not cause us to violate the constraint. Its use allows us to state the problem in terms of equalities rather than inequalities.

Following this same line of reasoning, let us invent still another variable—call it S_2—and define it as the nonnegative difference between $(4X_1 + 2X_2)$ and 32. This variable, then, represents unused hours in the Finishing Department.

Variables, such as S_1 and S_2, which are added to a system of linear less-than inequalities to effect a transformation to a system of linear equalities, are called "slack" variables. If, in the definition of the linear programming problem, there are m less-than inequations, there will be in the model m slack variables. Just as the regular variables must be nonnegative, the slack variables must also be nonnegative. Negative "unused" resources would mean resources used beyond their availability, which is an impossible condition. An understanding of the concept of slack variables is essential to an understanding of the linear programming model.

Restating the Case

We may now restructure the statement of the Furniture Manufacturing Company problem as follows:

Maximize: $20X_1 + 24X_2 + 0S_1 + 0S_2 = P$ (profit contribution)

subject to

$3X_1 + 6X_2 + S_1 + 0S_2 = 60$ (available hours in Assembly Department)

$4X_1 + 2X_2 + 0S_1 + S_2 = 32$ (available hours in Finishing Department)

where

X_1 = number of tables to produce daily

X_2 = number of benches to produce daily

S_1 = unused hours in the Assembly Department

S_2 = unused hours in the Finishing Department

with the further restriction that

$X_1 \geqslant 0, \quad X_2 \geqslant 0$ and $S_1 \geqslant 0, \quad S_2 \geqslant 0.$

Note that we have included all the variables in each of the equations. A complete mathematical formulation of a system of equations requires that any unknowns appearing in one equation must appear in all equations. In complying with this requirement, we have assumed that the slack variables S_1 and S_2 make no contribution—either positive or negative—toward profit; that is, we assume that no profit or loss is associated with unused units of the resources. These slack variables are thus written into the objective function with zero coefficients. Note also that, because a zero coefficient is assigned in each case, the addition of the slack variable S_2 to the Assembly Department constraint equation and the addition of the slack variable S_1 to the Finishing Department constraint equation does not in any way alter the basic relationships previously discussed between used and unused units of the resources.

SOME LINEAR PROGRAMMING TERMINOLOGY

Perhaps certain linear programming terminology should be introduced at this time.

Note that in the statement of the Furniture Manufacturing Company product mix problem there are four unknowns—X_1, X_2, S_1 and S_2—but only two equations. Whenever there are more unknowns than there are equations in a system, there can be no unique solution. However, given a system of m equations with $m + n$ unknowns, there does exist a unique solution if we set n of the variables equal to zero. In linear programming, a *basic solution* is a solution obtained by setting n variables equal to zero and solving the remaining m equations in m variables for the value of the m variables. The m variables are termed the *basic variables* or the *variables in solution* or the *basis*. The n variables which have zero values are termed *nonbasic variables* or the *variables not in solution*. There is a finite number of basic solutions. Not all basic solutions are feasible.

A *feasible solution* is a set of values for the variables in which all the restrictions of the problem situation are satisfied. The convex set outlined by the constraint equalities and inequalities is the collection of feasible solutions. There may be an infinite number of feasible solutions. On the other hand, if the set of constraints is such that no point in the positive quadrant satisfies all constraints, there will be no feasible solution.

A *basic feasible solution* is a feasible solution that is also a basic solution. A basic feasible solution always occurs where the feasible solution corresponds

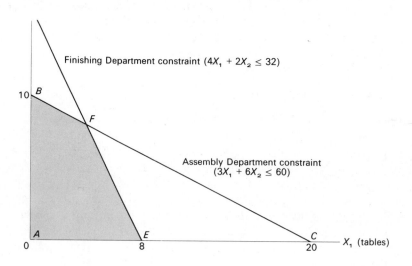

FIG. 4–1 Feasible, basic, and basic feasible solutions

to an extreme point, or a corner point, of the area of feasible solutions. There are only a finite number of basic feasible solutions.

Perhaps these terms can be more easily understood if we display them pictorially. In Fig. 4–1 the shaded area represents all "feasible" solutions. The "basic" solutions are at points A, B, D, F, E, and C. Note that at each of these points, two of the four variables have a zero value, two have a nonzero value: at point A, $X_1 = 0, X_2 = 0, S_1 = 60, S_2 = 32$; at point B, $X_1 = 0, X_2 = 10$, $S_1 = 0, S_2 = 12$; at point D, $X_1 = 0, X_2 = 16, S_1 = -36, S_2 = 0$; and so on. We see that at a basic solution the variables may have negative values. For this reason, not all basic solutions are feasible solutions. The "basic feasible" solutions are at points A, B, F, and E—the corner points of the area of feasible solutions.

An *optimal solution* is a basic feasible solution which optimizes the value of the objective function.

We have already defined a *slack variable* as a variable used to transform a less-than inequality into an equality. Let us call those variables that represent plans of action or strategies, such as X_1 and X_2 in the Furniture case, *activity variables or decision variables*.

THE INITIAL TABLEAU

Because the problem has been reduced to one of solving a set of linear equations, the mechanics of solving the equations are very similar to those of manipulating a Gaussian tableau. The simplex algorithm merely provides a systematic search process which assures an optimal solution in an orderly progression of steps, wherein each step improves the value of the objective function.

The initial simplex tableau is set up as follows:

A	I	b
$-c$	0	0

Matrix A constitutes the main body of the tableau and is made up of the coefficients of the activity variables. The entries in the I matrix are the coefficients of the slack variables and always constitute an identity matrix. Each column in the tableau is a column vector representing the coefficients of one of the variables, except that b is a vector representing the initial values on the right-hand side of the equations.

Each column, except the b column, is labeled with the variable it represents. The numbers in these columns, we shall see, represent exchange rates, or marginal rates of substitution, between the variables.

Each row in the tableau represents one equation, the bottom row (labeled $-c$) always representing the objective function equation. Each row in the initial tableau is labeled by the variable invented to transform that inequality into an equality.

The initial tableau for the Furniture Manufacturing Company is set forth in Fig. 4-2. Notice that each column is labeled with the name of the variable whose

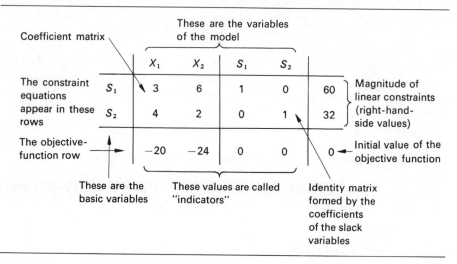

FIG. 4-2 *The initial tableau, Furniture Manufacturing Company Case*

coefficients appear therein.   Each row is labeled to denote the basic variable isolated in that equation.   The objective function coefficients are in the c vector and have been multiplied by a minus one.   (This manipulation will be explained fully in just a few moments).

The Slack Variables Are Isolated

The initial tableau assumes a starting point at the origin, where $X_1 = 0$ and $X_2 = 0$. In this way the slack variables are *isolated*.   A variable is said to be isolated in a Gaussian tableau if in its column vector the number one appears in the row that is labeled by this same variable and all other cell entries in the column are zeros.* These columns are also referred to as *control columns*.   The control column, or basic, variables are also the variables labeling the rows, and are called the *variables in solution*; that is, they are the variables which, at this point, have nonzero values.   The numbers in the rightmost column (the b vector) give the solution values of these variables.

---

* We will further explain the concept of isolating a variable in a Gaussian tableau when we discuss the procedure for reading the column entries as marginal rates of substitution.

The Row Labels and the b Vector

Mathematically speaking, in any equation in which a particular variable has a coefficient of unity and all other variables in the same equation either have coefficents of zero or have zero values themselves, the value of this particular variable appears on the right-hand side of the equation. For instance, consider the equation

$$3X_1 + 6X_2 + S_1 + 0S_2 = 60.$$

The variable S_1 has a coefficient of unity, S_2 has a zero coefficient, and both the other variables, X_1 and X_2, have been set equal to zero. Hence

$$3(0) + 6(0) + 1S_1 + 0S_2 = 60$$
$$S_1 = 60.$$

We may always read directly from the row labels and the b vector the basic variables and their values. Variables not used as row labels are nonbasic variables and have assumed zero values.

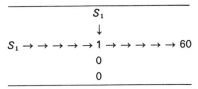

S_1
↓
$S_1 \rightarrow \rightarrow \rightarrow \rightarrow \rightarrow 1 \rightarrow \rightarrow \rightarrow \rightarrow \rightarrow 60$
0
0

FIG. 4–3 First row, third column of initial tableau

So we can read from the first row, third column of the initial tableau (see Fig. 4–3) that "$S_1 = 60$"; there are now 60 unused hours of assembly time. We can read from the second row, fourth column of this tableau (see Fig. 4–4) that "$S_2 = 32$"; there are now 32 unused hours of finishing time. We have manufactured no products and have used none of the scarce resources.

S_2
↓
0
$S_2 \rightarrow \rightarrow \rightarrow \rightarrow \rightarrow 1 \rightarrow \rightarrow \rightarrow \rightarrow \rightarrow 32$
0

FIG. 4–4 Second row, fourth column of initial tableau

The variables X_1 and X_2 are not basic variables; therefore they are not "in solution." They are, at this point, the variables with the zero values, or the nonbasic variables.

The Value of the Objective Function

The zero in the bottom row, rightmost column may be interpreted as the beginning value of the objective function. We have, as yet, realized no profit contribution.

A Technical Note on the
Objective-Function Row of the Initial Tableau

This text presents a method for entering the objective-function-row values of the initial tableau which is slightly different from that presented in many other linear programming texts. The method presented here was adopted because it is straightforward and easy to understand. However, a very important adjustment must be made in those special cases in which a variable in the initial basis has a nonzero objective-function coefficient! This adjustment is explained and illustrated in Chapter 16.

READING THE COLUMNS AS MARGINAL
RATES OF SUBSTITUTION

The numbers in the columns of the tableau represent marginal rates of substitution. It is essential that this concept be fully understood! Refer to Column 1 of the initial tableau (see Fig. 4–5) and note that **in order to gain one unit of** X_1 (a table)

	X_1	X_2	S_1	S_2	
S_1	3	6	1	0	60
S_2	4	2	0	1	32
	−20	−24	0	0	0

FIG. 4–5 *Column one of the initial tableau*

we must give up, or use, three units of S_1 (unused hours in the Assembly Department) **and four units of** S_2 (unused hours in the Finishing Department), **and in making this exchange we would lose minus \$20 in profit contribution.** Losing "minus" \$20 in profit contribution is exactly equivalent to gaining "plus" \$20! In everyday terminology, then, the column 1 numbers tell us that in order to make

	X_1	X_2	S_1	S_2	
S_1	3	6	1	0	60
S_2	4	2	0	1	32
	−20	−24	0	0	0

FIG. 4–6 *Column two of the initial tableau*

a table, we use three assembly hours and four finishing hours and by so doing we realize a profit contribution of $20.

The second column of the tableau (see Fig. 4–6) can be interpreted in this same manner. **To gain one unit of X_2 (a bench) we must give up, or use, six units of S_1** (unused hours in the Assembly Department) **and two units of S_2** (unused hours in the Finishing Department) **and to do so will result in the loss of minus $24 profit contribution.** And again, the loss of a minus $24 profit contribution is equivalent to the gain of a positive $24 profit contribution! Or in more practical terms, to make a bench, we must use six hours of assembly time and two hours of finishing time; and this action will increase the value of the objective function by $24.

The reason for the minus signs attached to the profit coefficients should be more apparent now. They make possible a consistent interpretation of the entire column vector. To "give up" a minus value is to "gain" a positive value.

Every column in the tableau, except the rightmost column, is read in this way. **To gain a unit of the column heading, we lose, or give up, (the cell value) units of the row label.**

Reading the Control Columns

Notice the interpretation of the control columns—the S_1 and S_2 columns in the initial tableau (see Fig. 4–7). We read "to gain a unit of S_1 we must give up one unit of S_1 (with no other effects); to gain a unit of S_2 we must give up one unit of S_2 (with no other effects)". These variables are expressed in terms of themselves —they have been "isolated". Variables that are not control column variables are expressed in terms of other variables. X_1, for example, was expressed in terms of units of S_1 and S_2. X_2 also was expressed in terms of other variables, S_1 and S_2.

	X_1	X_2	S_1	S_2	
S_1	3	6	1	0	60
S_2	4	2	0	1	32
	−20	−24	0	0	0

FIG 4–7   The control columns of the initial tableau

Initial Tableau Represents Marginal Rate of Substitution at Origin Only

The initial tableau presents the substitution picture at the "make zero units" solution. The marginal rates of substitution shown here are applicable to this point on the graph.   In later tableaus, from other corner points, different marginal rates of substitution prevail.   Nonetheless, the columns of the tableaus may always be read in the same way.

PIVOTING THE TABLEAU

The initial tableau represents one corner of the area of feasible solutions.   In order to move to another corner, the matrix must be altered so that one of the basic variables is changed to zero and one of the nonbasic variables is brought into solution.   The various coefficients and constants must be changed accordingly. This manipulation is effected by *pivoting* the tableau.   (A pivoting is also termed an *iteration* of the tableau.)   The tableau is pivoted about an element known as the *pivot number*.   The pivot number is always that number in the cell at the intersection of (1) the row corresponding to the basic variable which goes out of solution and (2) the column corresponding to the nonbasic variable coming into solution.

There are, then, two crucial decisions that must be made.   First, we must determine which nonbasic variable (if any) should be entered into the solution; and second, we must determine which basic variable should be eliminated from the basis.

Determining Which Variable will Enter into Solution

Let us refer to the numbers in the bottom row (the objective function coefficients) of the tableau, excluding the right-hand corner number, as *indicators*.   Recall that a negative number in this row represents a positive contribution to the objective.   Thus the variable labeling the column with the most negative indicator (the negative number farthest removed from zero, as shown in Fig. 4–8) is the

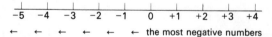

FIG. 4–8   The most negative numbers are those farthest removed from zero in the minus direction

variable that could, at this time, make the greatest profit contribution.   In choosing the variable to be entered into solution, it seems reasonable, since maximization of profit contribution is our goal, that we choose the variable that will make the greatest profit contribution; that is, we choose as the "incoming variable" the variable with the most negative indicator.   This column becomes the *pivot column* for the first iteration of the model.

Refer to Fig. 4–9 and note that the X_2 column is the column with the most negative indicator; thus this is the pivot column for the first iteration of the Furniture Company linear programming model.   The incoming variable is X_2, representing the number of benches to make each day.   Of the nonbasic variables— at this point these are X_1 and X_2—each unit of X_2 (each bench) makes a larger contribution to profit ($24) than does a unit of X_1 (a table, which contributes only $20). (Graphically, we have decided to move away from the origin by moving along the X_2-axis rather than along the X_1-axis.)

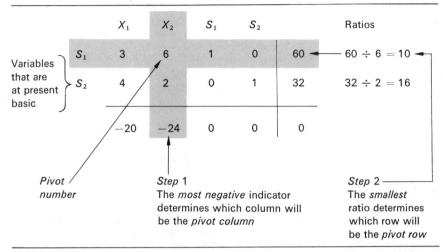

FIG. 4–9   *Selecting the pivot column and the pivot row. X_2 yields the highest contribution to profit per unit produced and is thus chosen as the variable to be entered into solution. Ten units of X_2 can be produced without violating the time constraint of either department. All unused hours of assembly time will be needed to produce the ten units of X_2; hence S_1 is the variable going out of solution.*

Determining Which Variable Will Go Out of Solution

Having decided which variable to introduce into solution, we must now determine how many units of this product we can introduce. (Graphically, we must determine how far along the X_2-axis we can travel before running into a constraint line.) We can make this determination by setting up ratios between the numbers in the rightmost column—the b vector—and the numbers in the pivot column, excluding those numbers from the objective function row.

We can interpret these ratios as follows:

For row 1, where the Assembly Department constraint is outlined, the ratio is $60/6 = 10$,

which indicates that because there is a total of 60 hours of Assembly Department time available, and because each unit of X_2 requires six hours in the Assembly Department, ten units of X_2 could be processed if the Assembly Department time were the only constraint.

For row 2, where the Finishing Department constraint is outlined, the ratio is

$32/2 = 16$,

which indicates that because a total of 32 hours is available in the Finishing Department, and because each unit of X_2 requires two hours of processing in this department, 16 units of X_2 could be produced if the time in the Finishing Department were the only constraint imposed on production.

Obviously, the most restrictive constraint insofar as X_2 is concerned is the time available in the Assembly Department; this is reflected by the fact that this row yielded the smallest ratio. We must live within the most limiting constraint. The maximum number of units of X_2 which we might produce without violating any constraint is ten. The row with the smallest ratio is the *pivot row* for this iteration of the tableau. The pivot row variable is completely utilized. When 10 units of X_2 are produced there will remain zero units of unused assembly time; thus S_1 is the variable going out of solution (see Fig. 4–9).

Importance of the Pivot Row and Pivot Column

Note these things about the selection of the pivot row in a "maximizing" linear programming model. The ratio dictating which row will be the pivot can never be infinity, nor can it be a negative number. An infinite ratio would arise when a variable used zero units of the variable currently described by the row, thereby indicating that as far as this row was concerned an infinite quantity of the column variable could be introduced. A negative ratio would indicate that introduction of the column variable would actually increase the supply of the row variable. This, of course, could be repeated forever before running out of the row variable. Hence, in a maximizing linear programming problem, ratios are not established for rows which have zero or negative values in the pivot column. Ratios are established only for rows with a pivot column value which is greater than zero. (Note that a negative ratio could arise if the value of the row variable in solution were negative. No variable in linear programming can assume a negative value. Therefore, this condition would indicate an error in the preceding tableau, probably a failure to select the most restrictive constraint.)

Actually, we would arrive at a correct solution even if we were to choose some column other than that column with the most negative indicator as the pivot column. The indicator merely denotes the profit to be gained by introducing a unit of that variable and to select a negative indicator other than the most negative indicator will only send us on a search pattern which will be generally longer. The pattern will lead us to the same place eventually. But we cannot arrive at a correct solution if the wrong ratio is selected. Selection of the incorrect ratio will lead to an impossible solution. Since the smallest ratio represents the quantity of the variable which will fully utilize the most restrictive constraint, to select another pivot would result in our exceeding this constraint.

Again, the pivot row variable is the outgoing or departing variable. After this tableau is pivoted, this variable will assume a zero value (become nonbasic). The pivot column variable is the incoming or entering variable; it will, generally, assume a nonzero value (become basic).

CALCULATING THE NEW PIVOT ROW

In order to bring a variable into solution, we must isolate that variable in a column. This means that the column for X_2, the incoming variable, must be transformed into this format:

$$
\begin{array}{c}
X_2 \\
\downarrow \\
X_2 \rightarrow \rightarrow \rightarrow \rightarrow \rightarrow \rightarrow 1 \rightarrow \rightarrow \rightarrow \rightarrow \\
0 \\
0
\end{array}
$$

To bring the pivot column variable into solution, we first divide the pivot row by the pivot number to obtain a "one" in the pivot number position. (The pivot number is always the number in the cell at the intersection of the pivot row and the pivot column.) Thus we make the computation:

(Old pivot-row values) ÷ (Pivot number) = (New pivot-row values)

(3 6 1 0 60)   ÷ (6)   = (1/2 1 1/6 0 10)

This result becomes the new row 1 in the next tableau. This new row 1 is labeled with the label of the incoming variable (see Fig. 4–10).

Partial Initial Tableau

	X_1	X_2	S_1	S_2		
S_1	3	6	1	0	60	(old pivot row)

The pivot number

The old pivot row is divided by the pivot number. The result is entered in the new tableau, labeled with the old pivot-column label.

Partial Second Tableau

	X_1	X_2	S_1	S_2		
X_2	1/2	1	1/6	0	10	(new pivot row)

↑
The row label
is that of the
incoming variable

FIG. 4–10   Calculation of the new pivot row

Converting from one Marginal Rate of Substitution to Another

Let us explain the manipulation just performed. Since the variable in the old solution (the pivot-row variable) is to be replaced by the incoming variable (the pivot-column variable), the row must be converted from a description of the former to a description of the latter. The pivot number in the old tableau represents the quantity of the variable going out of solution that will substitute for one unit of the incoming variable. We read that six units of S_1 (unused assembly hours) are needed for each unit of X_2 (bench). All the other numbers in the pivot row are substitution rates describing gains and losses in terms of the outgoing variable. In dividing these numbers by the pivot number, or multiplying by its reciprocal, we obtain marginal substitutions in terms of the new, or incoming, variable.

For example, the old pivot row values were these:

	X_1	X_2	S_1	S_2	
S_1	3	6	1	0	60

$\uparrow$

The values in this row tell us how many units of S_1 we would have to give up in order to gain one unit of the variable heading the column. That is, to gain one unit of X_1 (a table), we must give up three units of S_1 (among other things, which we need not consider at this time); to gain one unit of X_2, we must give up six units of S_1; and so on.

The variable X_2 is the variable coming into solution; S_1 is going out of solution. In the next tableau, we must be able to read from the first row the substitution rates between the variables heading the columns and X_2, rather than S_1. So we must make this conversion. The pivot number represents the marginal rate of substitution between the outgoing variable and the incoming variable:

$$S_1\text{-to-}X_2 \quad \text{or} \quad S_1/X_1 = 6/1 \quad \text{or} \quad 6\text{-to-}1.$$

It follows that the reciprocal of the pivot number would represent the marginal rate of substitution between the incoming variable and the outgoing variable:

$$X_2\text{-to-}S_1 \quad \text{or} \quad X_2/S_1 = 1/6 \quad \text{or} \quad 1\text{-to-}6.$$

Hence, by dividing each number in the old pivot row by the pivot number (which is equivalent to multiplying by the reciprocal of the pivot number), we effect the desired conversion. Let us see.

To gain a unit of X_2 we will have to give up six units of S_1. To gain a unit of X_1 we will have to give up three units of S_1. Now, if the exchange rate between S_1 and X_1 is three to one (we give up three S_1's to gain one X_1) while the exchange rate between S_1 and X_2 is six to one (we give up six S_1's to acquire one X_2), we shall have to give up $\frac{3}{6}$, or $\frac{1}{2}$, units of X_2 to gain one unit of X_1. In other words, $\frac{1}{2}$ unit of X_2 is substitutable for three units of S_1 which are, in turn, substitutable for one unit of X_1. Mathematically, we may state

$$\frac{S_1}{X_1} \times \frac{X_2}{S_1} = \frac{X_2}{X_1}$$

$$\frac{3}{1} \times \frac{1}{6} = \frac{3}{6} = \frac{1}{2}.$$

We enter into the new tableau the substitution rate between X_2 and X_1 as shown below:

$$X_1 \quad X_2 \quad S_1 \quad S_2$$
$$X_2 \quad 1/2$$
$$\uparrow$$

The next value entered into the new tableau is in the first-row, second-column position and represents the substitution rate between X_2 (the row variable) and X_2 (the column variable) as shown:

$$X_1 \quad X_2 \quad S_1 \quad S_2$$
$$X_2 \quad 1/2 \quad 1$$
$$\uparrow$$

We may actually use the same logic to explain this entry as we used to explain the preceding one. We are converting from substitution rates in terms of S_1 to substitution rates in terms of X_2. In the original tableau we saw that the substitution rate between S_1 and X_2 was six to one. Then,

$$\frac{S_1}{X_2} \times \frac{X_2}{S_1} = \frac{X_2}{X_2}$$

$$\frac{6}{1} \times \frac{1}{6} = 1$$

Next, if to gain a unit of X_2 is to give up six units of S_1, to gain a unit of S_1 is to give up $\frac{1}{6}$ units of X_2. And we fill in this cell in the new tableau accordingly:

$$X_1 \quad X_2 \quad S_1 \quad S_2$$
$$X^2 \quad 1/2 \quad 1 \quad 1/6$$
$$\uparrow$$

We actually computed

$$\frac{1}{1} \times \frac{1}{6} = \frac{1}{6}$$

The substitution rate in the last tableau between S_1 and S_2 was zero to one. Hence the entry in the S_2 column will not change.

$$X_1 \quad X_2 \quad S_1 \quad S_2$$
$$X_2 \quad 1/2 \quad 1 \quad 1/6 \quad 0$$
$$\uparrow$$

All the computations involved in bringing the pivot row from the old into the new tableau were of this basic form:

$$\begin{bmatrix} \text{Substitution rate} \\ \text{between outgoing} \\ \text{variable and} \\ \text{column variable} \end{bmatrix} \times \begin{bmatrix} \text{Substitution rate} \\ \text{between incoming} \\ \text{variable and} \\ \text{outgoing variable} \end{bmatrix} = \begin{bmatrix} \text{Substitution rate} \\ \text{between incoming} \\ \text{variable and} \\ \text{column variable} \end{bmatrix}$$

Computing the Value of the Incoming Variable

The last entry in the row is the value of the variable X_2 at this point. If we had 60 units of S_1 and each unit of X_2 requires six units of S_1, we would be able to produce ten units of X_2.

$$\begin{array}{ccccc} & X_1 & X_2 & S_1 & S_2 \\ X_2 & 1/2 & 1 & 1/6 & 0 & 10 \\ & & & \uparrow \end{array}$$

Thus, in dividing the old pivot row (representing the outgoing variable) by the pivot number (representing the marginal rate of substitution between the outgoing and the incoming variable), we convert the row from a description of the substitution rates for the outgoing variable to a description of the substitution rates for the incoming variable.

TRANSFERRING THE OTHER ROWS INTO THE NEW TABLEAU

However, the X_2 variable is isolated only if all other numbers in the X_2 column are forced to zero. This is accomplished, one row at a time, by multiplying the *new* pivot row by the number in the pivot column and subtracting this result from the row being transferred. The difference row is brought into the new tableau in that row position. Its label is not changed.

For example, to force a zero in the pivot column of the second row and thus obtain the second row for the new tableau, we proceed as follows:

1. Multiply the new pivot row by the number in row 2, pivot column of the original tableau:

$$(1/2 \quad 1 \quad 1/6 \quad 0 \quad 10) \times (2) = (1 \quad 2 \quad 1/3 \quad 0 \quad 20).$$

2. Subtract the result obtained in Step (1) from the old row 2:

$$(4 \quad 2 \quad 0 \quad 1 \quad 32) - (1 \quad 2 \quad 1/3 \quad 0 \quad 20) = (3 \quad 0 \quad -1/3 \quad 1 \quad 12).$$

3. Enter the result from Step (2) in the new tableau in the row 2 position. The row retains its previous label. (See Fig. 4–11.)

Partial Initial Tableau

	X_1	X_2	S_1	S_2		
						Old
S_2	4	2	0	1	32	row 2

↑
Pivot column

Partial Second Tableau

	X_1	X_2	S_1	S_2		
						New
X_2	1/2	1	1/6	0	10	pivot
						row

The calculations are made as follows:

1) New pivot row is multiplied by value from row 2 pivot column old tableau

(1/2 1 1/6 0 10) × (2) = (1 2 1/3 0 20).

2) The result is subtracted from the old row 2

(4 2 0 1 32) − (1 2 1/3 0 20) = (3 0 −1/3 1 12)′

3) The difference is entered into the new tableau in the row 2 position; this row retaining its original label.

Partial Second Tableau

	X_1	X_2	S_1	S_2	
X_2	1/2	1	1/6	0	10
S_2	3	0	−1/3	1	12

FIG. 4–11   Calculation of the new row 2

Computing the New Exchange Rates

Although this row is still in terms of the variable S_2 when it is transferred from the old tableau to the new tableau, it must reflect the marginal rates of substitution that exist at this basic feasible solution and not those that existed at the previous basic feasible solution. We can see from the graph in Fig. 4–12 that the first tableau represented the point of origin—point *A*—on the area of feasible solutions, where $X_1 = 0$ and $X_2 = 0$. When we decided to make as many units of X_2 as we could manufacture, we moved from point *A* along the X_2-axis to point *B*, where $X_1 = 0$ and $X_2 = 10$. The second tableau must represent this point. The exchange rates shown in the second tableau, then, must be those that prevail, not at the origin, but at corner point *B*.

The value at the intersection of the S_2 row and the X_1 column in the new tableau (see Fig. 4–13) indicates that to gain a unit of X_1 is to use three units of S_2. S_2 represents unused finishing time, and we recall from the statement of the problem that each X_1 requires four hours of processing in the Finishing Department. So let's see how this exchange rate was brought about. We are at the solution point at which, in order to gain an X_1 we must give up $\frac{1}{2}$ unit of X_2.

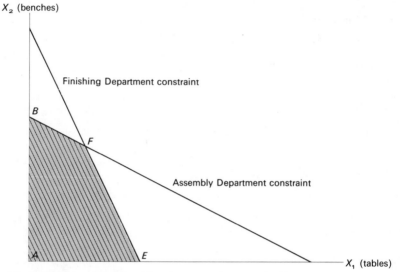

FIG. 4–12   *The area of feasible solutions: The second tableau will represent point B on the area of feasible solutions.*

Each X_2 manufactured requires two hours of finishing time (two units of S_2). In giving up $\frac{1}{2}$ unit of X_2, we regain $(\frac{1}{2})(2) = 1$ hour of finishing time. Hence the net effect of producing one unit of X_1, at this point, is to use

$$4 - (1/2)(2) = 3$$

units of S_2.

	X_1	X_2	S_1	S_2	
X_2	1/2	1	1/6	0	10
S_2	3				
	↑				

FIG. 4–13   *Partial second tableau*

From the X_2 column of the new S_2 row (see Fig. 4–14), we read that to gain a unit of X_2 is to use zero units of S_2. Again, from the original statement of the problem, we know that each unit of X_2 that is manufactured must be processed for two hours in the Finishing Department, and thus uses two units of S_2.

	X_1	X_2	S_1	S_2	
X_2	1/2	1	1/6	0	10
S_2	3	0			
			↑		

FIG. 4–14 *Partial second tableau*

However, at this corner point, the only way to gain an X_2 is to give up an X_2; therefore, the net effect is that

$$2 - (1)(2) = 0$$

units of S_2 will be exchanged for each unit of X_2.

	X_1	X_2	S_1	S_2	
X_2	1/2	1	1/6	0	10
S_2	3	0	−1/3		
			↑		

FIG. 4–15 *Partial second tableau*

Moving to the S_1 column (see Fig. 4–15), we read that to gain a unit of S_1 (a unit of unused assembly time) is to give up minus $\frac{1}{3}$ units of S_2, which is to gain $\frac{1}{3}$ units of unused finishing time. To gain one S_1 we must give up $\frac{1}{6}$ unit of X_2. Each X_2 requires two units of S_2. Hence the result is that for each unit of S_1 gained,

$$0 - (1/6)(2) = -1/3$$

units of S_2 are used.

	X_1	X_2	S_1	S_2	
X_2	1/2	1	1/6	0	10
S_2	3	0	−1/3	1	
			↑		

FIG. 4–16 *Partial second tableau*

The S_2 column of the S_2 row (see Fig. 4–16) reads "to gain a unit of S_2 is to give up a unit of S_2." The number results from the computation

$$1 - (0)(2) = 1.$$

We should note that S_2 is still a basic variable.

All these values in the new row were actually computed by:

$$\begin{bmatrix} \text{Old} \\ \text{exchange} \\ \text{rate} \\ \text{between} \\ \text{row} \\ \text{variable} \\ \text{and} \\ \text{column} \\ \text{variable} \end{bmatrix} - \begin{bmatrix} \text{New} \\ \text{exchange} \\ \text{rate} \\ \text{between} \\ \text{variable} \\ \text{coming} \\ \text{into} \\ \text{solution} \\ \text{and} \\ \text{column} \\ \text{variable} \end{bmatrix} \times \begin{bmatrix} \text{Old} \\ \text{exchange} \\ \text{rate} \\ \text{between} \\ \text{row} \\ \text{variable} \\ \text{and} \\ \text{variable} \\ \text{coming} \\ \text{into} \\ \text{solution} \end{bmatrix} = \begin{bmatrix} \text{New} \\ \text{exchange} \\ \text{rate} \\ \text{between} \\ \text{row} \\ \text{variable} \\ \text{and} \\ \text{column} \\ \text{variable} \end{bmatrix}$$

This is simply to say that the new exchange rate is the old exchange rate adjusted by the effect of our being forced to work through the incoming variable.

Computing the New b Vector Value

The number in the second row of the b vector (see Fig. 4–17) shows that the value of the variable S_2 is, at this corner point, 12. The computation was made

$$32 - (10)(2) = 12.$$

There were available—prior to the decision to bring X_2 into solution—32 hours of unused finishing time. Each unit of X_2 requires two hours of finishing time. We have tentatively decided to produce ten units of X_2, which would require that we use $(10)(2) = 20$ of those 32 hours of finishing time. This action would leave $32 - 20 = 12$ unused hours of finishing time.

	X_1	X_2	S_1	S_2	
X_2	1/2	1	1/6	0	10
S_2	3	0	−1/3	1	12
				↑	

FIG. 4–17   *Partial second tableau*

TRANSFERRING THE OBJECTIVE FUNCTION ROW

The old row 3, which is the objective function row, is brought into the new tableau in the same way as was row 2.

1. Multiply the new pivot row by the number in row 3, pivot column of the original tableau:

$$(1/2 \ 1 \ 1/6 \ 0 \ 10) \times (-24) = (-12 \ -24 \ -4 \ 0 \ -240).$$

2. Subtract the result from Step (1) from the old row 3:

$$(-20 \ -24 \ 0 \ 0 \ 0) - (-12 \ -24 \ -4 \ 0 \ -240) = (-8 \ 0 \ 4 \ 0 \ 240).$$

3. Enter the result from Step (2) into the row 3 position of the new tableau.

The completed second tableau is shown in Fig. 4–18.

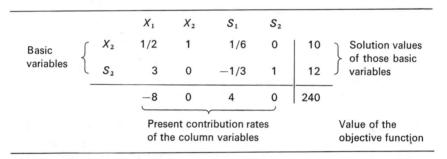

FIG. 4–18   *The completed second tableau*

Computing the New Contribution Coefficients

Again, let us move across this row from one number to the next and determine how these values were calculated and what they represent. Let us begin by referring to Fig. 4–19. Each unit of X_1 makes a profit contribution of $20. This

	X_1	X_2	S_1	S_2	
X_2	1/2	1	1/6	0	10
S_2	3	0	−1/3	1	12
	−8				
	↑				

FIG. 4–19   *Partial second tableau*

was shown as "-20" in the objective function row, X_1 column of the initial tableau. However, at this point, for each unit of X_1 we decide to make, we will have to give up $\frac{1}{2}$ unit of X_2 (see the X_1 column of Fig. 4–18). Now each unit of X_2 makes a profit contribution of $24. The net effect of producing a unit of X_1, then, is

$$(-20) - (1/2)(-24) = -8.$$

This indicates that we would now only increase the value of the objective function by $8 for each unit of X_1 we produce.

	X_1	X_2	S_1	S_2	
X_2	1/2	1	1/6	0	10
S_2	3	0	−1/3	1	12
	−8	0			
		↑			

FIG. 4–20   *Partial second tableau*

The new objective function value of X_2 is shown in Fig. 4–20 as zero. Although each unit of X_2 makes a $24 profit contribution, we can now gain an X_2 only by giving up an X_2. Thus the result insofar as the value of the objective function is concerned is

$$(-24) - (1)(-24) = 0.$$

The new tableau shows that to increase S_1 by one unit is to decrease the value of the objective function by four units (see Fig. 4–21). S_1 (unused units of assembly time) makes no direct contribution to profit. However, in order to gain a unit of

	X_1	X_2	S_1	S_2	
X_2	1/2	1	1/6	0	10
S_2	3	0	−1/3	1	12
	−8	0	4		
			↑		

FIG. 4–21   *Partial second tableau*

S_1, we have to give up $\frac{1}{6}$ unit of X_2 and each unit of X_2 makes a \$24 profit contribution. Thus the effect on the objective function is

$$0 - (1/6)(-24) = 4$$

which means we lose a \$4 profit contribution for every hour of assembly time we decide not to use. Recall that this solution required that all available assembly hours be utilized.

From the next column (see Fig. 4–22) we read that to gain a unit of S_2 is to have no effect on the value of the objective function. The variable S_2 does not make a direct contribution to profit. The way, at this solution point, to gain a unit of S_2 is only to give up a unit of S_2. To gain a unit of S_2 does not alter the solution value of X_2, which has an objective function coefficient of \$24. Thus the computation

$$0 - (0)(-24) = 0.$$

Notice that there are available unused units of finishing time.

	X_1	X_2	S_1	S_2	
X_2	1/2	1	1/6	0	10
S_2	3	0	−1/3	1	12
	−8	0	4	0	
				↑	

FIG. 4–22 Partial second tableau

Again, the computations of these values follow a pattern. Note that all the values in the objective-function row of the second tableau were obtained by the basic procedure:

$$\begin{bmatrix} \text{Prior} \\ \text{contribu-} \\ \text{tion to} \\ \text{objective} \\ \text{function} \\ \text{of column} \\ \text{variable} \\ \text{(multiplied} \\ \text{by } -1) \end{bmatrix} - \begin{bmatrix} \text{Exchange} \\ \text{rate} \\ \text{between} \\ \text{incoming} \\ \text{variable} \\ \text{and} \\ \text{column} \\ \text{variable} \end{bmatrix} \times \begin{bmatrix} \text{Contribu-} \\ \text{tion to} \\ \text{objective} \\ \text{function of} \\ \text{incoming} \\ \text{variable} \end{bmatrix} = \begin{bmatrix} \text{Current} \\ \text{net contri-} \\ \text{bution} \\ \text{of column} \\ \text{variable to} \\ \text{objective} \\ \text{function} \end{bmatrix}$$

Computing the New Value of Objective Function

The number in the b vector, objective-function row is the value of the objective function at this basic feasible solutions (see Fig. 4–23). The value of the objective function at the preceding solution point was zero. This solution introduces ten units of X_2, each unit making a contribution to profit of $24. Thus

$$0 - (10)(-24) = 240$$

is the objective function value of this solution.

	X_1	X_2	S_1	S_2	
X_2	1/2	1	1/6	0	10
S_2	3	0	−1/3	1	12
	−8	0	4	0	240
				↑	

FIG. 4–23 *Partial second tableau*

The rules for pivoting the simplex tableau are outlined in Fig. 4–24.

I. *Determine which variable will enter into solution.* Determine which nonbasic variable will, when increased, make the greatest per-unit contribution to the objective function. These contributions can be read from the "indicators"—the numbers in the bottom row of the tableau. Select the variable whose column has the most negative indicator. This column, let us assume it is column *j*, is the *pivot column.*

II. *Determine which variable will go out of solution.* Determine which basic variable reaches a zero value first as the entering variable is increased. This can be accomplished by setting up ratios between the numbers in the pivot column and numbers in the *b* vector. For each a_{ij} in column *j* which is greater than zero, find the quotient b_i/a_{ij}. The row that provides the smallest quotient becomes the *pivot row.* The a_{ij} is the *pivot number.*

III. *Determine the new basic feasible solution.* The rows from this tableau are carried forward into a new tableau by following these steps:

(A)   Divide the pivot row by the pivot number to obtain the new pivot row. Insert the new row in the position corresponding to the original row in the new tableau, labeling the new row with the label of the pivot column.

(B)   Move all other rows from the old tableau to the new tableau following this procedure:
1) Multiply the new pivot row by the number in the pivot column of the row being transferred.
2) Subtract the result obtained in (1) from the row being transferred.
3) Enter the result from (2) in the new tableau in the corresponding position of the old row being replaced.
4) Do not change the row label in the new tableau.

IV. *Determine whether or not this solution is an optimal solution.* After all rows have been transferred from the old tableau to the new tableau, check to see whether or not there are any negative indicators. If there is a negative indicator, return to Step I and repeat the steps outlined above. If there are no negative indicators, the process is complete and this tableau represents an optimal solution.

FIG. 4–24 *Procedure for pivoting the simplex tableau*

INTERPRETING THE SECOND TABLEAU

Let us see what we have accomplished. The row labels indicate those variables that are now in solution; the rightmost column indicates the solution quantities associated with these variables. Hence we are at the point at which ten units of X_2 (ten benches) are being produced and there are twelve units of S_2 remaining (twelve hours of unused time in the Finishing Department). The variables X_1 and S_1 are not in solution; this means that no units of X_1 (no tables) are being produced and there are no unused Assembly Department hours.

Let us check the consistency of these statements. We have these values for the variables:

$$X_1 = 0 \qquad S_1 = 0$$
$$X_2 = 10 \qquad S_2 = 12.$$

For the Assembly Department constraint, we obtain

$$3(0) + 6(10) + S_1 + 0S_2 = 60$$
$$S_1 = 0.$$

For the Finishing Department constraint, we obtain

$$4(0) + 2(10) + 0S_1 + S_2 = 32$$
$$S_2 = 12.$$

The number in the bottom cell of the right-hand column is the value of the objective function at this solution point. We see that

$$20(0) + 24(10) = 240.$$

Reading the X_1 Column

Still other information is available from the numbers in the body of the tableau. Let us interpret the exchange rates as shown in the X_1 column (see Fig. 4–25). To gain one unit of X_1 (one table) we would have to give up $\frac{1}{2}$ unit of X_2 ($\frac{1}{2}$ bench) and three units of S_2 (three hours of unused time in the Finishing Department)

	X_1	X_2	S_1	S_2	
X_2	1/2	1	1/6	0	10
S_2	3	0	−1/3	1	12
	−8	0	4	0	240

FIG. 4–25 Column one of the second tableau

and give up, as well, minus \$8 toward the objective (which is to gain a positive \$8 toward the objective). In other words, we could increase the total profit contribution by a maximum of \$8 if we produced one unit of X_1. The optimal way to produce one unit of X_1—the way that will yield the \$8 increase in the objective function value—is by producing $\frac{1}{2}$ unit less of X_2 and thereby using a net of three hours more in the Finishing Department. Let us check the consistency of these statements.

The variables would assume these values:

$$X_1 = 0 + 1 = 1$$
$$X_2 = 10 - \tfrac{1}{2} = 9\tfrac{1}{2}$$
$$S_1 = 0$$
$$S_2 = 12 - 3 = 9.$$

Unused hours in the two processing departments would become:

Assembly Department:
$$3(1) + 6(9\tfrac{1}{2}) + S_1 + 0S_2 = 60$$
$$S_1 = 0$$

Finishing Department:
$$4(1) + 2(9\tfrac{1}{2}) + 0S_1 + S_2 = 32$$
$$S_2 = 9.$$

Total profit contribution would become

$$20(1) + 24(9\tfrac{1}{2}) = 248$$

which is the same as

$$240 + 8 = 248.$$

Reading the S_1 Column

Column 3, the S_1 column, of this tableau (see Fig. 4–26) may be interpreted in a somewhat analogous manner. To gain one unit of S_1 (one unused hour of

	X_1	X_2	S_1	S_2	
X_2	1/2	1	1/6	0	10
S_2	3	0	−1/3	1	12
	−8	0	4	0	240

FIG. 4–26 *Column 3 of the second tableau*

Assembly Department time), we must give up 1/6 units of X_2 and minus 1/3 units of S_1 as well as four units toward profit contribution. In other words, we are at a point where we have no unused time in the Assembly Department. To obtain one hour of unused assembly time, we would be forced to make 1/6 of a unit fewer of X_2, we would gain 1/3 of an hour of unused Finishing Department time. (Recall that to give up a minus number is to gain a positive number.) In making this exchange we would lose \$4 profit contribution.

Again let us verify these statements. The values of the variables become

$$X_1 = 0$$
$$X_2 = 10 - \tfrac{1}{6} = 9\tfrac{5}{6}$$
$$S_1 = 0 + 1 = 1$$
$$S_2 = 12 + \tfrac{1}{3} = 12\tfrac{1}{3}$$

The constraint functions can be solved as follows:

Assembly Department:
$$3(0) + 6(9\tfrac{5}{6}) + S_1 + 0S_2 = 60$$
$$S_1 = 1$$

Finishing Department:
$$4(0) + 2(9\tfrac{5}{6}) + 0S_1 + S_2 = 32$$
$$S_2 = 12\tfrac{1}{3}.$$

Profit contribution would total

$$20(0) + 24(9\tfrac{5}{6}) = 236$$

which is \$4 less than before, or

$$240 - 4 = 236.$$

	X_1	X_2	S_1	S_2	
X_2	1/2	1	1/6	0	10
S_2	3	0	−1/3	1	12
	−8	0	4	0	240

FIG. 4–27 *Column 2 of the second tableau*

Both these columns—the X_1 column and the S_1 column—represent variables that do not appear in the solution at this juncture. These columns are interpreted in the light of the consequence of forcing one unit of the variable into solution.

The other columns in the body of the matrix represent variables presently in solution. An attempt to interpret these columns in the light of bringing another unit of the variable into solution is somewhat superfluous. For instance, we can read column 2 of the tableau (see Fig. 4–27) "to gain one unit of X_2 we must give up one unit of X_2 with no effect on the other variables nor on the objective function value."

ANOTHER ITERATION OF THE TABLEAU

Let us return to our search for the optimal solution to the problem facing Furniture Manufacturing Company. First, have we reached an optimal solution? We know that we have not because we have just seen that to introduce one unit of X_1 (a table) would increase profit contribution by $8. We also know, because the constraints are linear, that if it is desirable to introduce one unit of X_1 it will be desirable to continue to introduce more of these units, until we are stopped by a constraint. Graphically, if it is desirable to move along a constraint line, it will be desirable to continue along that line to a corner point.

We can also know by looking at the numbers on the bottom row of the tableau that this is not the optimal solution. A negative value among the indicator values always means that we can move closer to our objective by exchanging units that are presently in solution for other units that are not now in solution. *A negative indicator always means that another pivoting of the tableau is required.*

Selecting the Pivot Row and Pivot Column

Let us move to still another tableau then. To begin, the column with the most negative indicator—here it is the first, or X_1, column—is the pivot column. (See Fig. 4–28.) Ratios are set up to determine how many units of this variable can be brought into solution at this time.

For row 1 the ratio is

$$10 \div 1/2 = 20$$

which means that 20 units of X_1 could be introduced by exchanging them for X_2's.

For row 2 the ratio is

$$12 \div 3 = 4$$

which means that the constraint of remaining available time in the Finishing Department would keep us from producing more than four units of X_1.

The smallest ratio—the most restrictive constraint—is associated with the second row; this row, then, becomes the pivot row. Units of X_1 will be brought into solution; units of S_2 will go out of solution.

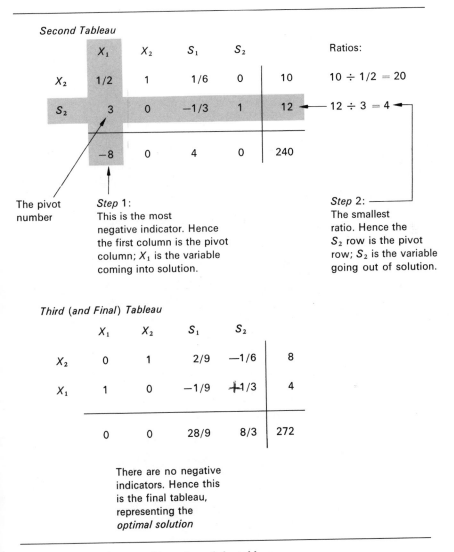

Second Tableau

	X_1	X_2	S_1	S_2		Ratios:
X_2	1/2	1	1/6	0	10	$10 \div 1/2 = 20$
S_2	3	0	−1/3	1	12	$12 \div 3 = 4$
	−8	0	4	0	240	

The pivot number

Step 1:
This is the most negative indicator. Hence the first column is the pivot column; X_1 is the variable coming into solution.

Step 2:
The smallest ratio. Hence the S_2 row is the pivot row; S_2 is the variable going out of solution.

Third (and Final) Tableau

	X_1	X_2	S_1	S_2	
X_2	0	1	2/9	−1/6	8
X_1	1	0	−1/9	+1/3	4
	0	0	28/9	8/3	272

There are no negative indicators. Hence this is the final tableau, representing the *optimal solution*

FIG. 4–28 *The second iteration of the tableau*

Calculations Required for the New Tableau

The row 2 column 1 cell contains the pivot number. In order to transfer the pivot row into the new tableau, we divide the pivot row by the pivot number:

$$(3 \quad 0 \quad −1/3 \quad 1 \quad 12) \div (3) = (1 \quad 0 \quad −1/9 \quad 1/3 \quad 4)$$

This result goes into the new tableau, labeled with the pivot column label;

that is,

$$X_1 \quad X_2 \quad S_1 \quad S_2$$

X_1	1	0	$-1/9$	$1/3$	4

All other rows in the second tableau must be transferred into the third tableau (the goal being to obtain a zero in the pivot column of each row). To transfer the first row, multiply the new pivot row by the number from the first row, pivot column cell to obtain:

$$(1 \quad 0 \quad -1/9 \quad 1/3 \quad 4) \times (1/2) = (1/2 \quad 0 \quad -1/18 \quad 1/6 \quad 2)$$

The difference between this result and the original first row

$$(1/2 \quad 1 \quad 1/6 \quad 0 \quad 10) - (1/2 \quad 0 \quad -1/18 \quad 1/6 \quad 2) = (0 \quad 1 \quad 2/9 \quad -1/6 \quad 8)$$

goes into the new tableau as the first row:

$$X_1 \quad X_2 \quad S_1 \quad S_2$$

X_2	0	1	$2/9$	$-1/6$	8

The bottom row is transferred in the same way. First, multiply the pivot row by the number from the bottom row, pivot column cell:

$$(1 \quad 0 \quad -1/9 \quad 1/3 \quad 4) \times (-8) = (-8 \quad 0 \quad 8/9 \quad -8/3 \quad -32)$$

Then subtract the result obtained above from the old bottom row:

$$(-8 \quad 0 \quad 4 \quad 0 \quad 240) - (-8 \quad 0 \quad 8/9 \quad -8/3 \quad -32) = (0 \quad 0 \quad 28/9 \quad 8/3 \quad 272).$$

This result goes into the new tableau as the new bottom row:

$$X_1 \quad X_2 \quad S_1 \quad S_2$$

0	0	28/9	8/3	272

The completed third tableau is shown in Fig. 4–28.

INTERPRETING THE FINAL TABLEAU

Let us pause and interpret this tableau   First, is this the optimal solution? We have noted previously that a negative indicator means that another iteration of the tableau is required. When there are no negative indicators on a tableau, that tableau is the final one; it represents the optimal solution to the problem outlined. The third tableau, shown in Fig. 4–28, then, represents the optimal solution to the Furniture Manufacturing Company's product-mix problem.

The Solution

The variables in solution are shown by the row labels; they are X_2 and X_1. The solution values associated with these variables are given in the rightmost column (the b vector). We read that eight units of X_2 (eight benches) and four units of X_1 (four tables) should be produced. From the lower right-hand corner, we read that this combination of tables and benches will result in a total profit contribution of

$20(4) + $24(8) = $272.

We also note that there are no unused resources. Both S_1 (unused hours of assembly time) and S_2 (unused hours of finishing time) are nonbasic variables; they have a solution value of zero. We can easily check to see that

Assembly Department constraint:

$$3(4) + 6(8) + S_1 + 0S_2 = 60$$
$$S_1 = 0$$

Finishing Department constraint:

$$4(4) + 2(8) + 0S_1 + S_2 = 32$$
$$S_2 = 0.$$

The X_1 and X_2 Columns

A great deal of information—information in addition to that concerning the optimal production combination—is available to us from the final tableau. Let us interpret the columns. Columns 1 and 2, the X_1 and X_2 column, represent the variables in the final solution. Their interpretation is rather simplistic and should be obvious. To gain a unit of X_1, we must give up a unit of X_1 with no effect on the other variables or on the value of the objective function. To gain a unit of X_2, we must give up a unit of X_2 with no effect on the other variables or on the value of the objective function.

The S_1 Column

The S_1 column, column 3, represents unused hours in the Assembly Department (see Fig. 4–29). We have learned that we can read the column as: to gain a unit of S_1 (another unused hour of assembly time), we would lose $28/9 of profit contribution. This, incidentally, is the *least* it would cost us to gain an hour of unused assembly time! We should accomplish this by giving up 2/9 units of X_2

(making 2/9 units fewer benches) and also giving up minus 1/9 of an X_1 (which would be to gain, or make, 1/9 units more tables).

	X_1	X_2	S_1	S_2	
X_2	0	1	2/9	−1/6	8
X_1	1	0	−1/9	1/3	4
	0	0	28/9	8/3	272

FIG. 4–29   The S_1 column of the final tableau

Let us note carefully what has happened. We started with $S_1 = 60$; that is, 60 hours of unused assembly time were available. The optimal solution required that all the assembly time be used; thus, in the final solution, $S_1 = 0$. We ask the question: How can we free-up one hour of this assembly time? How can we force $S_1 = 1$? How can we have one unused hour, rather than zero unused hours, of assembly time? What would be the effect of being allowed to use only 59, not 60, hours of the assembly time? We would want to accomplish this adjustment with the least undesirable effect possible on the value of the objective function. The answer to our question is:

1. Give up 2/9 units of X_2 so that

   $X_2 = 8 - 2/9 = 7\frac{7}{9}$.

2. Give up minus 1/9 units of X_1 so that

   $X_1 = 4 - (-1/9) = 4\frac{1}{9}$.

The value of the variables representing the unused resources will become:

Assembly Department:

$3(4\frac{1}{9}) + 6(7\frac{7}{9}) + S_1 + 0S_2 = 60$
$$S_1 = 1.$$

Finishing Department:

$4(4\frac{1}{9}) + 2(7\frac{7}{9}) + 0S_1 + S_2 = 32$
$$S_2 = 0.$$

Profit contribution is affected to the extent of

$20(4\frac{1}{9}) + 24(7\frac{7}{9}) = 268\frac{8}{9}$

which is the same as

$272 - 28/9 = 268\frac{8}{9}$.

The Worth of An Additional Unit of Assembly Time

Of equal and perhaps of even greater interest would be the question: What would happen if we could obtain one additional unit of the resource—if there were available for use 61, rather than 60, hours of assembly time each day? In terms of the linear programming model, we are now talking about a *decrease* in S_1 (*unused* units of the scarce resource).   We are talking about a unit of the resource added to the original supply.   The only reason we would be interested in an additional unit of the resource would be that we planned to use it.   (See Fig. 4–30.)

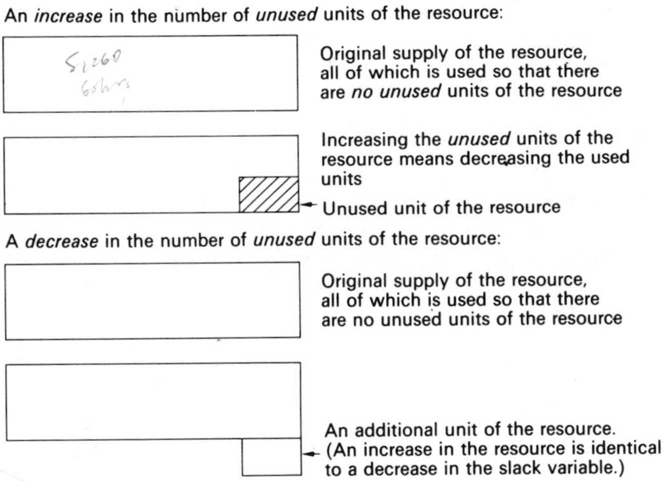

An *increase* in the number of *unused* units of the resource:

$S_1 = 60$
$60 hrs$

Original supply of the resource, all of which is used so that there are *no unused* units of the resource

Increasing the *unused* units of the resource means decreasing the used units

Unused unit of the resource

A *decrease* in the number of *unused* units of the resource:

Original supply of the resource, all of which is used so that there are no unused units of the resource

An additional unit of the resource. (An increase in the resource is identical to a decrease in the slack variable.)

FIG. 4–30   Changes in the supply of a scarce resource

To increase the amount of resource *used*, we must decrease the amount of *unused* units of the resource.   Recall how we obtained the variable S_1.   We restated the condition

$$3X_1 + 6X_2 \leqslant 60$$

in these terms:

$$3X_1 + 6X_2 + S_1 = 60.$$

Mathematically, if we want the used quantity to increase, the unused quantity must decrease.   *We interpret an increase in the resource as identical to a decrease in the slack variable.*

Previously we read the S_1 column in terms of an increase in the column variable.   In this instance, we want to interpret the column in terms of a decrease in the column variable.   Hence we must now reverse all algebraic signs and read directly: To gain a minus unit of S_1 we lose a minus 2/9 units of X_2 and a plus

1/9 units of X_1 and, thereby, lose a minus \$28/9 profit contribution. Or we may get rid of the double negatives and read: If we were to gain an additional unit of the resource, hours in the Assembly Department, we would be able to increase profit contribution by \$28/9 if we used the additional hour of assembly time to make 2/9 units more of X_2 (benches) and 1/9 units fewer of X_1 (tables).

Let us check these statements. The values of the activity variables will be

$$X_1 = 4 + (-1/9) = 3\tfrac{8}{9}$$
$$X_2 = 8 + (2/9) = 8\tfrac{2}{9}.$$

The scarce resources that are used are:

Assembly Department time:

$$3(3\tfrac{8}{9}) + 6(8\tfrac{2}{9}) = 60 + 1$$
$$61 = 61,$$

which is one unit more than the quantity originally specified in the model.

We may show that an increase in the supply of the resource is identical to a decrease in the value of the slack variable by the computation:

$$3(3\tfrac{8}{9}) + 6(8\tfrac{2}{9}) + S_1 + 0S_2 = 60$$
$$S_1 = -1.$$

Finishing Department time:

$$4(3\tfrac{8}{9}) + 2(8\tfrac{2}{9}) = 32$$
$$32 = 32$$

which has not changed.

Profit contribution becomes

$$20(3\tfrac{8}{9}) + 24(8\tfrac{2}{9}) = 272 + 28/9$$
$$275\tfrac{1}{9} = 275\tfrac{1}{9}.$$

The "28/9" and like numbers from the objective function row of the final tableau are often referred to as *shadow prices*. They represent the "worth" of an additional unit (above the original supply) of a scarce resource or the "cost" of using a unit fewer of the resource than was specified by the optimal solution. The shadow prices represent implicit or imputed values.

The S_2 Column

When we read column 4, the S_2 column (see Fig. 4–31), we see the effect that an additional unit of the resource, hours in the Finishing Department, would have on the solution. We read that an additional unit of finishing time could be used most advantageously by producing $\frac{1}{6}$ units fewer of X_2 (benches) and $1/3$ more of X_1 (tables), and that this would increase total profit contribution by $8/3$.

	X_1	X_2	S_1	S_2	
X_2	0	1	2/9	−1/6	8
X_1	1	0	−1/9	1/3	4
	0	0	28/9	8/3	272

FIG. 4–31   Column 4 of the final tableau

Let us see. The variables in solution would take on the values

$$X_1 = 4 + (1/3) = 4\tfrac{1}{3}$$
$$X_2 = 8 + (-1/6) = 7\tfrac{5}{6}.$$

Resources used are:

Assembly Department time:

$$3(4\tfrac{1}{3}) + 6(7\tfrac{5}{6}) = 60$$
$$60 = 60.$$

Finishing Department time:

$$4(4\tfrac{1}{3}) + 2(7\tfrac{5}{6}) = 32 + 1$$
$$33 = 33$$

which is one hour more than originally set forth in the model.

Profit contribution would now total:

$$20(4\tfrac{1}{3}) + 24(7\tfrac{5}{6}) = 272 + 8/3$$
$$274\tfrac{2}{3} = 274\tfrac{2}{3}.$$

Thus the values from the objective function row of the final tableau can be interpreted in much the same way as we interpret opportunity costs. We shall explore this idea further in the next chapter.

EXERCISES

1. A salesman must decide how to allocate his efforts between the different types of customers in his territory. He can call on either rural customers or city customers. A call on a

rural customer usually results in $12 in sales but requires four hours of time and six miles of driving. A call on a city customer usually results in only $8 in sales but requires only three hours and three miles.

The salesman uses an electric car and only 60 miles are available a week on the car. He also prefers not to work more than 50 hours each week.

a) Prepare a formal statement of the linear programming model. Graph the constraints of the model.

b) Convert all inequalities to equalities and restate the model, defining carefully all variables.

c) Set up the initial tableau. Explain in detail the information set forth in this tableau.

b) Pivot the tableau, explaining your choice of "incoming" and "outgoing" variables. Defend the logic of the computations performed in pivoting the tableau.

e) Was the tableau obtained in (d) the optimal solution? If not, continue manipulating the tableaus until the optimal solution is found. Relate the tableaus to the graph constructed in (a).

f) Explain the information given in the final tableau.

2. A firm manufactures two products, #67 generators and #109 generators. Two manufacturing processes are used in the production of these items. Generator #67 requires six hours of processing time in process A and 12 hours time in process B. Generator #109 requires 10 hours in process A and six hours in process B. There are available only 90 hours of processing time in process A and 120 hours in process B each day. Profit contribution for each #67 generator is $5 and for each #109 is $4. The firm would like to produce that combination of items which would maximize profit contribution.

a) Prepare a formal statement of the linear programming model. Graph the constraints of the model.

b) Convert all inequalities to equalities and restate the model, defining carefully all variables.

c) Set up the initial tableau. Explain in detail the information set forth in this tableau.

d) Pivot the tableau, explaining your choice of "incoming" and "outgoing" variables and the logic of the computations performed in pivoting the tableau.

e) Does the tableau obtained in (d) represent the optimal solution? If not, continue manipulating the tableaus until the optimal solution is obtained. Relate the tableaus to the graph constructed in (a).

f) Explain fully the information given in the final tableau.

3. The Newton Pigskin Company manufactures two lines of speciality hand-made leather footballs, the Collegiate and the Professional. The demand for both lines is great enough so that the firm is able to sell all of whatever it produces. The profit contribution for each Collegiate ball is $10; the profit contribution for each Professional ball is $16.

Each type of ball requires varying units of cutting and sewing, however, and the Newton Company wants to know what quantities of each type of ball it should produce in order to most profitably utilize the limited supply of cutting and sewing time available. Each Collegiate ball requires two hours of cutting; each Professional ball requires four hours of cutting. A total of 80 cutting hours are available daily. The Collegiate ball also requires four hours of sewing time; the Professional ball needs six hours of sewing. A total of 144 hours of sewing time are available each day.

Use the simplex method to find the optimal production strategy, given that the firm wishes to maximize profit contribution.

4. A manufacturing company produces vinyl-coated fabrics. Two standard products, Black and Red, go through the same coating and finishing processes. Both these processes must be considered to be "scarce resources" because of the limited machine time available for each process.

In the Coating Department, the Black fabric requires 2 machine hours per 1000 square feet processed and the Red fabric requires 4 machine hours per 1000 square feet processed. A maximum of 8 machine hours are available each day in the Coating Department.

In the Finishing Department, the Black fabric requires 8 machine hours per 1000 square feet processed, while the Red fabric requires 2 machine hours per 1000 square feet processed. A maximum of 16 hours of machine time are available each day in the Finishing Department.

The Black fabric yields a profit contribution of $100 per 1000 square feet and the Red fabric yields a profit contribution of $150 per 1000 square feet. Given that the company wishes to maximize profit contribution of the fabric produced, what is the optimum production level for the two types of fabric? What additional information can the company get from the final tableau of the linear programming model?

5. A company wishes to determine the optimal production and sales quantities for the next month.

A maximum amount of $1200 in cash will be available to meet production and selling expenses during the period. Product Able will require $2 per unit in cash outflow. Product Baker will require $3 per unit in cash resources.

Production time is limited to 1750 hours for the month. Two hours are needed to produce one unit of Able and three hours to produce one unit of Baker. The production process is completely adaptable to each type of unit.

The marketing department feels that a maximum of 500 units of Able and 300 units of Baker can be sold during the month.

Determine the product mix and the maximum profit contribution that can be earned during the month, given that each unit of Able yields a profit contribution of $90 and each unit of Baker yields a profit contribution of $160.

6. A manufacturer has three machines (M_1, M_2, and M_3) on which he can process two different products (P_1 and P_2). The unit hourly machine requirements for the products are as follows:

Product	Machine time (in hours)		
	M_1	M_2	M_3
P_1	1.0	0.5	0.7
P_2	1.2	1.0	0.9

The number of machine-hours available for use on each of the three machines during the next week are as follows.

Machine	Number of hours available
M_1	200
M_2	150
M_3	30

The unit contributions to fixed costs and profits are $10 for product P_1 and $8 for product P_2.

The manufacturer would like to know how to schedule production in order to maximize contribution to fixed costs and profits.

7. The Maple Manufacturing Company recently determined that in the warehouse there were miscellaneous units of materials which could be used to produce items A and B. These items could, in turn, be sold to local contractors for $19.50 and $17.00, respectively.

The stock on hand and the resources required to produce a unit of item A or B are as follows.

Resource	Units of resource required to produce one unit of		Units of resource on hand	Original cost of resource
	A	B		
Wood	1	1	12	$48
Steel	1	1/3	3	12
Plastic	0	1	3	6

Each unit of product A would require one man-hour of labor while each unit of product B would require two man-hours of labor. A man-hour of labor costs the company $2.50.

The company would like to know whether or not to use the materials to produce units of A and B and, if so, in what combination. The only alternative seems to be to to discard the materials as scrap or to continue to store them until another usage can be found.

8. Mr. Van Winkel is the investment manager of Recompense Insurance company (RIC), a medium-sized insurance company in New England. RIC typically invests in large construction projects and at this time Mr. Winkel has a choice of three such projects in which to invest. Mr. Winkel has calculated the net present value at RIC's cost of capital of each of the projects to be as follows.

Project	Net present value
I	$12,000
II	$14,000
III	$16,000

The outlays and cash inflows of each project for the next three years are as follows.

Project	Beginning of year 0	1	2
I	− 1,000,000	+ 200,000	+ 300,000
II	− 1,200,000	− 500,000	+ 200,000
III	0	− 1,000,000	− 800,000

(The minus signs indicate a cash outlay and the plus signs indicate a cash inflow.) After year 2, all cash flows are in until the end of the cash flow horizon.

Mr. Winkel will have the following funds to invest during the next three years.

Year	Funds from other sources available for investment
0	$2,000,000
1	500,000
2	400,000

RIC can take all or any portion of a project. Any part of a project which is not taken by RIC will be taken by a consortium of banks and other insurance companies. Mr. Winkel's problem is to decide which projects, or portions of projects, RIC should invest in during the three-year period. Any unused funds at the beginning of a year will be invested in one-year Certificates of Deposit at a return of 7.5% per annum.

Chapter 5

RIGHT-HAND-SIDE RANGING: THE STORY TOLD BY THE COLUMNS

In addition to wanting to know the optimal values for the activity variables, the decision maker will want to know how sensitive is the solution to the myriad changes that might occur in the problem environment. He may want to know how the solution would be altered by an increase, or decrease, in any of the resources or restrictions. He may wish to know how much it would "cost" to use a nonoptimal value for any of the activity variables. He will be concerned with the effect on the objective function value of a change in the contributions of any of the variables. What would happen if the cost of a raw material, or any other input to the system, changed? In many real-world linear programming problems, these considerations are just as important as finding the optimal solution to the case modeled. Much of this type of information can be gleaned from the simplex tableau.

THE SOLUTION VECTOR

Let us reexamine the rightmost column in the final tableau. In the Furniture Manufacturing Company case it is the vector

$$
\begin{array}{c}
X_2 \\
X_1 \\

\end{array}
\left(
\begin{array}{c}
8 \\
4 \\
272
\end{array}
\right)
$$

This is the *solution vector*. It gives us the quantities associated with the variables in solution as well as the solution value of the objective function. But, as we have noted, the linear programming model gives us much more than just the optimal solution strategy! Let us see what additional useful information is set forth in the columns of the final tableau.

THE COLUMN VECTORS AS EFFECTS OR CHANGE VECTORS

Columns containing the nonbasic variables, such as those headed S_1 and S_2 in the final tableau in the Furniture case, represent *effects vectors or change vectors. They outline the effect on the solution of a change in the number of units of that variable.* Let us explain.

The S_1 column in the final tableau (see Fig. 5–1) tells us that for each additional unit of the resource Assembly Department time we can obtain, we should make an extra $2/9$ units of X_2 (benches) but should give up $1/9$ units of X_1 (tables). This exchange would result in a $28/9 increase in total profit contribution. Hence, if Furniture Manufacturing Company could obtain an additional hour of assembly time, this column provides the plan for the most effective use of that time. The column also indicates the amount by which this additional unit of the resource would increase the value of the objective function.

	X_1	X_2	S_1	S_2	
X_2	0	1	2/9	−1/6	8
X_1	1	0	−1/9	1/3	4
	0	0	28/9	8/3	272

FIG. 5–1 The S_1 column from the final tableau

Likewise, the S_2 column in the final tableau (see Fig. 5–2) is an effects vector which tells us that for each extra unit of the resource Finishing Department time we can secure, we should make $1/3$ units more of X_1 (tables) and give up $1/6$ units of X_2 (benches). This exchange would increase total profit contribution by $8/3.

	X_1	X_2	S_1	S_2	
X_2	0	1	2/9	−1/6	8
X_1	1	0	−1/9	1/3	4
	0	0	28/9	8/3	272

FIG. 5–2 The S_2 column from the final tableau

EFFECT ON SOLUTION OF
ADDITIONAL UNITS OF RESOURCE

From the change vector, we see that if an additional unit of the resource Assembly Department time became available, the Furniture Manufacturing Company should increase its production of benches and decrease its production of tables. Let us use vector notation to show the effect that additional units of the resources would have on the solution strategy.

The effect on the solution vector of a one-unit increase in the resource Assembly Department time is:

$$
\begin{array}{c} \text{Original} \\ \text{solution} \\ \text{vector} \end{array} \qquad \begin{array}{c} \text{Effects} \\ \text{vector} \\ S_1 \end{array} \qquad \begin{array}{c} \text{Adjusted} \\ \text{solution} \\ \text{vector} \end{array}
$$

$$
\begin{array}{c} X_2 \\ X_1 \\ {} \end{array}
\begin{pmatrix} 8 \\ 4 \\ 272 \end{pmatrix}
+ (1)
\begin{pmatrix} 2/9 \\ -1/9 \\ 28/9 \end{pmatrix}
=
\begin{pmatrix} 8\frac{2}{9} \\ 3\frac{8}{9} \\ 275\frac{1}{9} \end{pmatrix}
$$

Because the marginal rates of substitution are constant, at least over a range, the second additional unit of assembly time would call for the same type of change in the solution as did the first. Hence, the effect on the solution of a two-unit increase in the resource, assembly time, would be:

$$
\begin{array}{c} \text{Original} \\ \text{solution} \\ \text{vector} \end{array} \qquad \begin{array}{c} \text{Effects} \\ \text{vector} \\ S_1 \end{array} \qquad \begin{array}{c} \text{Adjusted} \\ \text{solution} \\ \text{vector} \end{array}
$$

$$
\begin{array}{c} X_2 \\ X_1 \\ {} \end{array}
\begin{pmatrix} 8 \\ 4 \\ 272 \end{pmatrix}
+ (2)
\begin{pmatrix} 2/9 \\ -1/9 \\ 28/9 \end{pmatrix}
=
\begin{pmatrix} 8\frac{4}{9} \\ 3\frac{7}{9} \\ 278\frac{2}{9} \end{pmatrix}
$$

RANGE OF APPLICABILITY
OF EFFECTS VECTOR

Are we allowed to continue indefinitely adding units of Assembly Department time in this way? Over what range of values for the supply of this resource will these exchange rates and this shadow price remain in effect?

An additional 36 units of Assembly Department time would have this effect on the solution vector:

$$
\begin{matrix}
& \text{Original} & \text{Effects} & \text{Adjusted} \\
& \text{solution} & \text{vector} & \text{solution} \\
& \text{vector} & S_1 & \text{vector}
\end{matrix}
$$

$$
\begin{matrix} X_2 \\ X_1 \\ {} \end{matrix}
\begin{pmatrix} 8 \\ 4 \\ 272 \end{pmatrix}
+ (36)
\begin{pmatrix} 2/9 \\ -1/9 \\ 28/9 \end{pmatrix}
=
\begin{pmatrix} 16 \\ 0 \\ 384 \end{pmatrix}
\leftarrow \text{Outgoing variable}
$$

(The allowable amount of increase in the supply of the resource for the purposes of finding the right-hand-side range can be computed by dividing the numbers in the solution vector by the numbers in the appropriate column vector. For instance, to obtain the allowable increase in the resource, assembly time, we need consider only effects that will decrease values in the solution vector. So we need consider only the $-1/9$ in the S_1 column vector. We divide

$$4 \div (-1/9) = -36$$

and see that 36 such unit increases in the supply of the resource would decrease the solution value of X_1 from $X_1 = 4$ to $X_1 = 0$.)

Note what happens when we try to add the 37th extra unit of Assembly Department time:

$$
\begin{matrix}
& \text{Original} & \text{Effects} & \text{Adjusted} \\
& \text{solution} & \text{vector} & \text{solution} \\
& \text{vector} & S_1 & \text{vector}
\end{matrix}
$$

$$
\begin{matrix} X_2 \\ X_1 \\ {} \end{matrix}
\begin{pmatrix} 8 \\ 4 \\ 272 \end{pmatrix}
+ (37)
\begin{pmatrix} 2/9 \\ -1/9 \\ 28/9 \end{pmatrix}
=
\begin{pmatrix} 16\frac{2}{9} \\ -\frac{1}{9} \\ 387\frac{1}{9} \end{pmatrix}
\leftarrow \text{An illogical value in the solution vector}
$$

A minus value in the solution vector is nonsensical. (Furthermore it violates the nonnegativity requirement.) The Furniture Manufacturing Company cannot produce a minus number of units of a product. Whenever we obtain a zero in the solution vector, we have reached the limit for the applicability of the effects vector. A step beyond this point results in an illogical solution strategy. This fact gives rise to the concept of *right-hand-side ranging*.

Upper Limit of the Range

We started with 60 units of the resource and have added an extra 36 units before obtaining an infeasible solution, so we are thinking in terms of a range the upper limit of which is

$$60 + 36 = 96$$

hours of Assembly Department time. In this problem, we would call this point the upper limit of the range over which the effects vector S_1 would be applicable. At the end of the range, X_1 is labeled the "outgoing variable" since we have reached a point where units of X_1 are no longer in solution. This variable has assumed a zero value.

A Graphic Explanation

Figure 5–3 shows graphically what happens with increases in the supply of the resource, Assembly Department time. As more hours of the resource are made available for use, the constraint line moves, in a parallel fashion, farther and farther from the origin. The corner point (the point where the constraint lines cross) moves as well. More and more units of X_2 are made while fewer and fewer units of X_1 are made. We change the optimal strategy by moving along the Finishing Department constraint line. A point is eventually reached where $X_1 = 0$ and $X_2 = 16$. This is the upper limit of the range of values representing the available supply of the resource assembly time where this exchange rate is applicable.

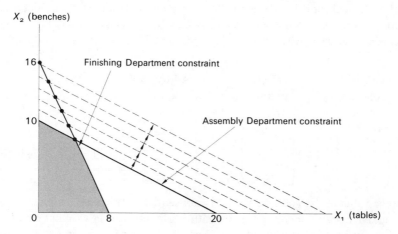

FIG. 5–3   The effect of increases in Assembly Department time available for use

Decreases in the Resource Supply

Suppose that, for whatever reason, the Furniture Manufacturing Company finds that is has available for use fewer than the 60 hours of assembly time originally thought available. We saw that when additional units of this resource were found to be available, the optimal strategy was to increase production of benches and to decrease production of tables. Then a decrease in the number of assembly hours available for use would have just the opposite effect; the Furniture Manufacturing

Company, in this situation, should decrease the number of benches produced and increase the number of tables.

A one-unit decrease in the number of assembly hours available for use would result in this adjusted solution vector:

	Original solution vector		Effects vector S_1		Adjusted solution vector
X_2	8		2/9		$7\frac{7}{9}$
X_1	4	$-(1)$	$-1/9$	$=$	$4\frac{1}{9}$
	272		28/9		$268\frac{8}{9}$

Note that the effects vector can be subtracted from the original solution vector only $8 \div 2/9 = 36$ times before the X_2 value becomes negative; that is,

	Original solution vector		Effects vector S_1		Adjusted solution vector	
X_2	8		2/9		0	← Outgoing variable
X_1	4	$-(36)$	$-1/9$	$=$	8	
	272		28/9		160	

We are thinking in terms of

$$60 - 36 = 24$$

hours of Assembly Department time. This, then, is the lower limit for the range over which this effects vector is applicable. At this end of the range, it is the variable X_2 that assumes a zero value; X_2 is, thus, termed the "outgoing variable."

Figure 5–4 illustrates what happens with decreases in the number of units of the resource "hours in the Assembly Department" that are available for use in producing tables and benches. With decreases in the supply of this resource, the constraint line moves, in a parallel fashion, closer and closer to the origin, stopping when it bumps into the constraint line for the other scarce resource, Finishing Department time. As fewer and fewer hours of Assembly Department time are available for use, the model tells us to produce more and more units of X_1 and fewer and fewer units of X_2. Again, although it is the assembly time that is decreased, the strategy is altered by movement along the Finishing Department constraint line. At the limit of the range of applicability for the change vector, we have reached a corner point. If further moves were to be made, they would be made along another constraint line and at another rate of exchange.

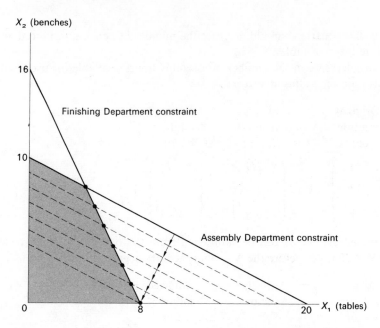

FIG. 5–4 The effect of decreases in Assembly Department time available for use

RIGHT-HAND-SIDE RANGING FOR THE RESOURCE

Anywhere within the range of from 24 to 96 hours of assembly time, the effects vector for S_1 that is shown in the final tableau will be applicable. The limits of this range are set forth in Table 5–1.

TABLE 5–1 Right-hand-side ranging for Assembly Department Time

Resource	Current value	Lower limit	Upper limit	Outgoing variable Lower	Upper
Assembly Department time (in hours)	60	24	96	X_2	X_1

When we state that this is the range over which the effects vector is applicable, we mean that within these limits (1) the shadow price shown in the final tableau measures the "worth" (contribution toward objective) of an additional unit of the scarce resource and (2) the exchange rates shown in the effects vector represent the marginal rates of substitution along this line segment. Beyond the limits of this range, we will be moving along some other constraint line where other rates of exchange are applicable.

This type of information is invaluable to the Furniture Manufacturing Company for planning purposes. The effects vector, along with the ranging information, allows the firm to plan for the most efficient usage of this resource.

RIGHT-HAND-SIDE RANGING
FOR THE OTHER RESOURCE

Now let us range the other resource, hours available in the Finishing Department. The effects vector from the final tableau is

$$
\begin{array}{c}
 & S_2 \\
X_2 & \left(\begin{array}{c} -1/6 \\ \\ 1/3 \\ \\ 8/3 \end{array} \right) \\
X_1 &
\end{array}
$$

Increases in the supply of the resource will cause us to produce fewer units of X_2. In fact, an additional 48 units of the resource would result in the production of zero of units of X_2 because

$$
\begin{array}{cccc}
 & \begin{array}{c}\text{Original}\\\text{solution}\\\text{vector}\end{array} & \begin{array}{c}\text{Effects}\\\text{vector}\\S_2\end{array} & \begin{array}{c}\text{Adjusted}\\\text{solution}\\\text{vector}\end{array} \\
X_2 & \left(\begin{array}{c} 8 \\ 4 \\ 272 \end{array} \right) & +(48)\left(\begin{array}{c} -1/6 \\ 1/3 \\ 8/3 \end{array} \right) = & \left(\begin{array}{c} 0 \\ 20 \\ 400 \end{array} \right) \leftarrow \text{Outgoing variable} \\
X_1 & & &
\end{array}
$$

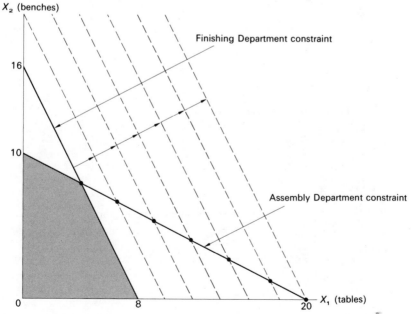

FIG. 5–5 The effect of increases in finishing Department time available for use

The upper limit of the range over which this effects vector is applicable is, then,

$$32 + 48 = 80$$

units of time in the Finishing Department. (See Fig. 5–5.)

When we decrease the number of hours of Finishing Department time available, we decrease the number of units of X_1 that should be produced. We may make a one-unit decrease in finishing time up to a maximum of twelve times. Let us see.

$$
\begin{array}{cc}
& \text{Original} \\
& \text{solution} \\
& \text{vector}
\end{array}
\quad
\begin{array}{c}
\text{Effects} \\
\text{vector} \\
S_2
\end{array}
\quad
\begin{array}{c}
\text{Adjusted} \\
\text{solution} \\
\text{vector}
\end{array}
$$

$$
\begin{array}{c}
X_2 \\
X_1 \\
\
\end{array}
\left(
\begin{array}{c}
8 \\
4 \\
272
\end{array}
\right)
- (12)
\left(
\begin{array}{c}
-1/6 \\
1/3 \\
8/3
\end{array}
\right)
=
\left(
\begin{array}{c}
10 \\
0 \\
240
\end{array}
\right)
\leftarrow \text{Outgoing variable}
$$

At this point

$$32 - 12 = 20$$

hours of finishing time are being used. (See Fig. 5–6.)

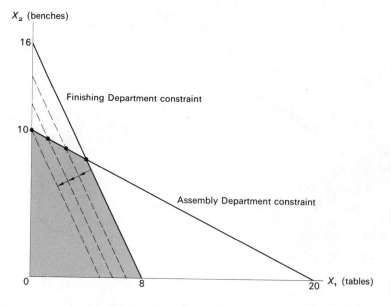

FIG 5–6 The effect of decreases in Finishing Department time available for use

Table 5–2 displays the appropriate ranging for both of the constraining resources, Assembly Department time and Finishing Department time.

TABLE 5–2 Right-hand-side ranging

Resource	Current value	Lower limit	Upper limit	Outgoing variable Lower	Upper
Assembly Department time (in hours)	60	24	96	X_2	X_1
Finishing Department time (in hours)	32	20	80	X_1	X_2

INFERRING "WORTH" OF THE RESOURCES BEYOND LIMITS OF THE RANGE

What can we infer about the "worth" of the resources beyond the relevant range of the change vectors? Does it not hold that the value of a resource decreases as the supply of that resource becomes more bountiful? Beyond the upper limit of the right-hand-side range for a given resource, this resource is so plentiful relative to the other resources that its "worth" will decline. In fact, we can see from Fig. 5–5 that even if more than 80 hours of Finishing Department time were available they would be "worthless"; they could not be used because of the Assembly Department constraint. Hence, beyond the upper limit of the range, the shadow price of a resource will be smaller.

By the same type of reasoning, does it not seem logical that below the lower limit of the range the shadow price of the resource will increase?

The shadow price, then, really contains three bits of information. For Assembly Department time, for example, the "28/9" tells us that (1) if between 24 and 96 hours of assembly time are available, the "worth" of one unit of assembly time is $28/9; (2) if fewer than 24 hours of assembly time are available, the "worth" of a unit of assembly time is greater than $28/9; or (3) if more than 96 hours of assembly time are available, the "worth" of one unit of assembly time is less than $28/9. For Finishing Department time, the shadow price "8/3" indicates that (1) if between 20 and 80 hours of finishing time are available, the "worth" of a unit of finishing time is $8/3; (2) if fewer than 20 hours of finishing time are available, the "worth" of a unit of finishing time is greater than $8/3; or (3) if more than 80 hours of finishing time are available, the "worth" of a unit of finishing time is less than $8/3.

THE EFFECT OF CHANGES IN THE SUPPLY OF ONE SCARCE RESOURCE ON THE OTHER SCARCE RESOURCES

Suppose that we are able to change the supply of one of the scarce resources limiting our model. What effect will this have on the other scarce resources?

The Adjusted Solution

Suppose that the Furniture Manufacturing Company found that it could obtain an extra 18 hours in the Assembly Department. The solution vector would be altered to this extent:

$$
\begin{matrix} X_2 \\ X_1 \\ {} \end{matrix}
\begin{matrix} \text{Original} \\ \text{solution} \\ \text{vector} \end{matrix}
\begin{pmatrix} 8 \\ 4 \\ 272 \end{pmatrix}
+ (18)
\begin{matrix} \text{Effects} \\ \text{vector} \\ S_1 \end{matrix}
\begin{pmatrix} 2/9 \\ -1/9 \\ 28/9 \end{pmatrix}
=
\begin{matrix} \text{Adjusted} \\ \text{solution} \\ \text{vector} \end{matrix}
\begin{pmatrix} 12 \\ 2 \\ 328 \end{pmatrix}
$$

Graphically, the constraint line for the scarce resource Assembly Department time moves farther out from the origin (from line BC to line GH on Fig. 5–7). The area of feasible solutions changes from the area $ABFE$ to the area $AGIE$. The optimal corner point moves from point F to point I. At this new solution point, two units of X_1 (tables) and twelve units of X_2 (benches) are produced, and there are no unused units of the resources. The value of the objective function increases to $328.

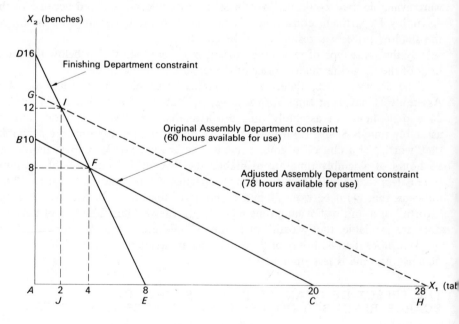

FIG. 5–7   Area of feasible solutions, assuming an additional 18 units of assembly time is made available for use

The Effect on the Other Resource

Now let us see what effect this will have on the "worth" of the other scarce resource, the marginal rate of substitution between the products, and the range over which this "worth" and marginal rate of substitution hold true. In ranging the resource, we must use the adjusted solution vector since it now represents the optimal solution. The old effects vector for the resource, finishing time, is still applicable. Note on Fig. 5–7 that we are still moving along the Finishing Department constraint line. Hence, the increase in Assembly Department time did not affect the prevailing marginal rate of substitution between the products nor the shadow price of finishing time.

We see that when we increase the finishing time available for use by 72 units, we obtain the result

$$
\begin{array}{cc}
& \text{Solution} \\
& \text{vector}
\end{array}
\quad
\begin{array}{c}
\text{Effects} \\
\text{vector} \\
S_2
\end{array}
\quad
\begin{array}{c}
\text{Adjusted} \\
\text{solution} \\
\text{vector}
\end{array}
$$

$$
\begin{array}{c}
X_2 \\
X_1 \\

\end{array}
\left(
\begin{array}{c}
12 \\
2 \\
328
\end{array}
\right)
+ (72)
\left(
\begin{array}{c}
-1/6 \\
1/3 \\
8/3
\end{array}
\right)
=
\left(
\begin{array}{c}
0 \\
26 \\
526
\end{array}
\right)
\begin{array}{l}
\leftarrow \text{Outgoing variable}
\end{array}
$$

This, then, is the new upper limit of the relevant range of this change vector. We

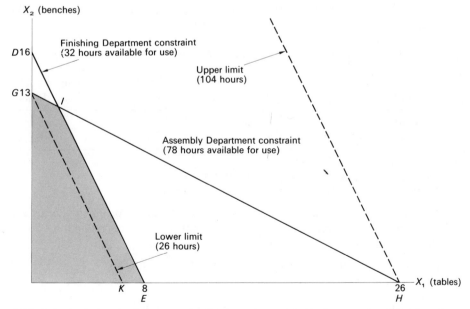

FIG. 5–8 Right-hand-side ranging for finishing time available for use, given 78 units of assembly time

have increased the supply of finishing time from 32 to

$$32 + 72 = 104$$

units. Graphically, we have pushed the constraint line DE out from the origin until we are stopped by the assembly time constraint line GH (see Fig. 5–8). We are now at the corner point H.

When we decrease the supply of finishing time by six units, we obtain this result:

$$
\begin{array}{cccc}
 & \text{Solution} & \text{Effects} & \text{Adjusted} \\
 & \text{vector} & \text{vector} & \text{solution} \\
 & & S_2 & \text{vector} \\
\end{array}
$$

$$
\begin{array}{c}
X_2 \\
X_1 \\

\end{array}
\begin{pmatrix} 12 \\ 2 \\ 328 \end{pmatrix}
- (6)
\begin{pmatrix} -1/6 \\ 1/3 \\ 8/3 \end{pmatrix}
=
\begin{pmatrix} 13 \\ 0 \\ 312 \end{pmatrix}
\leftarrow \text{Outgoing variable}
$$

The new lower limit for the range of applicability for this effects vector is, then,

$$32 - 6 = 26$$

hours of finishing time. The lower limit of the range is shown in Fig. 5–8 as the GK constraint line. We are stopped from making further decreases in the supply of finishing time by the assembly time constraint line GH. The solution now is at the corner point G.

Table 5–3 outlines the right-hand-side ranging for finishing time, given 78 units as the available supply of assembly time.

TABLE 5–3 Right-hand-side ranging for finishing time given 78 hours of assembly time

Resource	Current value	Lower limit	Upper limit	Outgoing variable Lower	Upper
Finishing Department time	32	26	104	X_1	X_2

THE IDEA THAT EACH RESOURCE FAVORS A PRODUCT

For every scarce resource there will be a "most favored" product. Let us explain what we mean. Insofar as the resource assembly time is concerned, we could use the 60 available hours to produce either

1. twenty units of X_1 for a total profit contribution of

   ($20) (20) = $400.

2. ten units of X_2 for a total profit contribution of

   ($24) (10) = $240.

We say that the resource assembly time "favors" product X_1 because a greater total profit contribution is realized when the resource is used to produce units of X_1 than would be realized if the resource were used to produce units of X_2. Since all relationships are linear, there would never be an advantage to a combination of products insofar as one constraint is concerned.

By the same token, we could use the 32 hours of finishing time that are available to produce either

1. eight units of X_1 for a total profit contribution of

   ($20) (8) = $160

or

2. sixteen units of X_2 for a total profit contribution of

   ($24) (16) = $384.

Clearly, the finishing time resource favors product X_2.

It is only because each product is favored by one of the scarce resources that each appears in the optimal solution. Unless a product is favored by some resource it will never appear in solution. This also explains, logically, why you never have more variables in solution than you have constraints defining the problem enviornment. (There is also a mathematical explanation for this, as you will recall.)

Now suppose that an extra unit of assembly time becomes available. How would you expect that it should be used? We have just seen that the resource assembly time favors product X_1. Intuitively, we would expect that an increase in the resource would result in an increase in the favored product. But refer again to the effects vector in the final tableau. It tells us that to increase assembly time available for use is to decrease X_1 and to increase X_2! Also, intuitively, we would expect that an increase in the resource finishing time would result in an increase in the product that this resource favors, product X_2. Yet the effects vector of the final tableau tells the opposite story; an increase in the available supply of finishing time results in a decrease in the number of units of X_2 produced and an increase in the number of units of X_1!

If we look closely we will see that this is not really a strange cause-and-effect. Extra units of resource #1 make this resource less scarce, and, thus, less valuable, relative to resource #2. Hence, the increased production will be in terms of an increase in the product favored by resource #2 and not in the product favored by resource #1. When the supply of resource #1 is increased, resource #2 becomes the more precious of the two and it is the resource we try to use most wisely. We increase the production of the product favored by the most precious resource.

In other words, you are at a status quo between two resources. Suddenly your supply of one resource is increased. It now becomes the less restricting resource, the less critical resource. So you look to see how you can use the other resource most effectively. Much decision-making is done in a manner contrary to this logic. This happens because the decision maker fails to consider the relationships that exist between the resources involved.

RIGHT-HAND-SIDE RANGING WHEN AN ACTIVITY VARIABLE IS NONBASIC

Both the nonbasic variables in the final solution in the previous illustration were slack variables. Often activity variables will be nonbasic in the final solution. For example, had the contribution of benches been $50 while the contribution of tables remained at $20, the objective function for the model would have been

Maximise: $20X_1 + 50X_2 = P$ (profit contribution)

Assuming that the two constraints modeled previously were still appropriate, the initial and final solutions shown in Fig. 5–9 would have resulted.

Initial Tableau:

	X_1	X_2	S_1	S_2		Ratios:
S_1	3	6	1	0	60	$60/6 = 10$
S_2	4	2	0	1	32	$32/2 = 16$
	-20	-50	0	0	0	

Second (and final) Tableau:

	X_1	X_2	S_1	S_2	
X_2	1/2	1	1/6	0	10
S_2	3	0	$-1/3$	1	12
	5	0	25/3	0	500

FIG. 5–9 Initial and final tableaus for "adjusted" Furniture Company Case

Note that the two basic variables are

$X_2 = 10$ and $S_2 = 12$.

The optimal course of action under these circumstances would be to manufacture ten benches. This would mean that 12 hours of the available finishing time would remain unused.

The nonbasic variables are X_1 and S_1. The optimal production plan includes no tables. All of the available assembly time would be used.

Now some interesting questions arise. What would happen if the company felt that it must include one table in the production plan? We see from the shadow price in the X_1 column (see Fig. 5–9) that such a move would decrease total profit contribution by \$5. The change in strategy should be brought about by decreasing the production of benches (X_2) by $\frac{1}{2}$ unit and by using three of the previously unused finishing hours. We are simply reading the X_1 effects vector: to gain a unit of X_1 we must give up $\frac{1}{2}$ units of X_2, three units of S_2, and five units toward the value of the objective function.

The adjusted solution vector would be

$$
\begin{array}{c}
\\
X_2 \\
S_2 \\
\\
\end{array}
\begin{array}{c}
\text{Solution} \\
\text{vector} \\
\left(\begin{array}{c} 10 \\ 12 \\ 500 \end{array} \right)
\end{array}
- (1)
\begin{array}{c}
\text{Effects} \\
\text{vector} \\
X_1 \\
\left(\begin{array}{c} 1/2 \\ 3 \\ 5 \end{array} \right)
\end{array}
=
\begin{array}{c}
\text{Adjusted} \\
\text{solution} \\
\text{vector} \\
\left(\begin{array}{c} 9\frac{1}{2} \\ 9 \\ 495 \end{array} \right)
\end{array}
$$

The adjusted strategy would include

$$X_1 = 1 \qquad S_1 = 0$$
$$X_2 = 9\tfrac{1}{2} \qquad S_2 = 9$$

This is a feasible, but not a basic feasible, solution. We can verify the values shown above by these computations:

Assembly Department constraint:
$$3(1) + 6(9\tfrac{1}{2}) + 0 + 0(9) = 60$$
$$60 = 60$$

Finishing Department constraint:
$$4(1) + 2(9\tfrac{1}{2}) + 0 + 1(9) = 32$$
$$32 = 32$$

Objective Function
$$20(1) + 50(9\tfrac{1}{2}) + 0 + 0 = 495.$$

The X_1 effects column, thus, outlines the effect of including one unit of X_1 in the strategy. We can determine the range over which this effects vector is applicable by computing the right-hand-side range. We see that X_1 could be increased by four units, at which time S_2 would assume a zero value, that is,

$$
\begin{array}{cc}
& \text{Solution} \\
& \text{vector}
\end{array}
\qquad
\begin{array}{c}
\text{Effects} \\
\text{vector} \\
X_1
\end{array}
\qquad
\begin{array}{c}
\text{Adjusted} \\
\text{solution} \\
\text{vector}
\end{array}
$$

$$
\begin{array}{c}
X_2 \\
S_2 \\

\end{array}
\begin{pmatrix}
10 \\
12 \\
500
\end{pmatrix}
-(4)
\begin{pmatrix}
1/2 \\
3 \\
5
\end{pmatrix}
=
\begin{pmatrix}
8 \\
0 \\
480
\end{pmatrix}
$$

Because in the optimal strategy X_1 is a nonbasic with a solution value of zero, it makes no sense to speak of decreasing its value; this would violate the non-negativity requirement. Hence, the lower limit of the right-hand-side range is zero.

The complete right-hand-side ranging for the final tableau shown in Fig. 5–9 is given in Table 5–4.

TABLE 5–4   Right-hand-side ranging for the "adjusted" Furniture Company Case

Resource	Current value	Lower limit	Upper limit	Outgoing variable Lower	Upper
Assembly time	60	0	96	X_2	S_2
Nonbasic activity variable:					
Tables (X_1)	0	0	4	—	S_2

Remember that the upper limit of the right-hand-side range does not represent the maximum number of tables that might be brought into solution but rather the maximum for which this effects vector is appropriate.

EXERCISES

1. The Ace Book Company has just received the rights to publish *What You Always Wanted to know about Linear Programming* (*but were afraid to ask*). The firm may publish the edition in paperback, hardback, or both. Ace estimates the profit contribution to be \$1 per paperback and \$2 per hardback sold. The demand for the book is so great that Ace believes it will be able to sell all of its production, of either the paperback or the hardback.

Both books must go through two production processes: printing and binding. The paperback version requires six units of printing and nine units of binding. The hardback, on the other hand, requires four units of printing and 12 units of binding. A total of 54 units of printing and 60 units of binding are available daily for the production of either paperback and/or hardback copies of this book.

The Ace Book Company desires to know what combination of paperback–hardback editions it should publish daily in order to maximize profit contribution.

Set up the linear programming model and solve for the optimal strategy using the simplex method. Interpret fully the final tableau. Establish the right-hand-side ranges for the nonbasic variables. Display these ranges graphically and explain carefully their significance.

2. Tucker's Machine Shop makes collets and set-rings from the same blank stock. Both types of items require machining time. The collets require one hour each of machine time and the set-rings require $\frac{1}{3}$ hour each. Both items also must go through a finishing operation. The collets require $\frac{1}{3}$ hour each of finishing time; the set-rings require $\frac{2}{3}$ hours finishing. Tucker's has available 60 machine hours each day and 40 finishing hours.

If the items make a contribution to profits of $10 per dozen for the collets and $6 per dozen for the set-rings, how many of each should Tucker plan to process each day, assuming his objective is the maximization of profit contribution?

How much should Tucker be willing to pay for an additional hour of machining time? If an additional hour of machining time were made available, how should it be used? If an additional hour of finishing time were made available, how should it be used? Over what range of quantities for the two resources would the column effects vectors of the final tableau show the appropriate marginal rates of substitution?

3. The XYZ Company must work within three current asset constraints. Due to credit problems, increases in accounts receivable have been limited to $30,000 during the next month. Cash outflows are limited to $32,000. Because of warehousing limits, available raw materials cannot exceed 8,000 units.

Three brands of product are produced and sold. Brand X sells for $3, Brand Y for $6, and Brand Z for $9. All sales are on credit. Each item uses one unit of raw material. Cash outflows for Y and Z are $1 for each unit produced; no cash outflows are expected for X. Profits per unit are $1 for X, $2.50 for Y, and $4 for Z.

Determine the optimal product mix. Interpret, fully, the final tableau. Compute and analyze carefully the right-hand-side ranges.

4. A farmer is considering the planting of 1000 acres of land with the intention of providing winter feed for his cattle. The only reasonable crops are coastal bermuda grass and alfalfa. The expected yield per acre of bermuda is 7 tons and for alfalfa is 4 tons. A cattle-feed-day of bermuda is 27 pounds and for alfalfa is 19 pounds.

Alfalfa requires a good deal of artificial watering (about 100 gallons per acre per day) while bermuda requires very little such watering (about 20 gallons per acre per day). The farmer can be assured of no more than 50,000 gallons of water per day.

On the other hand, bermuda requires a large amount of fertilizer (845 pounds per acre per season) while alfalfa requires only about 225 pounds per acre per season. The farmer has funds for no more than 300 tons of fertilizer.

How many acres of each crop should the farmer plant to maximize the total number of steer-feed-days of crop which can be harvested? Interpret fully the final tableau. Compute and analyze the right-hand-side ranges.

5. The Alpha-Beta Company has been manufacturing Betas for many years and has a reputation for making the best Betas in the business. They have decided to go into the Alpha business also. Even though their Alphas are to be priced considerably above

similar quality Alphas presently on the market, they feel that their reputation in Betas will allow them to sell the Alphas at this high profit margin.

Alpha-Beta's Betas are selling for $18.00, which has given them a profit contribution of $6.00 per unit. They have virtually no competition. The company plans to sell the Alphas for $18.00, also, which will give them a profit contribution of $7.00 per unit. But because of competitive pressures—similar Alphas are on the market selling for $12.00 each—Alpha-Beta can forecast sales of a maximum of 150 Alphas each week. In fact, competitive factors other than price would limit sales to 150 units weekly, even if prices were lower.

Alpha-Beta currently has a labor surplus; thus, labor is not a limiting constraint. Alphas will use two of the same raw materials that the production of Betas also requires. Alphas will use one unit of material M_1 and Betas use three units of this material. There are 400 units of the material M_1 available each week. Alphas use four units of material M_2 and Betas use three units of this material. There are 1600 units of material M_2 available each week.

Alpha-Beta is also wondering about the possibility of purchasing unlabeled Alphas from the Alpha-Alpha company for $12.00 each, spending $0.50 per unit to put the Alpha-Beta brand on it, and selling these units as their own for the originally planned $18.00.

Use a linear programming model to help Alpha-Beta arrive at the optimal production strategy.

6. A private clinical laboratory provides three types of clinical specimen examinations to physicians in the city. The examinations are parasitological (P), bacteriological (B), and serological (S). The lab has been realizing a net profit contribution from each specimen type as follows:

Type of specimen	Profit contribution
P	$2.00
B	$3.00
S	$1.50

There are two microbiologists, two technologists, and one laboratory helper in the lab. Each specimen is set up and tested by the technologists and then the microbiologists read and interpret the results. The lab helper cares for the test animals, washes glassware, and cleans up the examination area. The following outline shows the personnel time available and the required examination time per each specimen type:

Staff	Available personnel time per day (in hours)	Time required per specimen (in hours)		
		P	B	S
Microbiologist 1	4	0.4	0.3	0.2
Microbiologist 2	3	0.35	0.2	0.1
Technologist 1	5	0.45	0.4	0.15
Technologist 2	4	0.5	0.4	0.2
Lab helper	6	0.3	0.3	0.3

The lab always has more specimens coming in each day than they can process. The laboratory manager would like to determine what specimen-mix and how many of each type will maximize his profit. Furthermore, he would like to know the "worth" of an additional hour of work time each day for each member of the lab staff. The lab helper in particular has said that he would be willing to work two additional hours each day. Would it be profitable to allow him to work these additional hours? How much could the manager pay the lab helper for these work hours and still realize a profit on this time? How should the helper use these two additional hours?

If the laboratory manager felt that the lab should process at least one parasitological (P) specimen each day, how should he alter his strategy? If he felt that the lab should process at least one serological (S) specimen each day, how should he alter his strategy? What effect would each of the moves mentioned have on the total profit contribution?

7. Max, the mixologist, is planning for a bash. He has available the following amounts of liquid refreshments:

Amount (in fluid ounces)	Liquid
84	Vermouth
60	Bourbon
56	Scotch
48	Vodka

In addition, he has an unlimited supply of lemons, limes, orange juice, bitters, and other accompaniments.

Max mixes these masterpieces:

Masterpiece	Ingredients
Manhattan	$\frac{1}{2}$ ounce Vermouth $1\frac{1}{2}$ ounce Bourbon
Rob Roy	$\frac{3}{4}$ ounce Vermouth $1\frac{1}{2}$ ounce Scotch
Scotch-on-the-rocks	2 ounces Scotch
Martini	$\frac{1}{4}$ ounce Vermouth 1 ounce Vodka
Hulu cooler	$1\frac{1}{2}$ ounce Bourbon
Screwdriver	$1\frac{1}{2}$ ounce Vodka

Each drink will sell for $2 and Max knows he can sell as many drinks as he can make up. Which Masterpieces should Max mix in order to maximize his gross income? Explain the "worth" and optimal usage of additional units of the scarce resources, which Max might be able to obtain if he approached the right person.

Chapter 6

OBJECTIVE-FUNCTION-COEFFICIENT RANGING: THE STORY TOLD BY THE ROWS

We have been able to analyze the effects wrought by changes in the available supply of scarce resources. Of just as much interest to a decision maker would be the effects of changes in the contribution toward objective of the proposed courses of action. We have related the story told by the columns in the final tableau. What information can be obtained from the rows?

HOW THE SHADOW PRICE ON ASSEMBLY TIME IS DETERMINED

We have said that an additional unit of assembly time would be worth \$28/9 to the Furniture Manufacturing Company. Let us begin by determining how this "28/9" figure that is found in the objective-function row and the S_1 column (see Fig. 6–1) came about. If an additional unit of Assembly Department time could be obtained, it should be used to produce 2/9 units more of X_2 (benches) and 1/9 units fewer of X_1 (tables). Each bench contributes \$24 to profit while each

	X_1	X_2	S_1	S_2	
X_2	0	1	2/9	−1/6	8
X_1	1	0	−1/9	1/3	4
	0	0	28/9	8/3	272

FIG. 6–1 Column S_1 from the final tableau

table makes a contribution of $20. This exchange, then, would have the following net effect on total profit contribution

For the benches:	$(+2/9)\,(\$24) = +\$48/9$
For the tables:	$(-1/9)\,(\$20) = -\ 20/9$
Net effect:	$+\$28/9$

HOW THE SHADOW PRICE ON FINISHING TIME IS DETERMINED

The "8/3" value in the objective function row, S_2 column (see Fig. 6–2) can be explained in the same way; that is, an extra unit of Finishing Department time would most advantageously be used to produce 1/6 units less of X_2 (benches) and 1/3 units more of X_1 (tables) with the following net effect on total contribution;

For the benches:	$(-1/6)\,(\$24) = -\$24/6$
For the tables:	$(+1/3)\,(\$20) = +\ 20/3$
Net effect:	$+\$\ 8/3$

	X_1	X_2	S_1	S_2	
X_2	0	1	2/9	−1/6	8
X_1	1	0	−1/9	1/3	4
	0	0	28/9	8/3	272

FIG. 6–2   Column S_2 from the final tableau

THE SOLUTION VALUE OF THE OBJECTIVE FUNCTION

The solution value of the objective function is shown in the rightmost column of the objective function row as $272 (see Fig. 6–3). This was derived from the computation

$$(\$20)\,(4) + (\$24)\,(8) = \$272.$$

	X_1	X_2	S_1	S_2	
X_2	0	1	2/9	−1/6	8
X_1	1	0	−1/9	1/3	4
	0	0	28/9	8/3	272

FIG. 6–3   The solution vector from the final tableau

THE EFFECTS OF A CHANGE IN THE OBJECTIVE-FUNCTION COEFFICIENT OF A TABLE

The solution determined by the model to be optimal is based on the objective-function coefficients of $20 for X_1 (table) and $24 for X_2 (bench). What happens if these coefficients are changed? Beginning with X_1, what if tables made a profit contribution of $21 rather than $20?

On the Solution Value of the Objective Function

The value of the objective function would be affected in this way by a $1 increase in the profit contribution of X_1:

$$(\$20 + \$1)(4) + (\$24)(8) = \$276$$

which means that the value of the objective function would be

$$(\$1)(4) = \$4$$

greater than before. This $4 effect can be read directly from the cell at the intersection of the solution column and the row labeled X_1 in the final tableau. (See Fig. 6–4).

	X_1	X_2	S_1	S_2	
X_2	0	1	2/9	−1/6	8
X_1	1	0	−1/9	1/3	4
	0	0	28/9	8/3	272

FIG. 6–4   The X_1 row from the final tableau

On the Worth of a Unit of Assembly Time

Insofar as the S_1 column is concerned, the $1 increase in the profit contribution of X_1 would have this effect on the bottom row of the final tableau (where the shadow price of the resource is shown):

$$
\begin{aligned}
X_2: & \quad (2/9)(\$24) & = \$\ 48/9 \\
X_1: & \quad (-1/9)(\$20 + \$1) & = -21/9 \\
\hline
& & \$\ 27/9
\end{aligned}
$$

The net effect on the shadow price of assembly time is

Adjusted shadow price of S_1	*Original shadow price of S_1*	*Net effect of a $1 increase in O.F. coefficient of X_1 on the shadow price of S_1*
27/9	− 28/9	= − 1/9

This net effect, the $-1/9$, can be read directly from the intersection of the S_1 column and the X_1 row in the final tableau. (Refer again to Fig. 6–4.)

On the Worth of a Unit of Finishing Time

Turning to the S_2 column, we see that the shadow price on finishing time would be altered by a $1 increase in the objective-function coefficient of X_1 to this extent:

$$X_2: \quad (-1/6)\,(\$24) \qquad = -\$4$$
$$X_1: \quad (1/3)\,(\$20 + \$1) \ = +\ 7$$
$$\overline{\qquad\qquad}$$
$$\$3$$

The net change in the shadow price is

Adjusted shadow price of S_2	*Original shadow price of S_2*	*Net effect of a $1 increase in O.F. coefficient of X_1 on the shadow price of S_2*
3	− 8/3	= 1/3

This net figure can, too, be read directly from the X_1 row of the final tableau, in the S_2 column cell. (Refer to Fig. 6–4.)

Reading the Rows as Effects Vectors

Thus, we see that the net effects of a $1 increase in the objective-function coefficient of X_1 on the shadow prices of the resources and on the solution value of the objective function can be read directly from the X_1 row in the final tableau (ignoring the control columns). A $1 decrease in the objective-function coefficient of X_1 would have a similar effect but in the opposite direction. To read this effect from the final tableau, we would multiply through the X_1 row by a " − 1".

In the same manner, the effects on the shadow prices and on the value of the objective function of increases or decreases in the profit contribution of X_2 can be read from the X_2 row in the final tableau.

Hence, we see that the rows, as well as the columns, in the final tableau can be read as "effects vectors"; the rows reflect the effects of increases or decreases in the objective function coefficient of the variable labeling that row.

RANGING THE X_1 OBJECTIVE-FUNCTION COEFFICIENT: THE UPPER LIMIT

How high—or how low—could the profit contributions for tables and benches go before the current optimal strategy is altered?

We are able to range the objective-function coefficients just as we are able to range the supply of a scarce resource. This process tells us over what range of values for the objective-function coefficients this solution will be the optimal solution.

Consider the row vector as an effects vector, reflecting the effect of a \$1 increase in the objective-function coefficient for that variable. (When ranging the objective-function coefficients, we will ignore the control columns.) The effect of a \$1 increase in the profit contribution of X_1 (a table) can be calculated by

	S_1	S_2	
Objective-function row	(28/9	8/3	272)
Effect of a \$1 increase in profit contribution of X_1:	+(1) (−1/9	1/3	4)
Adjusted objective-function row:	(27/9	3	276).

Note that increases in the objective-function coefficient of X_1 result in decreases in the shadow price in the S_1 column. How many \$1 increases can we make before this number—the shadow price of S_1—turns negative? We recall that a negative number in the bottom row of the tableau means that another iteration of the tableau is necessary. And another iteration of the tableau means that another solution is optimal.

We see by computing $28/9 \div 1/9 = 28$ that twenty-eight \$1-increases in the profit contribution of X_1 would have the effect

	S_1	S_2	
Objective-function row:	(28/9	8/3	272)
Effect of 28 \$1-increases in the profit contribution of X_1:	+(28) (−1/9	1/3	4)
Adjusted objective-function row:	(0	12	384)
	↑		
	Incoming variable		

The "0" in the S_1 column of the objective-function row tells us that any additional increase in the profitability of X_1 would yield a negative indicator, calling for another pivoting of the tableau. In this next tableau, the variable S_1 would come into solution. Hence, the upper limit on the range of values for the X_1 objective-function coefficient over which this solution will hold is

$20 + $28 = $48.

A Graphic Explanation

Recall that the optimal corner point is found by considering both (1) the marginal rates of substitution in reference to usage of scarce resources and (2) the relative profitability of the products. We can see in Fig. 6–5 that the increase in the profit contribution of X_1 (when the profit contribution of the other product remains constant) will tilt the objective function—will cause its slope to become more negative. We had an original objective function of

$$20X_1 + 24X_2 = P.$$

In terms of X_2, the line is

$$24X_2 = P - 20X_1$$
$$X_2 = (P - 20X_1)/24.$$

The slope of this line is $-20/24$ or $-5/6$.

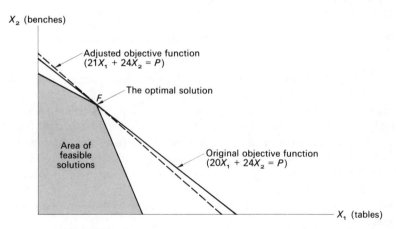

FIG. 6–5 *The effect of a $1 increase in the objective-function coefficient of X_1*

The adjusted objective function, using as the coefficient of X_1 the upper limit of the range, is

$$48X_1 + 24X_2 = P.$$

In terms of X_2 the function is

$$X_2 = (P - 48X_1)/24.$$

and it has a slope of $-48/24$ or -2.

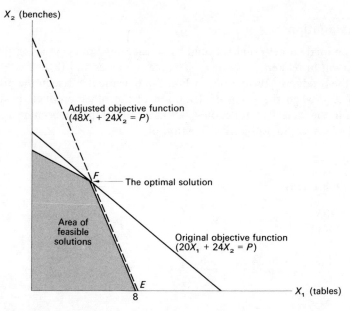

FIG. 6–6   Objective-function-coefficient ranging for X_1: upper limit

In Fig. 6–6 we have shown the slope of the objective function at the upper limit of the objective-function-coefficient range for X_1. Note that if the objective function tilts any further, the corner point $(X_1 = 4, X_2 = 8)$ will no longer be the optimal corner point. From Fig. 6–7 we can see that as an objective-function line with a slope more negative than -2 is pushed out from the origin as far as possible, the last common point between the objective-function line and the area of feasible solutions will no longer be at corner point F but will, instead, be at corner point E.

At the corner point E, the solution is $X_1 = 8, X_2 = 0$. Resources are used in this manner:

Assembly Department time:

$$3(8) + 6(0) + S_1 + 0S_2 = 60$$
$$S_1 = 36.$$

There are 36 unused hours of assembly time. For this reason, we note that S_1

(unused assembly time) is the "incoming variable." The variables in solution at this point are $X_1 = 8$ and $S_1 = 36$.

Finishing Department time:

$$4(8) + 2(0) + 0S_1 + S_2 = 32$$
$$S_2 = 0.$$

There are no unused finishing hours.

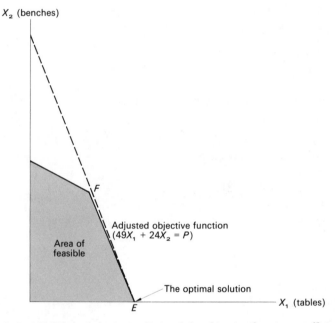

FIG. 6-7 *Beyond the upper limit of the objective-function-coefficient range for X_1 the solution changes*

Notice what has occurred. Tables (X_1) have become so profitable relative to benches (X_2) that all of the resources are being channeled into the production of tables. The most limiting resource is finishing time.

RANGING THE OBJECTIVE-FUNCTION COEFFICIENT FOR X_1: THE LOWER LIMIT

We have shown that—over a certain range—increases in the objective-function coefficient of the variable X_1 will change the shadow prices on the two nonbasic variables and will change the solution value of the objective function but will not alter the solution itself—make four tables and eight benches. Beyond this upper limit—and we found the upper limit to be \$48—further increases in the profit contribution of X_1 would lead to a new optimal solution.

By the same token, it may be possible to decrease the objective-function co-efficient of X_1 without altering the optimal solution. What would happen, for instance, if the profit contribution of X_1 were only $19 rather than $20?

First, the solution value of the objective function would become

($20 − $1) (4) + ($24) (8) = $268.

Shadow prices for the slack variables would be affected to the extent:

S_1 (unused assembly hours):

(2/9) ($24) + (−1/9) ($19) = $29/9

S_2 (unused finishing hours):

(−1/6) ($24) + (1/3) ($19) = $7/3.

The net changes in the shadow prices, and in the value of the objective function, are:

	S_1	S_2	
Shadow prices and value of objective function after objective-function coefficient of X_1 is decreased by $1:	(29/9	7/3	268)
Original objective-function row as shown in final tableau:	−(28/9	8/3	272)
Net effect of a $1-decrease in the objective-function coefficient of X_1 (which is the same as the X_1 row in the final tableau multiplied by −1):	(1/9	−1/3	−4)

With each unit decrease in the objective-function coefficient of X_1, the "worth" of additional units of assembly time increases while the "worth" of additional units of finishing time decreases. Eight $1-decreases in the objective-function coefficient of X_1 would produce a change like this:

	S_1	S_2	
Objective-function row from final tableau:	(28/9	8/3	272)
Effect of eight $1-decreases in the profit contribution of X_1:	−(8) (−1/9	1/3	4)
Adjusted objective-function row:	(4	0	240)

$$\uparrow$$
Incoming
variable

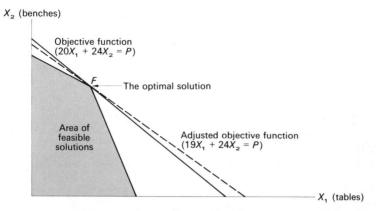

FIG. 6–8 The effect of a \$1 decrease in the objective-function coefficient of X_1

In Fig. 6–8 we see that decreases in the profit contribution of X_1 tilt the objective-function line to make it less and less negative. The original objective function

$$20X_1 + 24X_2 = P$$

has a slope of $-5/6$. The objective function adjusted for the decrease in the profit contribution of X_1 (using \$20 − \$1(8) = \$12 as the objective-function coefficient of X_1) is

$$12X_1 + 24X_2 = P$$
$$X_2 = (P - 12X_1)/24.$$

The adjusted objective function has a slope of $-1/2$. See Fig. 6–9.

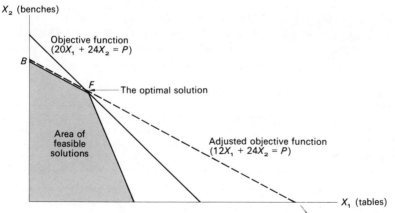

FIG. 6–9 Objective-function-coefficient ranging for X_1: lower limit

If the objective-function coefficient of X_1 were less than \$12, the function would have a slope such that the corner point F would no longer be the optimal solution. Notice in Fig. 6–10 that with a slope of less than $-\frac{1}{2}$, the objective-function line will last touch the area of feasible solutions at corner point B. Hence, with this slope, the optimal solution will be $X_1 = 0$, $X_2 = 10$.

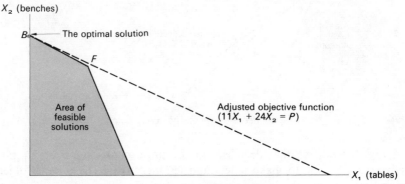

FIG. 6–10 *Beyond the lower limit of the objective-function-coefficient range for X_1 the solution changes*

With this product combination all the available assembly time will be used; that is,

$$3(0) + 6(10) + S_1 + 0S_2 = 60$$
$$S_1 = 0.$$

However, there will be twelve unused hours in the Finishing Department;

$$4(0) + 2(10) + 0S_1 + S_2 = 32$$
$$S_2 = 12.$$

The variables in solution at this corner point are $X_2 = 10$ and $S_2 = 12$.

Notice again what has happened. X_1 has become so unprofitable relative to X_2 that all of the available resources are being devoted to the production of units of X_2. The most restrictive resource is assembly time.

TABLE 6–1 *Objective-function-coefficient ranging for X_1*

Variable	Current value	Lower limit	Upper limit	Incoming variable Lower	Upper
X_1 (tables)	\$20	\$12	\$48	S_2	S_1

In Table 6–1 we have noted that the objective-function coefficient of X_1 (tables) could range from a low of \$12 to a high of \$48 and this solution—make four tables and eight benches—would still be the optimal solution. Outside this range, some other product combination would be optimal. This range is constructed on the assumption that the profit contribution of X_2 remains constant at \$24.

RANGING THE OBJECTIVE-FUNCTION COEFFICIENT FOR X_2

Let us review objective-function-coefficient ranging by ranging the coefficient of X_2 (benches). The row vector from the final tableau is:

$$\begin{array}{ccc} & S_1 & S_2 \\ X_2 & (2/9 & -1/6 & 8) \end{array}$$

This vector reflects the effect of a unit increase in the profit contribution of X_2. We have used a profit contribution of \$24 for X_2. A \$1 increase—to \$25—would have this effect on the bottom row of the final tableau:

	S_1	S_2	
Objective-function row from final tableau:	(28/9	8/3	272)
Effect of \$1 increase in the profit contribution of X_2:	+(1) (2/9	—1/6	8)
Adjusted objective-function row:	(30/9	15/6	280)

Sixteen \$1-increases in the profit contribution of X_2 would result in

	S_1	S_2	
Objective-function row from final tableau:	(28/9	8/3	272)
Effect of 16 \$1-increases in the profit contribution of X_2:	+(16) (2/9	—1/6	8)
Adjusted objective-function row:	(60/9	0	400)
		↑	
		Incoming variable	

Thus, the upper limit of the range of values for the objective-function coefficient of X_2 over which this solution ($X_1 = 4$, $X_2 = 8$) is optimal is

\$24 + \$16 = \$40.

If X_2 yielded a profit contribution greater than \$40, the current solution would no longer be optimal. Figures 6–11 and 6–12 illustrate the effect of an increase in the profit contribution of X_2. As X_2 becomes more profitable relative to X_1, X_1 drops out of solution and only units of X_2 are produced. The limiting constraint is time available in the Assembly Department. There are unused hours of Finishing Department time; hence, S_2 (unused Finishing Department time) is said to be the incoming variable.

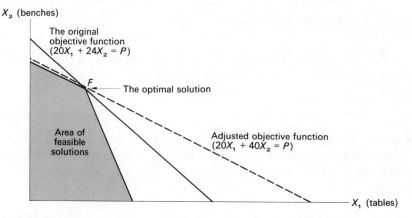

FIG. 6–11   *Objective-function-coefficient ranging for X_2: upper limit*

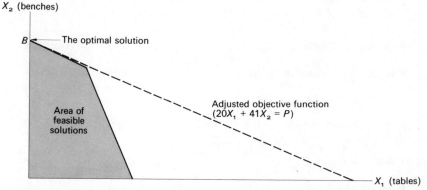

FIG. 6–12   *Beyond the upper limit of the objective-function-coefficient range for X_2 the solution changes*

A \$1 decrease in the objective-function coefficient of X_2 has the following effect on the bottom row of the final tableau:

	S_1	S_2	
Objective-function row from final tableau:	(28/9	8/3	272)
Effect of a \$1-decrease in the profit contribution of X_2:	$-(1)$ (2/9	—1/6	4)
Adjusted objective-function row:	(26/9	17/6	268)

Fourteen $1-decreases in the profit contribution of X_2 would result in this adjusted objective function row:

	S_1	S_2	
Objective-function row from final tableau:	(28/9	8/3	272)
Effect of 14 $1-decreases in the profit contribution of X_2:	$-(14)$ (2/9	$-1/6$	4)
Adjusted objective-function row:	(0	30/6	216)

↑
Incoming variable

Decreases in excess of $14 in the profit contribution of X_2 would result in a negative indicator and would force a new solution. Hence, the lower limit for the range of values of the objective function coefficient of X_2 over which this solution is optimal is

$$\$24 - \$14 = \$10.$$

Figures 6–13 and 6–14 illustrate graphically what has taken place. X_2 has become so unprofitable relative to X_1 that all of the available resources are spent on the production of units of X_1. Finishing Department time becomes the most restrictive constraint.

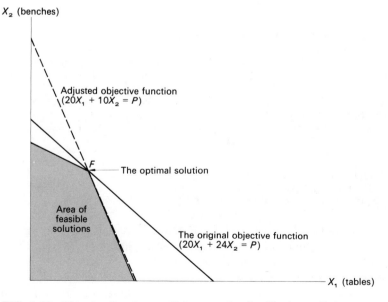

X_2 (benches)

Adjusted objective function
$(20X_1 + 10X_2 = P)$

F — The optimal solution

Area of feasible solutions

The original objective function
$(20X_1 + 24X_2 = P)$

X_1 (tables)

FIG. 6–13 Objective-function-coefficient ranging for X_2: lower limit

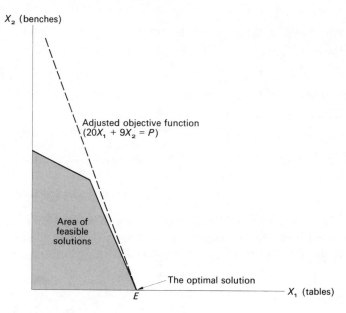

FIG. 6–14   Beyond the lower limit of the objective-function-coefficient range for X_2: the solution changes

A complete tabulation of the objective-function-coefficient ranging for the Furniture Manufacturing Company case is shown in Table 6–2.

TABLE 6–2   Objective-function-coefficient ranging

Variable	Current value	Lower limit	Upper limit	Incoming variable Lower	Upper
X_1 (tables)	$20	$12	$48	S_2	S_1
X_2 (benches)	$24	$10	$40	S_1	S_2

RANGE OF VARIATION PERMITTED IN SLOPE OF OBJECTIVE FUNCTION WITH NO CHANGE IN THE OPTIMAL SOLUTION

A close examination of Figs 6–6, 6–9, 6–11, and 6–13 reveals that the slope of the objective function could vary anywhere between the slope of the Finishing Department constraint line and the slope of the Assembly Department constraint line without altering the optimal solution. From Fig. 6–15 we see that the profit line could rotate anywhere within the shaded area (between the *BFC* line and the *DFE* line) and the optimal solution would remain at point *F*.

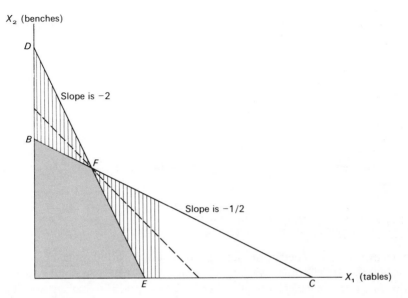

FIG. 6–15 Range of variation permitted in slope of objective function with no change in the optimal strategy

The constraint line BC has a slope of $-1/2$. (We can recheck this value by computing

$$3X_1 + 6X_2 = 60$$
$$X_2 = 10 - (1/2)X_1.$$

The slope is given by the coefficient of X_1 to be $-1/2$; the value of X_2 changes by $-1/2$ for each $+1$ change in the value of X_1.)

The slope of the constraint line DE is -2.

The slope of the profit function could be anywhere within the range

$$-1/2 > \text{slope of objective function} > -2$$

before a change in strategy (away from point F) would be in order.

We ranged the objective-function coefficient of one variable assuming that the objective-function coefficient of the other variable would remain constant. Naturally, both these coefficients could have changed simultaneously. Let us write the objective function as

$$c_1X_1 + c_2X_2 = P$$

where c_1 and c_2 represent the respective contributions of the two variables. Now when the function is rewritten in terms of X_2

$$X_2 = (P/c_2) - (c_1/c_2)X_1$$

we see that the slope is $-c_1/c_2$. Then, the optimal strategy will be at point F for so long as

$$-1/2 > -c_1/c_2 > -2.$$

To simplify matters, we may multiply through by -1 and obtain

$$1/2 < c_1/c_2 < 2.$$

In other words, the relative contribution to the objective of X_1 to X_2 can be anywhere between 1/2 and 2 and the optimal solution to the model will remain unchanged.

CONCOMITANT CHANGES IN THE CONTRIBUTION COEFFICIENTS

The objective-function-coefficient ranging for a given variable presupposes that the coefficients of all other variables remain constant. Assuming that the objective-function coefficient for all other variables will not change, we range a particular variable to determine how its coefficient could vary without altering the optimal strategy. Many times, however, the objective-function coefficients of the activity variables are interrelated so that if one coefficient changes the others change as well, though not always to the same extent. If the activity variables represent products to be manufactured, the coefficients might be simultaneously affected by a change in the cost of a direct raw material that is used by each of the products. Or a change in the labor wage rate might cause the contributions of all activity variables to change at the same time.

It is possible to analyze the effect of concomitant changes in the objective-function coefficients of activity variables by combining the proper row effects vectors in the proper proportions. Let us suppose that both the tables and benches produced by the Furniture Manufacturing Company use a basic white pine lumber. Quantity-wise, a bench requires twice as much of the lumber as does a table. The cost of this raw material was considered when the profit contributions of the items were calculated. Now assume that the cost of the lumber increases so that the quantity required to make one bench now costs $1.00 more than before. The profit contribution of a bench decreases by this same amount. We have seen that the effect of a $1.00 decrease in the objective-function coefficient of the bench (X_2) is shown by the X_2 row effects vector multiplied by -1; that is,

Effect of a $1 decrease
in objective-function
coefficient of X_2: $\qquad (-1) \times (2/9 \quad -1/6 \quad 8) = (-2/9 \quad 1/6 \quad -8).$

Because the tables use the same lumber, the objective-function coefficient of X_1 (tables) will decrease as well. A table, however, uses only half as much of the lumber as does a bench. Thus, there will be only a $0.50 decrease in the profit contribution of a table. This effect is given by

Effect of a $0.50 decrease
in objective-function
coefficient of X_1: $(-0.50) \times (-1/9 \quad 1/3 \quad 4) = (1/18 \quad -1/6 \quad -2)$.

The total effect of this change in the raw material cost will be seen by summing the individual effects of the two variables; that is,

$$(-2/9 \quad 1/6 \quad -8) + (1/18 \quad -1/6 \quad -2) = (-3/18 \quad 0 \quad -10).$$

We readily see that because of these changes in the coefficients of the variables, the total value of the objective function would decrease by $10. The shadow price of S_2 would not be affected; the shadow price of S_2 would remain at $8/3. The shadow price of S_1 would, however, decrease by $3/18; the shadow price of S_1 would become

$28/9 - $3/18 = $53/18.$

We can verify that these are the new shadow prices by these computations:

For S_1:

X_2:	$(2/9) \times (\$24 - \$1)$	$= \$ 46/9$
X_1:	$(-1/9) \times (\$20 - \$0.50)$	$= -39/18$
		$\$ 53/18.$

For S_2:

X_2:	$(-1/6) \times (\$24 - \$1)$	$= -\$23/6$
X_1:	$(1/3) \times (\$20 - \$0.50)$	$= 39/6$
		$\$ 8/3$

and the total profit contribution would become

X_2:	$(8) \times (\$24 - \$1)$	$= \$184$
X_1:	$(4) \times (\$20 - \$0.50)$	$= 78$
		$\$262$

OBJECTIVE-FUNCTION-COEFFICIENT RANGING
FOR A SLACK VARIABLE

Now let us investigate objective-function-coefficient ranging for slack variables. The "adjusted" Furniture Company model

Maximize: $20X_1 + 50X_2 + 0S_1 + 0S_2 = P$ (profit contribution)

subject to

$$3X_1 + 6X_2 + S_1 + 0S_2 = 60 \quad \text{(Assembly Department constraint)}$$
$$4X_1 + 2X_2 + 0S_1 + S_2 = 32 \quad \text{(Finishing Department constraint)}$$

where

X_1 = number of tables to produce each day

X_2 = number of benches to produce each day

S_1 = unused hours of assembly time

S_2 = unused hours of finishing time

resulted in the final tableau reproduced in Fig. 6–16.

	X_1	X_2	S_1	S_2	
X_2	1/2	1	1/6	0	10
S_2	3	0	−1/3	1	12
	5	0	25/3	0	500

FIG. 6–16 Final tableau for "adjusted" furniture company case

Note that one of the basic variables is the activity variable X_2 (benches) and that the other is the slack variable S_2 (representing unused hours of finishing time).

The slack variables were assigned coefficients of zero in the objective function of the model because it was believed that an unused unit of the resources made no contribution—positive or negative—to profit. However, the assumption that unused resources have no cost, or have no worth, is not always tenable. Various reasons why it might be costly to have unused units of a resource may be suggested: labor morale problems may arise if labor hours are unused; storage costs may be associated with unused units of raw material; and so on. In some cases it may be appropriate to attach a premium to unused units of a scarce resource. There may exist alternative uses for the resource—uses which are outside of the current model—that would justify the attaching of a positive objective-function coefficient to the slack variable. In a maximizing linear programming model,

1. a positive objective-function coefficient attached to a slack variable indicates that there is a contribution to the objective associated with not using the resource in this model; and

2. a negative objective-function coefficient attached to a slack variable indicates that there is a cost to the objective associated with not using the resource in this model.

It is certainly not unusual for firms to have a bias against unused resources or to have many alternative uses for the resource.

It is helpful, then, to find a "range of indifference" for the costs or premiums associated with unused units of scarce resources. The limits of the range would be determined by how large, or how small, an objective-function coefficient could be attached to the slack variable before obtaining a negative indicator and, thereby, forcing a new optimal solution.

The effect of increasing the objective-function coefficient of S_2 by \$1 is shown by the S_2 row vector in the final tableau. Had, then, the coefficient of S_2 been $+\$1$ rather than zero, the adjusted objective-function row shown below would have resulted:

	X_1	S_1	
Objective-function row (ignoring control columns):	(5	25/3	500)
Effect of using $+1$ as the objective-function coefficient of S_2:	$+(1)(3$	$-1/3$	12)
Adjusted objective-function row:	(8	24/3	512)

A positive coefficient attached to S_2 in the objective function indicates that that there is a premium associated with having unused finishing hours. The maximum positive coefficient is \$25; that is,

	X_1	S_1	
Objective-function row (ignoring control columns):	(5	25/3	500)
Effect of using $+25$ as the objective-function coefficient of S_2:	$+(25)(3$	$-1/3$	12)
Adjusted objective-function row:	(80	0	800)

$\uparrow$
Incoming variable

If unused finishing hours were more valuable than \$25 each, it would be advantageous for the company to abandon the optimal solution given earlier and make neither tables nor benches but, instead, have 32 hours of unused finishing time.

We can see the effect of attaching a negative objective-function coefficient to S_2—which would indicate a cost associated with having unused finishing hours—by multiplying the S_2 row vector in the final tableau by a minus number.

Had the coefficient of S_2 been $-\$1$, for example, the adjusted objective-function row shown below would have resulted:

$$X_1 \quad S_1$$

		X_1	S_1	
Objective-function row (ignoring control columns):	(5	25/3	500)	
Effect of using -1 as the objective-function coefficient of S_2:	$-(1)(3$	$-1/3$	12)	
Adjusted objective-function row:	(2	26/3	488)	

The most negative coefficient for S_2 over which the current strategy would be optimal would be $-5/3$. For a cost of unused finishing hours greater than $\$5/3$, the production should shift from units of X_2 (benches) to units of X_1 (tables). This shift could result in zero unused finishing hours.

We see, then, that the objective-function coefficient for the variable S_2 (representing unused finishing hours) could range from $+\$25$ to $-\$5/3$ and the solution given—make ten units of X_2—would still be optimal. This range is shown in Table 6–3.

TABLE 6–3 Objective-function-coefficient ranging, "adjusted" furniture case

Variable	Current value	Lower limit	Upper limit	Incoming variable Lower	Upper
X_2 (benches)	$50	$40	∞	X_1	—
S_2 (unused finishing) hours)	$0	$-\$5/3$	$+\$25$	X_1	S_1
X_1 (tables)	$20	$0	$25	—	X_1

The basic variable X_2 is also ranged in Table 6–3. The lower limit of the range is $40. If the contribution of X_2 were less than $40, it would be profitable to allocate some of the resources to the production of X_1. The upper limit of the range is plus infinity. With a profit contribution of $50 for X_2, it was most profitable to use all resources in this production of this product. Certainly, if the item were even more profitable than $50, this strategy would still be optimal.

OBJECTIVE-FUNCTION-COEFFICIENT RANGING FOR A NONBASIC ACTIVITY VARIABLE

Take special notice of the objective-function-coefficient ranging for the nonbasic activity variable X_1 as shown in Table 6–3. Because it is a nonbasic variable, it has no row vector in the final tableau so we must range this variable by looking at its shadow price. First, the lower limit is $0. If with a contribution of $20 it was not profitable to include units of X_1 in the production strategy, it will still not be profitable to include them should the contribution decrease. Zero is a practical lower limit (minus infinity is the real lower limit). The upper limit of $25 was derived following this line of reasoning: In the initial tableau the number in the X_1-column, objective-function row cell was -20. In the final tableau this number had been changed to $+5$. Now if the beginning value had been 5 smaller than it was, the ending number would have been zero; that is, if the beginning value had been -25, the ending number would have been zero. If the beginning value had been less than -25, the number in the X_1 column of the last tableau would have been negative and the tableau would have been pivoted again, resulting in a new optimal strategy. Hence, the objective-function coefficient of X_1 could have been anywhere between zero and $25 and the current solution would have remained optimal.

STABILITY OF THE MODEL

If the solution is relatively insensitive to changes in the objective-function coefficients, the model is said to be a *stable* one whereas if only slight changes in the coefficients would result in a new optimal strategy, the model is said to be *unstable*.

The identification of those objective-function coefficients to which the solution is most sensitive permits the decision maker to concentrate on improving these estimates.

RE-PIVOTING THE TABLEAU

Should the objective-function coefficient of a variable change so that a new solution is called for, it is not necessary to return to the original model and begin all over again with the simplex manipulations. We can simply insert the adjusted objective-function row in the last tableau and continue from this point.

For example, the final tableau of the "adjusted" Furniture Company Case is shown in Fig. 6–17. The model used here was built on an objective-function coefficient of $50 for X_2. We see from Table 6–3 that had the contribution coefficient been less than $40, the current strategy would no longer be optimal. So let us change the coefficient from $50 to $24. We can effect this change by multiplying the X_2 row vector in the final tableau by a scalar that represents the change we wish to make. We want to effect a $26 decrease in the X_2 coefficient so we mutliply the X_2 row (ignoring control columns always) by "-26", as

$$(-26)(1/2 \quad - \quad 1/6 \quad - \quad 10) = (-13 \quad - \quad -13/3 \quad - \quad -260).$$

Final tableau for model using \$50 as the objective-function
coefficient of X_2

	X_1	X_2	S_1	S_2	
X_2	1/2	1	1/6	0	10
S_2	3	0	−1/3	1	12
	5	0	25/3	0	500

Tableau with the objective-function row adjusted for a \$26 decrease
in the objective-function coefficient of X_2

	X_1	X_2	S_1	S_2	
X_2	1/2	1	1/6	0	10
S_2	3	0	−1/3	1	12
	−8	0	4	0	240

Final tableau for model using \$24 as the objective-function
coefficient of X_2

	X_1	X_2	S_1	S_2	
X_2	0	1	2/9	−1/6	8
X_1	1	0	−1/9	1/3	4
	0	0	28/9	8/3	272

FIG. 6–17 Re-pivoting the tableau

This result is combined with the old objective-function row in the final tableau:

$$
\begin{array}{rrrrr}
(& 5 & 0 & 25/3 & 0 & 500) \\
+ (-13 & - & -13/3 & - & -260) \\
= (& -8 & 0 & 4 & - & 240)
\end{array}
$$

Now we replace the old objective-function row with the adjusted row and pivot the tableau as usual. (See Fig. 6–17.)

EXERCISES

1. People's Clothing Company makes shirts and blouses. Both types of items are processed through the cutting and stitching departments of the plant and the resources of both of these departments are severely limited. There are only 120 hours of time available each day in the cutting department and 160 hours available in the stitching department.

Each shirt requires four hours of cutting time and four hours of stitching time; each blouse requires three hours of cutting time and five hours of stitching time.

The firm wishes to plan production so as to maximize its profit. The profit associated with each shirt is $6 and with each blouse is $5.

Set up and solve a linear programming model to aid in this decision. What strategy is optimal? What is the profit contribution of this strategy? By how much would profit be increased if five additional hours of time were available in the cutting department each day? What changes in the product mix would this increase in cutting time call for? What would be the effect of a 5-hour increase in the stitching time available each day? Suppose that the profit on each shirt increased by $1. What effect would this change have on the optimal strategy? Set up both the right-hand-side and the objective-function coefficient ranges and explain carefully their significance.

Suppose that the cotton cloth used in the production of these items increased in price by $0.10 a yard. Two yards of the cloth are used in each blouse and one yard is used in each shirt. What effect does this change have on the final solution?

2. The following linear programming model

Maximize: $50X_1 + 20X_2 + 10X_3$ (profit)

subject to

$$6X_1 + 2X_2 + X_3 \leqslant 500 \qquad \text{(Resource \#1)}$$
$$2X_1 + X_2 + X_3 \leqslant 200 \qquad \text{(Resource \#2)}$$
$$3X_1 + 4X_2 + 5X_3 \leqslant 1000 \qquad \text{(Resource \#3)}$$

where X_1 = number of units of Product #1 to produce, X_2 = number of units of Product #2 to produce, X_3 = number of units of Product #3 to produce, yielded this final tableau:

	X_1	X_2	X_3	S_1	S_2	S_3	
X_1	1	0	− 0.5	0.5	− 1	0	50
X_2	0	1	2	−1	3	0	100
S_3	0	0	− 1.5	2.5	− 9	1	450
	0	0	5	5	10	0	4500

a) Compute and explain the right-hand-side and the objective-function-coefficient ranges.

b) If ten additional units of Resource #1 were made available, how should they be utilized? What is the worth of these ten units?

c) If four units of X_3 had to be produced, what would be the best product mix, and what would be the resulting profit?

d) If conditions changed so that X_2 became $2 more profitable per unit, what would an additional unit of Resource #2 be worth?

e) Show the effects vector which reflects the fact that Resource #2 has become $1 per unit more costly. Over what range of price changes in Resource #2 would this final tableau still hold?

f) If Resource #3 were labor, what cost would have to be attributed to idle time for the model to decrease the unused labor time?

3. A company manufactures three products (#1, #2, and #3) which sell for $80, $30, and $65, respectively. The resources used in the manufacture of these products, their costs and availabilities are as follows:

Resource	Units of the resource required to produce one unit of the products			Per unit cost of the resource	Total number of units of the resource available for use
	#1	#2	#3		
Raw material I	1	0	3	$4	1000
Raw material II	1	1	2	$1	unlimited quantity
Raw material III	2	1	1	$5	1500
Labor level 1	20	14	16	$1	unlimited supply
Labor level 2	5	1	3	$5	6000

The products are seasonal products and will have to be warehoused for a period of time after their manufacture until they are delivered to the buyers. The company has available for use 900 square feet of warehouse space. Each unit of each of the products requires one square foot of storage space.

Use a linear programming model to help the company decide upon a production strategy. Find the range over which cost of raw material I can vary, still maintaining the same optimal production strategy. Find the same range for raw material II and raw material III. What would be the effect of adding $1 per unit: To the cost of raw material I? To the cost of raw material II? To the cost of raw material III?

4. The Aurora Corporation produces three products for commercial sale—a deluxe model called the Australis, a regular model, the Borealis, and an economy model, the Corona. The marketing department of Aurora has done extensive research concerning the quantities of each product that can reasonably be expected to be sold each day. The conclusion of this research is that the probability of selling more than 150 Coronas each day is very, very small. Otherwise, it seems that as many units of the other models as can be produced can be sold.

In addition to other materials which are in plentiful supply, each of these products requires certain amounts of buckles, belts, and clamps. Aurora purchases these materials from outside suppliers at a cost of $0.13, $0.12, and $0.10 per unit, respectively. A finished Australis requires 5 buckles, 6 belts, and 3 clamps. A finished Borealis requires 7 buckles, 4 belts, and 3 clamps. A finished Corona requires 2 buckles, 2 belts, and 2 clamps. The daily supply of the raw materials is limited to 730 buckles, 680 belts, and 470 clamps.

Aurora is only one of many producers of products similar to Australis, Borealis, and Corona, and, therefore, must sell these products at a price established by the market. Presently the Australis can be sold for $2.25 per unit, the Borealis for $2.00 per unit, and the Corona for $1.15 per unit.

Aurora desires to find out how many of each product to produce to maximize daily profit. What is the "worth" of an additional unit of each of the scarce resources? How should these additional resources be used?

If the cost of belts increased to $0.15, what changes should be made in the production strategy?

5. Fergusen Engineering, Inc., was founded by John Fergusen, a mechanical engineer specializing in hydraulic system components. Mr. Fergusen developed a new chatter-resistant shuttle valve and patented the design of the valve spindle. He found he could sell the spindles alone to manufacturers of certain types of hydraulic equipment or he could sell assembled valves by machining a sleeve for each spindle. Recently, he succeeded in obtaining orders from automotive manufacturers for a valve block assembly which contains two of the patented valve spindles and a machined valve block. Fortunately, the market is such that the entire output of each type of product can be sold.

The profit per unit for each type of product is as follows:

Valve spindle	$10.00
Valve assembly (consisting of one spindle and one sleeve)	20.00
Valve block assembly (consisting of one valve block plus two spindles)	60.00

The shop at Fergusen Engineering is of limited size and available machine time, as well as assembly and inspection and test time, is limited. The machining time available each week for each function and the time required for each machining step for each main product component is as follows:

Machining time required (minutes per unit)

Machine	Valve spindle	Valve sleeve	Valve block	Total available minutes each week
Turret lathe	10.0	15.0	25.0	25,000
Polish-grinder	5.0	5.0	10.0	15,000

Processing time required (minutes per unit)

Process	Valve spindle	Valve sleeve	Valve block	Total available minutes each week
Inspection	5.0	5.0	10.0	
Testing	—	5.0	20.0	
Total	5.0	10.0	30.0	

	Valve spindle	Valve assembly	Valve block assembly	45,000
Assembly	0	5.0	10.0	

Mr. Fergusen wishes to produce those products which will maximize his profit. Use linear programming to help Mr. Fergusen analyze the production possibilities. Extract as much information from the linear programming model as you can.

6. The Gem Ring Company produces a line of quality, hand-crafted men's and women's 14k gold rings. Each ring requires two processes: molding and finishing. A woman's ring requires four units of molding and six units of finishing. A man's ring requires five units of molding and four units of finishing. A total of 100 units of molding and 120 units of finishing are available daily for the manufacture of rings.

The Gem Company exists in a purely competitive market situation; it can sell whatever it produces. Gem achieves a total profit of $7 each for the men's rings and $8 each for the women's rings.

Gem desires to know what combination of men's and women's rings it should produce in order to maximize profits. Set up the linear programming model and solve by the simplex method. Interpret fully the final tableau. Find the ranges for the objective-function coefficients. Display these ranges graphically and explain carefully their significance. Also establish the right-hand-side ranges. Discuss thoroughly the information provided by the linear programming model.

7. The Lasting Leather Company has 200 square yards of untanned leather that can be used to produce either fancy leather belts or leather billfolds. Each of the belts requires 0.1 square yards of leather and each of the billfolds requires 0.05 square yards.

Before the leather can be used for either item, however, it must go through a tanning process. The leather to be used in belts requires $\frac{1}{4}$ hour of tanning for each square yard processed; the leather to be used in billfolds requires $\frac{3}{4}$ hours of tanning for each square yard processed. One hundred hours of tanning time is available.

The belts are decorated with brass nails. Each belt requires one dozen of these nails. The company has in stock twelve gross of these nails but will be unable to obtain any additional nails.

Each type of item makes about the same contribution to profit. Thus, the company would like to know how many units of each type of item they should produce in order to maximize the total number of items produced.

8. An electronics design engineer is confronted with a problem in choosing components for a 10 kHz oscillator. He may have up to a total of 70 devices each of 20 ohms impedance in his circuit to restrict current flow. Since all components will function with the same 10 kHz signal, they can be either 20 ohms of pure resistance, or 20 ohms of capacitive or inductive reactance. Capacitors and inductors cannot be mixed in the same circuit because of their opposite phase characteristics, so he has decided to narrow his choice of mix to six resistors and 0.8 microfarad capacitors (which both have an effective resistance or impedance of 20 ohms).

For each resistor the engineer can use instead of an inductor, the firm will save 4¢ per circuit board. The corresponding figure for each capacitor is 2¢.

Each 20 ohm resistor takes up $\frac{1}{4}$ square inch of circuit board while each 0.8 microfarad capacitor takes up 0.4 square inches of circuit board. Area measurements include space for leads. The total space available on the board is 25 square inches.

The problem with the resistors is that they generate heat. Specifically, each resistor can be expected to raise the temperature of the board by $\frac{1}{4}$ degrees above the $70°$ temperature its cooling system is designed to maintain. Capacitors, on the other hand, dissipate very little heat and should raise the temperature by no more than 0.05 degrees per capacitor. The maximum permissible temperature deviation is $10°$.

What mix should this engineer use in maximizing the firm's savings? List as much additional information given by the final tableau as you possibly can.

9. The B. K. Goober Company is engaged in the exportation of domestically grown and processed peanuts. Being a relatively new firm, it has thus far developed a market for its products in only three countries: France, India, and Argentina. (None of its products are sold in the United States.) Furthermore, only two grades of peanuts are marketed: Superior (highest-quality) and Fine (lower-quality). Even then, only the lower-quality product is marketable in India because of a licensing restriction imposed by the Indian government. The company exports the peanuts in case-size lots, C.I.F., from two ports: New York (peanuts bound for France and India) and New Orleans (peanuts bound for Argentina). Goober Company has available to it all the peanuts it can process and sell in any given month.

The company has determined from its production runs over the past year that to process a case of the lower-quality peanuts requires from 28 to 32 minutes. From this data, it seems reasonable to assert that 30 minutes is the processing time required for a case of the Fine peanuts. Similarly, repeated random samples of production runs of the Superior peanuts established the fact that the time required for this process lay within 57 and 63 minutes. Thus, the company feels justified in asserting that one hour is the processing time required for a case of the Superior peanuts.

The current labor contract by which the Goober Company is bound calls for two ten-hour shifts (straight-time pay only) per day on a five-day week, four weeks per month basis. With 250 machines at its plant, this provides the company with a total of 100,000 machine-hours per month.

As a result of its marketing research endeavors, the company has found that the French populace prefers the Superior peanut to the Fine by a ratio of 3-to-1 whereas the Argentines prefer the Fine over the Superior by a 2-to-1 ratio. From its demand studies, the company had found that total demand, in cases per month, for both grades of peanuts does not exceed 40,000 for France, 20,000 for India, and 30,000 for Argentina.

The company is required by the banks with which it maintains its accounts to retain in reserve a certain percentage of the drafts loaned to the company as insurance against default by its export agents. The company has available only $50,000 per month for this purpose. Due to the distances and risks involved, the banks require these reserves as a percentage of revenue per case exported: France, 5%; Argentine, 7%; and India, 9%.

The variable costs associated with producing a case of peanuts for export is explained as follows. The resource peanuts cost a straight $2 per case regardless of quality of finished product, which is solely a function of processing. The company has determined its packaging costs to be $1 a case, again irrespective of grade. The processing costs (composed of labor and machines) is $4 an hour.

The transportation costs are based on the shipping distances involved and are $1 a case for cases shipped to France, $1.20 a case to India, and $1.50 a case to Argentina. Insurance costs are 10% of port cost (plant plus transportation costs).

The revenue associated with a case of each grade peanut is as follows: French Superior, $11.00; French Fine, $7.95; Argentine Superior, $10.49; Argentine Fine $8.00; and Indian Fine, $8.50.

The company would like to determine how many cases of each grade of peanut to produce and export to its various markets in order to maximize its profits in any given month.

Chapter 7

BUILDING A
LINEAR PROGRAMMING
MODEL

Linear programming can be a powerful tool for providing informative answers to perplexing questions. The versatility of the technique, its adaptability to myriad types of problem situations, is truly a manifestation of its usefulness. Nonetheless, the mathematical algorithm known as linear programming is endowed with no magical powers that enable it to extract meaningful and valuable answers from a poorly formulated description of the relevant aspects of the situation under study.

The model is an aid to, never a substitute for, sound human judgment. In fact, the usefulness of the technique depends upon the soundness of the judgment of its user. The greatest pitfall, the greatest danger, in the use of linear programming, or any other mathematical model, is the tendency of the user to become the model's slave rather than its master. Too often data, of whatever significance and validity, are fed into the model and "iron-clad" strategies, of no greater significance or validity, pour forth from the model. All too frequently we forget that no solution method, however refined, can overcome basic deficiencies present in the structure of the system or in the data input to that system.

With the successful user, the real thinking in modeling goes into the structuring of the model and into collecting the required data inputs. The manipulation of the model itself is usually a rather routine clerical operation, handled more often than not by a high-speed electronic computer. The analyst concentrates on isolating those aspects of the problem situation most important for analysis, determining relationships between relevant variables, deciding upon the appropriate parameters and—after a solution has been obtained—evaluating its feasibility.

Modeling has an inherent advantage in that the construction of the model helps one to put the complexities and uncertainties attending a decision-making situation into a logical framework, one amenable to comprehensive analysis. A mathematical model is a functional account of the relationship between pertinent variables under study. It is an abstraction that isolates those factors of a problem situation that are most germane to a solution. It clarifies the decision alternatives and their anticipated effects. Modeling, thus, is a vehicle for arriving at a well-structured view of a real-world problem environment.

The practical use of linear programming requires that the conceptual model of the phenomena under consideration be translated into a concrete description of these phenomena. It requires a fairly precise mathematical statement of the situation under study, the objective sought, the variables most directly related to the achievement of that goal, the restrictions imposed upon activities by the environment in which they are carried on, and the contributions of the alternative activities toward the objective.

It is the ability to build a model consistent with the real-world as characterized by the use of appropriate restrictions, meaningful coefficients and contributions, and the securing of accurate input data to feed into the model that is the critical phase of modeling. Although a mathematical model does not attempt to portray reality—it is an abstraction, an oversimplification—if the answers provided by the model are to be useful in the real-world environment, the input into the model must have real-world validity. The greater the difference between the real-world problem and the problem modeled, the less satisfactory will be the solution provided by the model in relation to the real-world problem.

DEFINING THE OBJECTIVE FUNCTION

The first step, and a most important one, is a thorough thinking-through of the problem at hand. What general plans of action are under scrutiny? What questions are being asked? (How many units of each type of product should be manufactured? How should the advertising budget be spent? How should a feed-mix be blended?) However, none of these questions can be fully answered except in terms of a goal or a target. How many units of each type of product should be manufactured—in order to accomplish what end purpose? How should the advertising budget be spent—to achieve what mission?

To complicate matters further, it may be a very distorting oversimplification to assume that any specific problem situation is governed by a single objective. More often than not, there are many objectives, some of which may not be compatible, may even be conflicting. The sales function of a firm might be interested in determining the product mix that would maximize current dollar sales; the financial function of the same firm could be more interested in the product mix that would maximize current profits. And these two goals may not be strictly compatible. Moreover, the market research group of the company may be primarily concerned with the product combination that would best exploit future growth potential while the production department wants to keep the labor force busy, and the controller wants to minimize costs. Precise specification of an objective is prerequisite to construction of the linear programming model.

The linear programming model requires a *single* objective function. In the product-mix problem alluded to above, the model might be structured around any one of the objectives mentioned, or many others which were not mentioned. Each different objective function would possibly result in an entirely different optimal solution. The decision maker might, in fact, want to use the model with various objective functions and compare the different solutions to see what would be sacrificed in terms of, say, current profits in order to maintain full employment of the labor force, or, perhaps, how the sales volume would be affected if current profits were to be maximized. (We already know that much of the same type of information can be gleaned from the sensitivity analysis—the right-hand-side and the objective-function-coefficient ranging.)

Although the linear programming model does require a single objective function which is to be maximized or minimized, this one objective need not be allowed to subvert other legitimate goals. It is possible to include other objectives as "constraints" in the model. In the hypothetical product mix problem we have been referring to, the objective function for the model might be to maximize current profit contribution; then, restrictions could be included in the model that would require that labor-hours used be not fewer than a specified minimum, or that at least a minimum quantity of each product be produced, and so on. Thus, the model requirement that a single objective be used is not as restrictive as it might at first appear to be. Note that when using constraints as a means of including multiple objectives in a linear programming model, the model will satisfy the constraints first, and within these limitations will maximize (or minimize) the objective function. Careful thought must be given to the matter of which objectives should be included as constraints and which one should be expressed as the objective function.

One very rigid restriction does exist regarding the criterion given the linear programming model to use as a basis for selecting an optimal plan of action. The objective function must be couched in numerical terms. The contribution of various activities to this goal must be measurable quantitatively. So we are barred from thinking along the lines of such broad generalities as "maximize goodwill", or "maximize future market potential," or "maximize company well-being." Even such objectives as "maximize profit" or "minimize cost" are rather ambiguous since there are many different varieties of "profit" and many types of "costs." We must must define the objective in such a way that we are able to outline a procedure for measuring degree of achievement of the objective, in numerical terms.

DEFINING THE ACTIVITIES

Once an overall goal for the decision-making situation is established, the analyst returns to the possible alternative plans of action in order to subject these to more careful consideration. The activity variables will evolve from these alternative courses of action.

We have stressed the idea that the activity variables of a linear programming model must (1) be controllable and (2) provide a definite plan for action. Beyond these criteria, activities may be defined as broadly, or as narrowly, as is consistent with the aims of the study. Two alternative courses of action represent different activities if they differ in respect to resource usage, if they produce different end products, if they use the same proportions of the same resources to produce different products, if they use different proportions of the same resources in producing the same product, or if they are subject to different restrictions of whatever nature. Two alternative courses of action are representative of two different activities if they contribute to the achievement of the stated objective at different rates.

Two activities, although not precisely identical, may be treated as if they were the same if they have identical entries in the same rows of the simplex tableau, or if the coefficients of one are a simple multiple of the coefficients of the other. This condition would indicate that the contributions of the two actions are in the same ratio as are the respective resource inputs into the activities.

The model, naturally, can consider only those activities that are defined for it. Thus, the model builder should make a special effort not to overlook alternative courses of action that might be significant.

The definition of the activities, of course, requires a parallel definition of resource restrictions and contributions to objective.

DEFINING THE RESTRICTIONS

Much of the success of any linear programming model depends upon the ingenuity of the builder of that model in establishing restrictions which are relevant in number and in magnitude. There are many types of restrictions that might enter into a situation: physical, technical, legal, or institutional. Restrictions that are subjective or personal in nature may also play a major role in defining a linear programming model.

Technically, the number of activities in the optimal solution cannot exceed the number of constraint equations in the model. Thus, defining the relevant number of restrictions is synonomous with specifying the maximum number of activity variables which can be included in the final solution. If man-hours of labor is the only restriction used in a model, for example, the final strategy will never include more than one activity—that activity which, in terms of the objective function, most efficiently utilizes man-hours of labor. If another restriction is added to the model—to represent available supply of a scarce raw material, for example—then the final strategy can include, at the most, two activities; these will be the two activities most efficient in terms of labor and raw material usage.

We are not trying to suggest that the number of constraint equations should be made to exactly correspond to the number of activity variables. Not at all. Only those variables that are appropriate should be defined in the model, just as only those restrictions that are relevant should be included. However, this mathematical "peculiarity" of the linear programming model does necessitate a careful analysis of the optimal solution provided.

Suppose that a firm has a product line consisting of 50 different items. Then assume that there are only five logical restrictions for a linear programming model designed to determine the optimal product mix. Given accurate objective function and constraint coefficients for the activity variables, the model will provide a technically correct plan of action, one that will call for the manufacture of, at the most, five products. And the firm may well wish to follow this plan of action. Still, it does not seem unreasonable to believe that the decision maker might wish to alter this plan to bring into play other items in the product line. The firm may not wish to become highly specialized but may feel that diversification, within certain limits, will tend to stabilize the flow of income over the years or to minimize certain market risks and that these factors are more important than current profit maximization. Restrictions might be included in the model to provide for minimum production quantities of specified products. This is tantamount to specification that the objective is not solely one of profit maximization but one of a proper combination of profit and income stability, as exemplified by diversification of the product line. If it is not desirable that such restrictions on activity levels be included in the model itself, the shadow prices from the solution tableau will be useful in determining the "cost" of including certain activities in the strategy that is finally adopted.

CONSIDERING THE ASSUMPTIONS OF THE MODEL

These factors—the objective function, the activity variables, and the restrictions—contribute the framework of the model. The model itself is based on certain assumptions regarding these factors and the interrelationships prevailing among them.

Linearity

The linear programming model rests on the assumption that the relationships between the variables are *linear*. This means, for one thing, that only equations with variables in the first power can be used to represent the existent relationships.

TABLE 7–1   An example of a linear relationship between X and Y

$$Y = 20 - 4X \qquad X = 0, 1, ..., 5$$

The value of X is:	The value of Y is:	The change in X is:	The change in Y is:
0	20	—	—
1	16	+1	−4
2	12	+1	−4
3	8	+1	−4
4	4	+1	−4
5	0	+1	−4

When two variables are linearly related, a change in one causes an exactly proportionate change in the other, as illustrated in Table 7–1. Note that whenever X changes by one unit, Y changes by four units. This relationship is constant for the entire range of values for X.

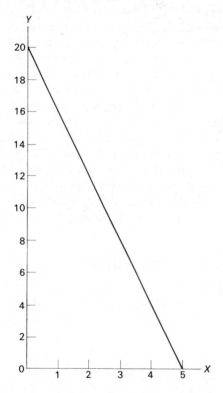

FIG. 7–1   *A linear relationship between X and Y*

A linear relationship always graphs as a straight line, as shown in Fig. 7–1. The slope of the line, representing the change in Y relative to a unit change in X, is constant.

An example of a nonlinear relationship between two variables is given in Table 7–2. In this example, a one-unit change in the value of X cause a differentially increasing change in the value of Y. When these pairs of values are plotted on a graph, they do not take the form of a straight line, but rather of a line with a changing slope (see Fig. 7–2).

The linearity assumption implies constant returns to scale and precludes the possibility of economies or diseconomies of scale. When a resource-usage coefficient is assigned to a variable in a product-mix problem, for instance, it is assumed that this value will be reliable over a wide range of volume variations in the

TABLE 7–2 *An example of a nonlinear relationship between*
X and Y
$$Y = X^2 \qquad X = 0, 1, ..., 5$$

The value of X is:	The value of Y is:	The change in X is:	The change in Y is:
0	0	—	—
1	1	+1	+1
2	4	+1	+3
3	9	+1	+5
4	16	+1	+7
5	25	+1	+9

production of the variable. If one hour of labor is required to make one unit of product X, it is assumed that 1000 hours of labor will be required to make 1000 units of X. If X represents an activity variable which has been assigned an objective function coefficient of \$5, linear programming assumes that this \$5 value will be

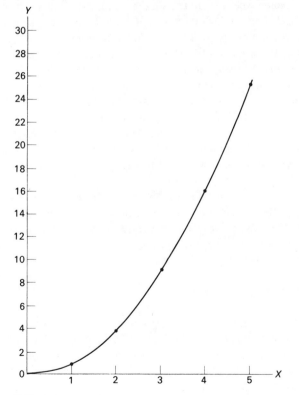

FIG. 7–2 *A nonlinear relationship between X and Y*

the true per unit contribution of that activity whether the output level be one unit, 1000 units, or 10,000 units.

This underlying assumption of linearity presents many difficulties; but these do not invalidate the usefulness of the model. Many features of business and industrial operations are linear: regular hourly wage rates, machine outputs per hour, chemical analyses of raw materials. If a worker is paid $4 an hour, he is paid $8 for two hours, and $12 for three hours and so on (for the first forty hours of a week). If the rated output capacity of a machine is 100 units per hour, the output for two hours should be 200 units, for three hours 300 units. If one unit of a grain provides one unit of a nutrient, two units of the grain should provide two units of the nutrient.

Other relationships are clearly in violation of the linearity rule. Freight rates are based on weight brackets; the per pound rate declines as the total weight of a shipment becomes larger. Utility rates usually decline as the kilowatt-hours used increases. The production of large quantities of an item may result in substantial reductions in raw material costs through quantity purchasing discounts.

Some functions are piecewise linear. Regular hourly wage rates apply usually for the first 40 hours of work each week; then, the wage rate jumps to an overtime rate which is ordinarily 150% of the regular rate and is applicable for the first eight hours of overtime. After eight hours of overtime, a double-time rate of 200% of the regular rate is paid. Thus, the wage bill for a worker, relative to the number of hours worked each week, is linear in segments.

Sometimes relationships, although clearly curvilinear, can be satisfactorily approximated by linear functions. We shall see in a later chapter that we can, at times, approximate a nonlinear objective function by linear functions. We wish to emphasize here that the linearity assumption does constitute a prominent source of difficulty in building the model; and, while it can often be handled without undue compromise, it should not be overlooked when formulating, and interpreting, a model.

Problems involving nonlinear relationships which are clearly not suitable for solution by the linear programming method may be subjected to other solution techniques. In nonlinear programming, for example, the quantity to be maximized or minimized need not be expressed as a linear function, nor do the restrictions on the variables need to be in the form of linear equations.

Additivity

An assumption concomitant to that of linearity is the assumption of *additivity*. The activities of a linear programming model must be additive in the sense that when two or more are used, their total product must be the same as the sum of their individual products. If we are thinking about utilization of scarce resources, for example, we mean by additivity that the total amount of a resource used by several activities must be equal to the sum of the resources used by the individual activities.

If we are thinking in terms of the objective function, its total value must be equivalent to the sum of the variables at their individual contribution rates.

Hence, no joint interactions are allowed between the activities whereby the amount of resource usage required by one unit of output of the activities is altered depending on whether activities are undertaken alone or in various proportions with other activities. In the same manner, the objective function, measuring the effectiveness of the activities in goal-achievement must be characterized by this same lack of interaction. The total measure of effectiveness and each total resource usage resulting from the joint performance of the activities must equal the respective sums of these quantities resulting from each activity being conducted individually.

Let us use a specific example to illustrate the concept of additivity of activities. Product A and product B are each produced by the same type of labor and each uses the same raw material. Each unit of product A requires one unit of labor and two units of raw material. Each unit of product B requires three units of labor and two units of raw material. These activities are pictured in Fig. 7–3. Point R on the chart represents output of 20 units of product A, requiring 20 units of labor and 40 units of raw material. Point S represents an output of 10 units of product B, requiring 30 units of labor and 20 units of raw material. The two activities are additive because the sum at point T represents an output of 20 units of A and 10

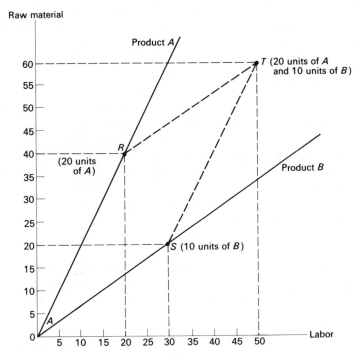

FIG. 7–3 *Activities that are additive*

units of B, requiring in total $20 + 30 = 50$ units of labor and $40 + 20 = 60$ units of raw material. If the output of 20 units of A and 10 units of B were forthcoming from any other combination of labor and material—let us say, 50 units of labor and 50 units of material—the two activities would not be additive.

Graphically, if points R and T and S and T are connected with straight lines, a parallelogram is formed; this configuration denotes additive activities. (A parallelogram is a plane figure with four sides, having the opposite sides parallel and equal.) A line connecting R and T is parallel to a line connecting the origin and S; likewise, a line connecting S and T is parallel to a line connecting the origin and R.

A common case of two activities that are not additive with respect to resource usage occurs where a by-product is produced from the scrap material of a primary product. The primary raw material would have to be procured whether or not both products were produced. Thus, the total material requirements when both are produced is less than the sum of the requirements when each is produced individually.

To explore another aspect of additivity, let us suppose a firm is considering producing two products which would compete for the same market. Let us say that if the first product were produced at level X_1 and the second were not produced at all, profit from the sale of the first would be $c_1 X_1$. Let us further assume that if the first product were not manufactured at all while the second was produced at a level of Y_1, profit from the second product would be realized at the rate of $d_1 Y_1$. Now these activities are additive only if, when both products are produced at levels X_1 and Y_1 respectively, total profit can be measured by the sum $c_1 X_1 + d_1 Y_1$. If prices have to be lowered on one, or both, of the products in order to market both instead of just one or the other, the activities would not be additive.

While additivity may, indeed, be an aspect of many real problems, the assumption is one that a real-world relationship would have little difficulty in violating. Common instances of interactions between activities might be (1) where the price of a product X and the level of output of the product are interrelated, the price per unit depending on the total output; (2) where the demand for product X and product Y, they being either complementary or competitive products, are interrelated; or (3) where profit per unit of product X is related to profit per unit of product Y. Interactions of this nature must be considered carefully when structuring a linear programming model.

Divisibility

The linear programming model assumes that each activity is continuous, is infinitely divisible. This implies that all activity levels and all resource usages are permitted to assume fractional as well as integer values. Therefore, the model will often specify a program of activities that produce activity X at a level of $10/3$ units and Y at a level of 99.875 units, or to use material at the level of 0.85 units or labor at a level of 34.2 hours a week. There is no promise at all that the procedure will yield an integer solution.

In many cases, resources may be used in fractional units. In other cases, the decision variables may have significance only if they have integer values, or some may be used only in blocks. This assumption of divisibility, however, may not present a serious limitation since the values of the variables can often be rounded to include activities to the nearest whole unit without causing significant decision-making errors. Such rounding, while perhaps not creating serious distortions, may not yield an optimal solution. *Integer programming* is a technique used for obtaining the optimal solution with integer values for all the decision variables.

The Assumption of Certainty

The standard linear programming model is based on the premise that the parameters of the model—resource supplies, resource usages, contributions of activities, and so forth—are all known with certainty. At least, no significant variations are expected in the parameters of the model. This assumption is clearly unrealistic in most situations; often the parameters of a situation are no more known than they are constant. Again, the sensitivity analysis of the optimal solution allows much useful analysis and interpretation along these lines.

A great deal of research is being carried on in the area of *stochastic programming*, wherein decisions are based on anticipations regarding the probable values of the various relevant factors.

DETERMINING THE APPROPRIATE COEFFICIENTS

Within this framework, the analyst must determine the appropriate coefficients for the variables, both for the constraint equations and for the objective function. He must also determine the limiting values for the restrictions. The analyst is now transforming his conceptual model into very specific terms; this is a critical step in the modeling process.

Data Requirements

Certain data requirements are established and these must be met by the user of the model if the model is to supply meaningful information to that user. It is the work that goes into collecting the data for use by the model, and not simply the mathematical procedures followed in computations, that determines whether or not sensible results will be forthcoming.

The input data are generated, not from a single source, but from many, all of which must be cognizant of the strategic data requirements of the model. Precise pricing and cost data, so critical for the success of a linear programming model, must be furnished by the cost accounting function or by a skilled cost analyst. Production data relating to productivity measures for workers and machines, production time required by each unit of product, raw material and other resource requirements for each item, along with production capacity constraints, usually come from the industrial engineering team. Information concerning availability of raw materials may emanate from the purchasing function. Financial constraints under which the company must operate may be set forth by the financial officers of the firm. Data concerning marketing demand and other marketing conditions may come from a marketing research department. Other operating criteria may be established by other members of the top management team.

Unfortunately, the data needed for the model are not always easily obtained. Accounting records necessarily reflect a great many crude approximations and arbitrary allocations. Extraction of unit costs and unit contributions from ordinary accounting records may be a virtual impossiblity. Reliable sales forecasts may be still more difficult to obtain. Input and output rates for production facilities may not be readily available. Securing the information needed for the model may prove to be a real test of the ingenuity of the analyst.

Real, rather than Nominal, Restrictions

In quantifying the restrictions, the model builder must remember that it is often the *effective* supply of a resource, rather than the *nominal* supply, that is important. A warehouse that is 200ft by 200ft will probably not have 40,000 square feet of usable floor space; provision must be made for aisles and walkways and the like. A worker who is at the plant for eight hours a day will not usually have eight productive work hours because of the lunch hour and rest periods. There may be a real difference between the quantity of funds a firm might be able to borrow and the quantity of funds the firm is willing to borrow. The quantity of a scarce resource listed in the model is probably not the absolute maximum quantity obtainable by the utmost diligence in purchasing; it is probably that quantity which is reasonably available. Shadow prices from the final tableau will indicate the "worth" of additional units of the scarce resources.

The Concept of Relevant Costs

In decision-making or planning situations, costs to a firm are assumed to belong to one of two broad categories, *fixed costs* and *variable costs*. Those costs that do not change appreciably with changes in the level of a firm's business activity are considered to be fixed costs for that activity. Examples of fixed costs for a manufacturing firm might include executive salaries, property taxes, depreciation of plant. Variable costs, on the other hand, are those costs which vary almost directly with changes in volume or output. For the manufacturing firm, these are primarily direct labor and raw material costs, and direct factory overheads.

Although we assume that fixed costs do not change in total in the short-run, we know from practical experiences that small changes in them may occur. Nonetheless, these changes are probably not directly proportional to changes in activity level, so that the assumption of constant fixed costs does not detract appreciably from the validity of decisions made thereon.

Likewise, it is true that while we define variable costs as those that vary directly with volume, this relationship does not hold perfectly. Suppose that a company manufactures tables and that each table requires five board-feet of lumber. Two tables should require ten board-feet of lumber, and so on. The cost of lumber, a direct raw material, should increase directly in proportion to the volume of output. However, if the lumber is purchased in large quantities, quantity purchasing discounts might come into play and the unit cost per table for the lumber might be reduced when the tables are produced in great quantities. Also raw materials are subject to waste or misuse. Many factors can enter into the process to keep variable costs from being perfectly variable and fixed costs from being perfectly fixed. Nonetheless, we learn to live with these facts, and for a given decision, we treat a specified cost as if it were either fixed or variable.

Fixed costs are not decision-making costs in the short-run. These are costs not related to a single activity and should not be subtracted from the revenue of a single activity in determining its contribution. These costs represent commitments which will not be altered by the adoption of one short-term strategy as opposed to another. If such a cost were allocated to the various activities when determining their contribution, the model would act as if these costs increased or decreased as the level of the activity increased or decreased. If an activity is such that it does require an investment involving additional fixed costs, these costs should be included in the computation of net contribution but should not be included in the computation of the contribution coefficients.

Variable costs, on the other hand, are associated with a particular activity; these are costs whose total amount is a function of the level of the activity to which they apply. While fixed costs should never, for decision-making purposes, be subtracted from the revenue generated by a single activity, variable costs should be deducted from the revenue of the activity to which they apply. It is for this reason that, in a maximizing situation, the objective-function coefficients of the activity variables ordinarily represent, not "profit" but "net contribution to fixed costs and profit." Contribution is defined as revenue per unit minus direct decision costs per unit. Fixed costs are not included. A strategy that maximizes contribution toward fixed factors will also maximize profits to the firm. When the objective function represents contribution, fixed costs must be deducted from the solution value of the function in order to obtain "net profit."

As an illustration, for linear programming purposes the annual depreciation on a warehouse owned by the firm should not be allocated to each unit of the product when attempting to determine the optimal product-mix since this depreciation will will not be altered if one strategy rather than some other is followed. Now if the warehouse space were scarce, the model could be asked how best to allocate this scarce resource. This should be handled through a constraint equation, however, and not through the objective function. On the other hand, if the production of a particular item necessitated the incurrence of additional storage costs—if containers had to be purchased, for instance, for each unit stored—this storage cost will vary directly with the number of units of that product produced. This variable cost should be attached to the item for decision-making purposes.

Still, many costs ordinarily considered to be direct costs may not, in a specific situation, be direct at all. For instance, will the factory labor bill for a company vary directly with production in the short run? It may be that it will. But it is not necessarily true that it will. Suppose that the firm believes that it should employ a labor force of a stated size and should work these men for a stated number of hours each day. The direct labor cost has become, in effect, a fixed cost.

We can visualize situations wherein direct raw material might be considered "free" insofar as a decision on whether or not to use it in a particular way is concerned. Consider a shipment of zepthis, purchased with more zeal than perception, which has been stored in the warehouse since its receipt. There seems to be only one feasible use for the material—the manufacture of zepths. Now while zepthis is exceedingly costly, zepths can be sold at only a very moderate price. Should the cost of the zepthis, although it is a direct raw material, be considered when making the decision as to whether or not to manufacture the zepths? If these items will produce revenue sufficient to cover their other costs of manufacture and sale, should they not be produced?

Discretion, then, must be used in determining the contribution of the activities to the objective. Those costs that should be allocated are the costs that will be affected by the decision at hand. This is the "decision costing" concept; only those costs that change with the decision being made should be allocated to the alternative activities under consideration.

Chapter 8

CASETTES FOR DISCUSSION

The casettes in this chapter are designed to highlight many of the pitfalls encountered in building linear programming models. Many are classic examples of how *not* to build and use a model! Others simply illustrate some of the problems that must be faced in using the linear programming model.

THE PHAEDRA SAILBOAT COMPANY CASE

The Phaedra Sailboat Company is a producer of two-man sailboats which employs 50 skilled craftsmen at $5.00 an hour (based on a 40-hour work week). Phaedra manufactures one type of sailboat with the profit for that entire finished boat being $200.

Due to an exclusive processing method which costs Phaedra $100 a day to maintain, the boats' wooden parts, their rudders, centerboards, and masts, can be sold for profits of $50, $25, and $50, respectively. This process involves a massive oven which uses an exclusive sealant mist (applied under extreme pressure) to permeate the wooden parts. After the process is applied, the wooden parts are resistant to water, bacterial growth, barnacles, and other forms of biological growth. The process also causes the parts to have miraculously low resistance to wind and water, and to have that certain degree of flexibility necessary for perfect stability afloat while gaining maximum speed. Phaedra has the following limited resources which must be allocated to its manufacturing processes:

2000 man-hours per week;
160 machine-saw hours per week;
240 machine-sander hours per week;
80 lathe-hours per week.

It takes the following amount of these resources for the manufacture of each of Phaedra's products:

Masts: 6 man-hours and 2 lathe-hours;
Rudders: 10 man-hours, 2 saw-hours, and 2 sand-hours;
Centerboards: 4 man-hours, 1 saw-hour, and 1 sand-hour.

And for the boats (aside from the resources necessary for one mast, one rudder, and one centerboard):

25 man-hours for the hull shaping and molding; and
5 man-hours for assembly of the final product.

Phaedra's production manager, who is trying to maximize his weekly profit through selection of an optimal product mix, is puzzled as to the manner in which he should allocate the cost of the sealant process to the various parts and to the finished boats. The process costs $500 per week, since the cost of maintaining the oven over the week-ends is negligible.

The only element in the problem which prevents a straight-forward linear programming solution is that of cost allocation for the sealant process. This process, which must be continued at a cost of $500 per week whether one wooden part or a multitude of these parts is processed during that period, cannot properly be allocated to the individual parts. Therefore, it must be regarded as a "sunk cost" to Phaedra and ignored in attempting to gain a final solution to the problem of mix.

Since the profit contribution for each wooden part is known, all that is further required is to obtain the constraints and variables, and to set up the objective function.

The production manager decided these should be the variables:

X_1 = the number of rudders to be produced per week to be used in boats;
X_2 = the number of centerboards to be produced per week to be used in boats;
X_3 = the number of masts to be produced per week to be used in boats;
X_4 = the number of boats to be produced per week, exclusive of their wooden parts;
X_5 = the number of rudders to be produced per week for final, individual sale;
X_6 = the number of centerboards to be produced per week for final, individual sale;
X_7 = the number of masts to be produced per week for final, individual sale.

Since the contribution to profit of the wooden parts totals

$50	one rudder
25	one centerboard
50	one mast
$125	total

the profit contribution by the remainder of the boat is $200 - \$125 = \$75$. Thus, the objective function is

Maximize: $50X_1 + 25X_2 + 50X_3 + 75X_4 + 50X_5 + 25X_6 + 50X_7$

subject to the constraints

Man-hours: $10X_1 + 4X_2 + 6X_3 + 30X_4 + 10X_5 + 4X_6 + 6X_7 \leqslant 2000$
Saw-hours: $\ \ 2X_1 + 1X_2 + 0X_3 + \ \ 0X_4 + \ \ 2X_5 + 1X_6 + 0X_7 \leqslant \ \ 160$
Sand-hours: $2X_1 + 1X_2 + 0X_3 + \ \ 0X_4 + \ \ 2X_5 + 1X_6 + 0X_7 \leqslant \ \ 240$
Lathe-hours: $0X_1 + 0X_2 + 2X_3 + \ \ 0X_4 + \ \ 0X_5 + 0X_6 + 2X_7 \leqslant \ \ \ \ 80.$

The solution tableau is as follows

	X_1	X_2	X_3	X_4	X_5	X_6	X_7	S_1	S_2	S_3	S_4	
X_4	1/15	0	0	1	2/30	0	0	1/30	-2/15	0	-1	$37\frac{1}{3}$
X_2	2	1	0	0	2	1	0	0	1	0	0	160
S_3	0	0	0	0	0	0	0	0	-1	1	0	80
X_3	0	0	1	0	0	0	1	0	0	0	1/2	40
	5	0	0	0	5	0	0	2.5	15	0	17.5	8800

This indicates that $37\frac{1}{3}$ X_4's (boats without rudders, centerboards, and masts) along with 160 X_2's (centerboards for boats) and 40 X_3's (masts for boats) should be produced each week. The production manager is dumbfounded. This is obviously an untenable solution and he cannot imagine what happened. After all, he used a linear programming model!

The flaw in the model lies in the selection of the variables. The variables must answer two key questions:

1. What items are completely controllable? and
2. Do these variables, when assigned proper scalar coefficients, provide sufficient information to solve the problem?

Phaedra *must* provide one rudder, one centerboard, and one mast for each finished boat. The X_1, X_2 and X_3 variables, as stated above, are not controllable. They must be incorporated into the finished-boat variable, X_4 to be controlled properly. Therefore, there are only four properly-defined variables necessary to satisfy the second question. These variables are:

X_1 = number of finished boats to be produced per week, including one rudder, one centerboard, and one mast per finished boat;
X_2 = numbers of rudders to be produced per week for final, individual sale;
X_3 = number of centerboards to be produced per week for final, individual sale;
X_4 = number of masts to be produced per week for final, individual sale.

Accordingly, the corrected constraints and objective function are:

Man-hours: $50X_1 + 10X_2 + 4X_3 + 6X_4 \leqslant 2000$

Saw-hours: $3X_1 + 2X_2 + 1X_3 + 0X_4 \leqslant 160$

Sander-hours: $3X_1 + 2X_2 + 1X_3 + 0X_4 \leqslant 240$

Lathe-hours: $2X_1 + 0X_2 + 0X_3 + 2X_4 \leqslant 80$

Maximize: $200X_1 + 50X_2 + 25X_4 + 50X_4$.

Now the solution tableau is:

	X_1	X_2	X_3	X_4	S_1	S_2	S_3	S_4	
X_1	1	0.06	0	0	0.03	−0.125	0	−0.09	35
X_3	0	1.81	1	0	−0.09	1.375	0	0.28	55
S_3	0	0	0	0	0	−1	1	0	80
X_4	0	−0.06	0	1	−0.03	0.125	0	0.59	5
	0	4.688	0	0	2.34	15.625 0		17.97	8625

Thus Phaedra should produce each week:

35 completed boats, including rudder, centerboard, and mast,
55 centerboards for final, individual sale, and
 5 masts for final, individual sale.

The maximum profit for such an output is $8625 per week, over and above direct costs.

THE TIP TOP TOY COMPANY CASE

A large national firm as part of its expansion policy has just purchased a small manufacturer, Tip Top Toy Company. TTT produces four items which sell all the year round. Because of industry conditions, they can sell all of each that they can produce, at the going price. Raw materials are available in any quantities needed. Each of the four products sells for $1.00; however, the cost of producing them varies. Product A costs 50¢ to manufacture while B and C cost 70¢, and D costs 80¢.

The principal constraint in producing these items is time. Each day the firm has available only 12,000 minutes of production time. Each A and each B requires 4 minutes, each C requires 3 minutes, and each D requires 1 minute. Packaging time is limited to 1800 minutes per day with each A using 0.4 minutes, each B using 0.5 minutes, each C using 0.3 minutes and each D using 0.2 minutes. Likewise, inspection time is restricted to 960 minutes a day with each A and each B requiring 0.2 minutes, and each C and each D requiring 0.1 minutes.

The new manager sent in by the acquiring company reviewed this report of the situation and instructed his assistant to prepare a linear programming model that will give the maximum-profit production plan. As it was management's general policy to produce only products whose controllable profit was 25% of its revenue, product D was immediately eliminated from consideration since it netted only 20%. The resulting model was as follows:

The controllable variables were:

X_1 = number of A's to produce each day;
X_2 = number of B's to produce each day;
X_3 = number of C's to produce each day.

The objective function was:

Maximize $0.5X_1 + 0.3X_2 + 0.3X_3$

The constraints were:

Production time: $4X_1 + 4X_2 + 3X_3 \leqslant 12000$
Packaging time: $0.4X_1 + 0.5X_2 + 0.3X_3 \leqslant 1800$
Inspection time: $0.2X_1 + 0.2X_2 + 0.1X_3 \leqslant 960$.

The final tableau was:

	X_1	X_2	X_3	S_1	S_2	S_3	
X_1	1	1	3/4	1/4	0	0	3000
S_2	0	1/10	0	−1/10	1	0	600
S_3	0	0	−1/20	−1/20	0	1	360
	0	1/5	3/40	1/8	0	0	1500

The model indicates that if profit is to be maximized the company should produce 3000 units of product A and none of the other items. Following this strategy would result in daily profits of \$1500. Production time would be fully utilized but there would be 600 minutes of unused packaging time and 360 minutes of unused inspection time each day.

There is one very serious error in the model and thus in the solution. The problem was presolved by the elimination of one of the variables, the number of units of product D to produce; the model was never given a chance to consider production of D. In some situations this might not have mattered in the solution; but in this case it did matter.

When an X_4 column (1, 0.2, 0.1, −0.2) vector is added to the initial tableau, the following final solution results:

	X_1	X_2	X_3	X_4	S_1	S_2	S_3	
X_1	1	3/4	3/4	0	1/2	−5/2	0	1500
X_4	0	1	0	1	−1	10	0	6000
S_3	0	−1/20	−1/20	0	0	−1/2	1	60
	0	11/40	3/40	0	1/20	3/4	0	1950

Thus, had the model been given an opportunity to consider product D, product D would have been included in the optimal production plan with the resulting daily profit being \$450 greater than when D was left out of the model; this is an increase of 30% in the profit figure.

THE INTRICATE ASSEMBLY COMPANY CASE

The Intricate Assembly Company, currently under contractual agreement to furnish the army with 15 A's, 26 B's, 40 F's and 49 G's by June 1st, has been notified by the sole supplier of raw materials W and Z that, due to a new revolution in their country, they will not be able to supply the Intricate Assembly Company with W and Z until after the revolution has been put down.

W and Z are used exclusively in sub-assemblies X and Y which are in turn used exclusively in final assemblies A, B, C, and E. Each A requires two X's, each B requires one Y, each C requires three X's and two Y's, and each E requires four X's. Currently the company's inventory records indicate that the only finished products on hand or in process are one A, one B, forty F's, and forty-nine G's. There are no X's or Y's on hand or in process.

The contract covering the A's, B's, F's, and G's to be furnished to the army follows the general military practice of pricing products requiring sub-assembly units. The unit price established for the four products was in part determined by pricing each sub-assembly unit separately. Sub-assemblies X and Y were priced at \$4 and \$3 each respectively in the contract price for the indicated products.

The Company's plant manager, upon hearing that the Company would not be able to secure further shipments of W and Z, examined the specification sheets for sub-assemblies X and Y with the plant engineer. The specification sheets indicated that each X required two W's and one Z and each Y required one W and three Z's. Recognizing that the company had only 105 units each of W and Z, the plant manager asked the plant engineer to determine the optimum use that might be made of W and Z. The plant engineer asked the plant manager what he meant by the optimum use. The plant manager replied that since X's sold for \$4 and Y's sold for \$3, he wanted to know how they might best utilize the 105 units of W and the 105 units of Z in products X and Y in order to receive the largest revenue from their sale. He said further that the cost of W and Z were immaterial since they were sunk costs and there was no possibility of securing additional units of W and Z after the present supply was used up.

The plant engineer, armed with the above information, immediately recognized that the problem would lend itself to a linear programming solution. The results of the plant engineer's work are as follows:

Variables:

X_1 = number of units of sub-assembly X to produce;

X_2 = number of units of sub-assembly Y to produce.

Objective function:

Maximize: $4X_1 + 3X_2$.

Constraints:

$2X_1 + X_2 \leqslant 105$ Number of W's available;

$X_1 + 3X_2 \leqslant 105$ Number of Z's available.

Final tableau:

	X_1	X_2	S_1	S_2	
X_2	0	1	2/5	$-1/5$	21
X_1	1	0	$-1/5$	3/5	42
	0	0	2/5	9/5	231

The plant engineer, following the completion of his work, informed the plant manager that revenue from the use of W and Z would be maximized if 42 X's and 21 Y's were produced. He said further that production of these quantities of X and Y would exhaust the supply of W and Z and would yield $231 profit. He pointed out to the plant manager that it was a shame they did not have more units of Z since each additional unit would add $1.80 to revenue.

The plant manager thanked the plant engineer for a job well done and immediately issued a production order for 42 X's and 21 Y's.

On June 2nd, the Intricate Assembly Company was sued by the army for breach of contract. On June 3rd, the plant manager was fired.

The plant manager's interest in utilizing the raw materials, W and Z, in the optimum manner and the plant engineer's approach and solution were correct in every respect except for one glaring oversight. The company's objective, relative to the utilization of the raw materials, W and Z, was to maximize revenue; but this objective was restricted by a contract requiring delivery of 15 A's and 26 B's on June 1st to the army. Because of this contract the company really had no control over the number of X's and Y's to produce. Since there was only one A and one B in inventory, an additional 14 A's and 25 B's would have to be produced in order to comply with the terms of the contract. In order to produce 14 A's and 25 B's, 28 X's and 25 Y's must be produced since each A requires two X's and each B requires one Y. The requirements for W and Z in the production of X and Y are two units of W and one unit of Z for an X, and one unit of W and three units of Z for a Y. The individual product requirements of W and Z for the contract are, therefore, 56 units of W and 28 units of Z for an X and 25 units of W and 75 units of Z for a Y for a total requirement of 81 units of W and 103 units of Z. Since the company has only 105 units each of W and Z, it is impossible to produce any combination of X's and Y's other than 28 X's and 25 Y's and honor the contract.

The plant manager's decision to produce 42 X's and 21 Y's resulted in a final production of 21 A's and 21 B's which meant that the company was short four B's and was unable to comply with the contract.

THE JACKSON'S ENGINE REPAIR SERVICE CASE

Bob Jackson operates a service station in a suburban community. For the past several years, he has also repaired and sold small gasoline engines of the type found in lawnmowers.

The small-engine work has complemented his other activities by furnishing work for his employees during the slack periods, and this endeavor has been well received in the community. Last year he added a line of lawnmowers and was able to sell his entire inventory during May and June.

In late April of this year, he attended a government surplus auction and was able to buy a lot of 350 gasoline engines which could be used in lawnmowers. He only bid $1500 for them although they were new engines and would have cost $28 each wholesale.

Naturally Mr. Jackson wanted to put these engines to the most profitable use so he explored all possible applications. First, he considered making new lawnmowers and his past experience convinced him that he could sell the entire 350 lawnmowers that he might make with these engines if he priced them at $45 each. The housings, handles, blades, and wheels were available locally for $15 per set, and each unit would only take one hour to assemble.

Several people had inquired recently for portable power units, and Jackson felt that he could sell up to ten of these during the summer for $120 each. The generator, pulleys, belts, electrical cord, and base would cost him a total of $80 per unit and assembly would require two hours.

Another possible application would be in portable air compressor units used for painting or to charge SCUBA tanks, and Jackson felt he could sell up to 20 of these during the summer for $110 each. The compressor and other hardware for each unit would cost $60 and it would take about three hours to assemble.

All the items would have to be sold during the summer, since Jackson did not want to carry any inventory over the winter. Thus all work would have to be completed during May, June, and July, and Mr. Jackson felt that only 380 man-hours would be available, without overtime, since he had to maintain his service station equipment. Since he paid his employees $2.00 an hour, overtime labor would cost $3.00 an hour, if any were required.

One of Mr. Jackson's customers suggested that a linear programming model could be used to determine the most profitable mix of applications and to indicate whether of not overtime would be justified. If any engines were not used in any of the applications, they could easily be sold at wholesale for $28, so any slack engines would add to the profit contribution of the final linear programming solution.

This is the model used.

Variables:

X_1 = number of lawnmowers to be built;
X_2 = number of compressor units to be built;
X_3 = number of Emergency Power Units (EPU) to be built.

Constraints:

Engines: $X_1 + X_2 + X_3 \leqslant 350$
Labor: $X_1 + 3X_2 + 2X_3 \leqslant 380$
Compressor market: $X_2 \leqslant 20$
EPU market: $X_3 \leqslant 10$.

Profit contribution:

Maximize: $30X_1 + 50X_2 + 40X_3$.

Final tableau:

	X_1	X_2	X_3	S_1	S_2	S_3	S_4	
X_1	1	0	1/2	3/2	$-1/2$	0	0	335
X_2	0	1	1/2	$-1/2$	1/2	0	0	15
S_3	0	0	$-1/2$	1/2	$-1/2$	1	0	5
S_4	0	0	1	0	0	0	1	10
	0	0	0	20	10	0	0	10800

All of the engines are utilized in the final solution so none should be sold independently. Overtime would be worth $10 per hour for the first ten extra hours, however; and at a cost of $3 per hour, would add $70 to the total profit contribution. Thus, by using ten hours of overtime, total profit contribution could be $10,870.

But Mr. Jackson made one simplification in building the model that was a mistake. He knew the motors could be sold wholesale for $28 each and knew that if the model did not find a use for all of the motors he would dispose of them in this way. However, the model should have been allowed to weigh this alternative along with the others in determining the best plan of action regarding the motors. If the variable X_4, representing the number of motors to be sold wholesale, is added to the model and the term $28X_4$ is included in the objective function, this final tableau results:

	X_1	X_2	X_3	X_4	S_1	S_2	S_3	S_4	
X_1	1	0	0	0	0	1	-3	-2	300
X_2	0	1	0	0	0	0	1	0	20
X_4	0	0	0	1	1	-1	2	1	20
X_3	0	0	1	0	0	0	0	1	10
	0	0	0	0	28	2	16	8	10960

The corrected model allows a value to be placed on the engines themselves. Thus, the number of lawnmowers is reduced to allow the necessary time to build the more profitable compressors and EPU's. Overtime is not warranted since it is only worth $2 per hour and the workers would have to be paid $3 per hour for any overtime.

THE POOR'S DEPARTMENT STORE CASE

Poor's is one of the larger and more successful department stores in the South with its base in the Greater Atlanta metropolitan area. This corporation has its main store in downtown Atlanta and branch stores in the many suburban shopping centers which have been built in the past five to ten years. It is of the general merchandising type outlet.

Organizationally, each store is broken up into departments with the manager of the downtown store department also being the general manager over all branch store managers of the same department. As the general manager of all the branch store departments as well as the main store department, each such individual has a large record-keeping responsibility which is necessary not only for his own information in managing his departments but also for furnishing higher echelon management with their various required reports.

Mr. Grossman is a newly appointed general manager of the drapery department at Poor's. Upon assuming his responsibilities at the downtown office, he was greatly surprised at the lack of any type of systematic record storage system. Files, papers, records, documents, and so forth, received from branch store managers, outside vendors, higher echelon managers as well as copies of materials sent out by his office were scattered throughout the office. There was great difficulty in locating needed papers as well as in storing and filing the many types of documents, papers, and so on, that were continually being received and sent.

Mr. Grossman realized that he needed help. Therefore, he sent for a clerk who professed some skill in the used of mathematical models. Mr. Grossman informed the clerk that his problem of the lack of a filing system would easily be corrected if he had sufficient filing cabinets into which he could organize all of the various papers. He told the clerk further, however, that his office is not very large and that after considering what was necessary to keep in the office (that is, desks, chairs, office machines, and so on) he can not spare more than 144 square feet of floor space for the filing cabinets. Also, the store policy, for reasons of safety and insurance, requires that file cabinets may not be stacked on top of each other.

It is determined that Mr. Grossman's budget allows him to spend no more than $768 on filing cabinets and that all such filing cabinets must be purchased from a local firm, Maynard's Office Supply Company, Inc., with whom Poor's has a contract.

Maynard's is contacted and it is found that they have two types of filing cabinets which have the following characteristics:

Model A costs $48 each, requires six square feet of floor space and has a usable filing capacity of 27 cubic feet.

Model B costs $32 each, requires eight square feet of floor space and has a usable filing capacity of 24 cubic feet.

Mr. Grossman wants to know how many of each type of filing cabinet to buy so that he gets as much filing cabinet capacity as possible without exceeding his limitation of floor space and budget money.

The aspiring young clerk thought that the problem lent itself very well to the technique of linear programming and proceeded to build the model outlined below:

Variables:

X_1 = number of filing cabinets of Model A to purchase;

X_2 = number of filing cabinets of Model B to purchase.

The objective is to maximize the number of cubic feet of filing capacity; that is,

Maximize: $27X_1 + 24X_2$.

However, this must be done subject to floor space requirement and the budget restriction:

$6X_1 + 8X_2 \leqslant 144$ (square feet of floor space);

$48X_1 + 32X_2 \leqslant 768$ (budget dollars available).

The final tableau was this:

	X_1	X_2	S_1	S_2	
X_2	0	1	1/4	$-1/32$	12
X_1	1	0	$-1/6$	1/24	8
	0	0	3/2	3/8	504

The pleased clerk went to Mr. Grossman with this solution and this interpretation. If Mr. Grossman had or could get one square foot more of floor space, all other things remaining the same, then he could increase his filing capacity by 3/2 cubic feet. He could do this by purchasing 1/4 more Model B's and 1/6 less Model A's. Of course, since we are dealing with indivisible filing cabinets, we cannot purchase fractional units. Thus, a realistic physical interpretation would be that for every additional 12 square feet of floor space gained, Mr. Grossman can increase his filing capacity by 18 cubic feet. He would accomplish this by purchasing three additional Model B's and two less Model A's.

Obviously, Mr. Grossman cannot continue following this strategy indefinitely for there are only 8 Model A's to be given up. It can be seen that if Mr. Grossman gained an additional 48 square feet of floor space, he would increase his filing capacity by 72 cubic feet. He could do this by purchasing 12 additional Model B's and purchasing 8 less Model A's. Since, at the optimal, Mr. Grossman had purchased only 8 Model A's this indicate that we have reached the upper limit of floor space that Mr. Grossman can realize by following the strategy outlined above.

We can similarly reason in the other direction. If Mr. Grossman needed more floor space for something else, or if he were required to give up some of his floor space, what strategy should he follow in giving up filing cabinets so that his filing capacity is decreased as little as possible? For every 12 square feet of floor space which he has to give up, he can hold his decrease in filing capacity to a minimum by giving up three Model B's and purchasing two additional Model A's. This will result in a decrease in his filing capacity of 18 cubic feet.

As before, Mr. Grossman cannot continue this strategy indefinitely as he has only 12 Model B's which he can give up. Therefore, if he has to give up more than 48 square feet, he should change his strategy. However, in giving up 48 square feet of floor space or less, he should continue to follow the strategy outlined. Thus, the limits between which he will follow the above strategy without change are a lower limite of 96 square feet and an upper limit of 192 square feet.

Now, let's examine what strategy Mr. Grossman should follow if his budget allowance of $768 were increased or lowered so that he would either continue to maximize increasing his filing capacity or limit his loss of filing capacity to as little as possible.

If Mr. Grossman had or could get $1 more, all other things remaining the same, then he could increase his filing capacity by as much as 3/8 cubic feet. He could accomplish this by purchasing 1/24 more Model A's and 1/32 less Model B's. As before, we realize that since we are dealing with indivisible filing cabinets that we cannot purchase fractional cabinets. Realistically, Mr. Grossman must deal in multiples. What this means physically is that for each additional $96 gained, Mr. Grossman can increase his filing capacity by as much as 36 cubic feet. He can accomplish this by purchasing four additional Model A's and three less Model B's.

Conversely, if Mr. Grossman's budgeted amount were cut by $96, he can limit his loss of filing capacity to 36 cubic feet by giving up four Model A's and purchasing three model Model B's.

If, for every $96 lost Mr. Grossman's strategy is to give up four Model A's and purchase three Model B's, it should be clear that he can do this twice only since at the optimal Mr. Grossman only purchased 8 Model A's. Thus, the lower limit of his budget in which he should continue to follow this strategy is $768 − (2) ($96) = 576. If Mr. Grossman were allowed a budget that is less than $576 then it would be necessary to recalculate in order to determine the best strategy for him to follow.

If, in fact, Mr. Grossman's budgeted amount were increased by $96, the best strategy for him to follow is to buy four Model A's and give up three Model B's. However, since Mr. Grossman, at the optimal, only bought 12 Model B's, he can make this type of exchange only three times. Hence the upper limit of his budget in which he should continue this strategy is $768 + (3) ($96) = 1056. If Mr. Grossman's budget were no more than $1056, he should recalculate the best strategy to follow.

Mr. Grossman was so impressed with the clerk's presentation that he immediately ordered from Maynard's Office Supply Company eight Model A's and twelve Model B's. Fortunately, Maynard's was temporarily out of stock on these items.

Suppose, upon delivery of the cabinets, it was discovered that the 144 square feet into which they are to be placed is dimensioned 1 ft. by 144 ft. and that neither of the filing cabinet models could fit into these dimensions. What was beautifully formulated and solved as a linear programming model is simply something that cannot be implemented.

Further, even if the dimensions of the office were not as extreme as described above, they might well be such that the optimum solution of installing 8 Model A's and 12 Model B's might not be possible. In addition to the maximization of filing capacity problem, there may still remain a layout problem which may well cause the optimum solution to be modified or even rejected.

The major point here is that linear programming is only a tool, although a powerful one, which a manager may use to aid him in his decision making. Be constantly aware, prior to implementation, of factors which the model did not or could not consider but which may have considerable influence on whether or not to implement the linear programming solution.

The clerk accepted Mr. Grossman's analysis and facts without checking them them for himslef. There may well have been factors which Mr. Grossman may have missed which would have led to perhaps another objective (such as an analysis of just which reports are necessary and which are not) or perhaps have caused him to have considered solving Mr. Grossman's problem by other means than filing cabinets (such as the use of microfilm).

There is another aspect of this case which deserves some discussion and from which insight can be gained. In this case, the product (filing cabinets) is indivisible as is the case with many other types of products. Suppose the optimal solution had not been integer in form. Then, it would have been necessary to determine whether to buy the next higher number of cabinets or the next lower, or just how

to round the numbers. In this case, the two products cost only $32 and $48 each and the difference in filing capacity is only 3 cubic feet. Thus, the consequences of purchasing one less or one more than the optimum is probably not great. Suppose, instead, that the products which were being considered were two large supersonic airplanes, one of which costs $3.2 million and the other $4.8 million. Now, if the optimum solution was to purchase 7.3 of the cheaper and 11.6 of the more expensive plane, the decision to purchase one more or less might well be a critical one. Because of this additional complication, the consultant might well have decided that another type of model should have been used.

THE CAPITAL WAREHOUSE COMPANY CASE

The Capital Warehouse Company was recently faced with an interesting problem. Golden Coffee Company anticipated a strike by the ILA in approximately four months and wanted to ensure a supply of raw materials during the potential strike period. They had on hand at a portside warehouse the equivalent of 225 carloads of green coffee and 50 carloads of boxes for packaging (k-d cartons). Golden had to move the green coffee and the k-d cartons before the strike because the ILA would set up picket lines at all dockside facilities in the city if the strike were to occur, thereby causing Golden's supplies to be immovable. Faced with this situation, Golden requested, within a 24-hour period, rates for the storage and handling of these materials.

The warehouse manager at Capital found that he had available 75,000 square feet of storage space. Handling the materials would be no problem, as he had sufficient labor at his disposal; however, he had on hand only enough pallets to palletize 75 carloads of green coffee, and all of the green coffee offered by Golden was non-palletized. The boxed coffee was palletized.

The fact that any green coffee over the first 75 carloads could not be stored on pallets would cause the warehouse to incur handling costs which would be double its normal amount. This would occur because the green coffee, instead of being palletized and then stacked by machine, would be palletized for transfer into the warehouse and then removed from the pallets and stacked by hand. This same double-handling would occur again when the goods were removed from the warehouse.

Accordingly, the manager of the warehouse quoted the Golden representative rates of $105 for a carload of palletized green coffee, $170 for a carload of unpalletized green coffee, and $90 for a carload of palletized k-d cartons.

Golden accepted the rates and asked the warehouse how many carloads it would accept. The warehouse manager knew that his direct cost on each carload would be $45 for the palletized green coffee, $90 for the unpalletized green coffee, and $30 for the palletized k-d cartons. Furthermore, he knew that, per carload, the palletized green coffee would occupy 450 square feet of storage space, the unpalletized coffee would occupy 400 square feet, and the k-d cartons would occupy 300 square feet.

He felt that a linear programming model would be useful in deciding how best to allocate this space. He wanted to maximize profit contribution, so he established this objective function:

Maximize: $60X_1 + 80X_2 + 60X_3$

where

X_1 = number of carloads of palletized green coffee to be accepted by the warehouse;

X_2 = number of carloads of unpalletized green coffee to be accepted by the warehouse;

X_3 = number of carloads of k-d cartons to be accepted by the warehouse

and the coefficients are the quoted per carload rates minus the direct costs.

These constraints seemed to be appropriate:

Total storage space: $450X_1 + 400X_2 + 300X_3 \leqslant 75000$

Green coffee: $X_1 + X_2 \leqslant 225$

Cartons: $X_3 \leqslant 50$

Pallets for green coffee: $X_1 \leqslant 75$.

This is the final tableau:

	X_1	X_2	X_3	S_1	S_2	S_3	S_4	
X_2	9/8	1	6/8	1/8	0	0	0	187.5
S_2	−1/8	0	−6/8	−1/8	1	0	0	37.5
S_3	0	0	1	0	0	1	0	50
S_4	1	0	0	0	0	0	1	.75
	30	0	0	10	0	0	0	15000

The strategy implied is that the warehouse accept 187.5 carloads of the unpalletized green coffee at a profit of $15,000.

There is one flaw in the model which causes it to create an undesired result. The flaw centers around the fact that Golden Coffee Company will naturally expect Capital to accept the first 75 carloads of green coffee in the palletized form before it will be willing to pay the higher costs for the non-palletized coffee to be handled and stored. This means that the fourth constraint should have been written as an exactly-equal-to constraint; that is,

$X_1 = 75$.*

---

* The "exactly-equal-to" constraint will be discussed in depth in Chapter 9.

Then the final tableau would be:

	X_1	X_2	X_3	S_1	S_2	S_3	S_4	
X_2	0	1	6/8	1/8	0	0	−9/8	103⅛
S_2	0	0	−6/8	−1/8	1	0	1/8	46⅞
S_3	0	0	1	0	0	1	0	50
X_1	1	0	0	0	0	0	1	75
	0	0	0	10	0	0	−90	12,750

Although this is obviously a satisfying solution in the short-run, it will most likely be the profit maximizing solution in the long-run, as the Golden account will be likely to return to Capital with business in the future. This wouldn't occur with the first strategy.

THE HOLT MANUFACTURING COMPANY CASE

Holt Manufacturing Company is in need of funds for capital expansion and has decided to go into the market with an issue(s) of new securities. The company figures that it can profitably employ as much capital (within reason) as it can raise, and considers three types of securities at its disposal as allowed by corporate charter and company policy: common stock, first mortgage bonds, and convertible debentures.

After having contacted several insurance companies, private funds, and individual investors, it has been determined that the new issues can be disposed of through direct placement, thus avoiding the commission costs involved with a public offering through a brokerage house. The placement can be consumated under the following terms:

Common Stock, $20 per share, 25¢ quarterly dividend;

Bonds, $1000, 20-year maturity, 6% annual interest;

Convertible Debentures, $1000, 20-year maturity, 4% annual interest, convertible at holders option into 25 shares of common stock.

Because this is a direct placement, securities may be issued in fractional denominations.

The issue of new securities are subject to the following restrictions:

Only 30,000 additional shares of common stock are authorized.

There is an agreement with the bankers that there will be no more than $700,000 in additional funded debt.

In addition, management realized that it will take several years before the additional investment will have a favorable impact upon profits and cash flow. So as to protect against a possible cash strain, a limit of $50,000 per year has been placed upon the servicing of any new issue(s). Although payment of dividends is optional, Holt Manufacturing has a long and proud record of payment and considers itself under strong moral obligation to continue. A reduction or omission of dividends would be resorted to only in the face of financial crisis.

This being the situation, the financial vice president was faced with the decision of what mix of securities to offer in order to maximize the amount of capital raised. While pondering the problem, a young clerk, who had been exposed to linear programming, offered the following solution.

Variables:

X_1 = number of shares of common stock to issue;

X_2 = number of first mortgage bonds to issue;

X_3 = number of convertible debentures to issue.

Objective function:

Maximize: $20X_1 + 1000X_2 + 1000X_3$.

Constraints:

Maximum shares of common stock: $X_1 + 25X_3 \leqslant 30,000$

Maximum funded debt: $1000X_2 + 1000X_3 \leqslant 700,000$

Maximum cash to service: $X_1 + 60X_2 + 40X_3 \leqslant 50,000$.

Final tableau

	X_1	X_2	X_3	S_1	S_2	S_3	
X_1	1	0	0	1/3	1/30	5/9	160,000/9
X_3	0	0	1	1/45	1/750	$-1/45$	4400/9
X_2	0	1	0	$-1/45$	$-1/3000$	1/45	1900/9
	0	0	0	80/9	1/3	100/9	1,055,555

The clerk explained that by issuing 17,777.8 shares of common stock, 488.9 convertible debentures, and 211.1 bonds, a total of $1,055,555.56 in new capital could be raised.

The financial vice president was very much impressed with his clerks' ability at mathematical manipulation; however, he detected a mistake in setting up the problem which might have a decided effect upon the outcome. Dividends are not tax deductible and are, therefore, payable on an "after tax" basis. Assuming a 50% tax rate, $2 must be generated for every $1 paid out in dividends. This change was reflected in the third constraint of the new tableau. With the adjusted model, this solution was obtained:

Final tableau:

	X_1	X_2	X_3	S_1	S_2	S_3	
S_1	0	-35	0	1	$-5/1000$	$-1/2$	1500
X_3	0	1	1	0	$1/1000$	0	700
X_1	1	10	0	0	$-20/1000$	$1/2$	11,000
	0	200	0	0	0.6	10	920,000

By issuing 11,000 shares of common stock and 700 convertible debentures, $920,000 could be raised. This represents a decrease of over $135,000 from the previous strategy. But taxes are facts of life.

Still, for some strange reason, the financial manager felt dissatisfied with the plan. He then realised that he had not given sufficient consideration to the fact that each of the debentures was convertible at the holder's option into 25 shares of common stock. And it is not outside the realm of possibility that the holders of the debentures will elect to convert them to common stock. This means that for each debenture outstanding there is a possible call on 25 shares of common stock. This means that Holt Manufacturing Company is, in effect, contingently liable for the payment of $25 in dividends for each conversion, which represents $50 before taxes. So that it reflects this contingency, the third constraint is rewritten

$$2X_1 + 60X_2 + 50X_3 \leqslant 50,000.$$

The final tableau is now:

	X_1	X_2	X_3	S_1	S_2	S_3	
S_1	0	-30	0	1	0	0	500
X_3	0	1	1	0	$1/1000$	0	700
X_1	1	5	0	0	$-25/1000$	$1/2$	7500
	0	100	0	0	1/2	0	850,000

The plan now calls for the issuance of 7500 shares of common stock and 700 debentures, resulting in $850,000 additional capital.

THE SPATIAL FACIAL COMPANY CASE

Mr. I. Uplift, owner of the Spatial Facial Company, has must received notice from his basic chemical supplier that they have technologically upgraded and repriced some of their basic chemicals that are used in his products and that these new chemicals are available for immediate delivery.

The Spatial Facial Company mixes, packs, and sells three different facial cremes within the local area. The three facial cremes are trademarked by the brand names of Starkiss, Moonview, and Galaxy Delight. The basic chemicals which affect the mix are a new emulsifier which is used in one-ounce units for each jar of Starkiss; a new solvent which is used in one-ounce units for each jar of Moonview; and a new resin which is used in one-ounce units for each jar of Galaxy Delight. The nature of the basic chemical compound changes are such that they can be substituted directly and on a unit for unit basis for their respective end products. The new basic chemical changes do not substantially cause changes in the quality of their respective products. Therefore, they can be substituted in their respective mixes without loss of brand integrity. However, because of chemical reactions the new basic chemicals cannot be mixed with their counterparts which they are replacing.

The cost of the new emulsifier is $6/20$ of a dollar per ounce; the emulsifier which has been obsoleted cost $3/20$ of a dollar per ounce. The new solvent will cost $3/20$ of a dollar per ounce and the old cost was $2/8$ of a dollar per ounce. The new resin will cost $8/40$ of a dollar per ounce whereas the old resin cost was $12/40$ of a dollar per ounce.

Mr. Uplift already had purchased and had just received in his raw material inventory 2000 ounces of the old type resin, 5000 ounces of the old type solvent and 1000 ounces of the obsoleted type of emulsifier prior to receiving the notice of discontinuance from his basic chemical supplier. Because of certain governmental regulations, he cannot keep these chemicals for cosmetic use for more than 30 days. None of these unused chemicals have any salvage value.

Mr. Uplift's packaging machinery will handle only 10,000 jars of facial creme in a month's time period. Each brand requires as much packaging time as any other. The nature of Mr. Uplift's market is such that his distributors can sell all of the products he produces with the exception of Moonview, which has a maximum market of 4000 jars.

Other raw material and direct labor costs for Starkiss total $33/20$ of a dollar per jar. Other raw materials and direct labor total $13/8$ of a dollar per jar for Moonview and $67/40$ of a dollar per jar for Galaxy Delight. Mr. Uplift will receive $23/10$ of a dollar for each jar of Starkiss sold to his distributors. He will receive $24/10$ of a dollar for each jar of Moonview sold and $47/20$ of a dollar for each jar of Galaxy Delight sold.

Faced with this decision, Mr. Uplift's objective was to determine how to maximize profits for the coming month. He thought the use of linear programming would lead him to the correct strategy for doing this. Since the old chemicals had been replaced by a new line which is directly substitutable in their respective products, he decided that the new cost would be the appropriate variable cost for use in each of the three products.

Variables:

   X_1 = number of jars of Starkiss to be mixed and sold;
   X_2 = number of jars of Moonview to be mixed and sold;
   X_3 = number of jars of Galaxy Delight to be mixed and sold.

	X_1	X_2	X_3
Revenue:	23/10	24/10	47/20
Costs:			
New raw material cost:	6/20	3/20	8/40
Other raw material and direct labor:	33/20	13/8	67/40
	7/20	5/8	19/40

Objective function:

   Maximize: $(7/20)X_1 + (5/8)X_2 + (19/40)X_3$.

Constraints:

   $X_1 + X_2 + X_3 \leqslant 10{,}000$ jars that can be packaged;
   $X_2 \leqslant 4000$ jars of Moonview maximum that can be sold;
   $X_3 \leqslant 2000$ ounces of old type resin available;
   $X_2 \leqslant 5000$ ounces of old type solvent available;
   $X_1 \leqslant 1000$ ounces of old type emulsifier available.

Final tableau:

	X_1	X_2	X_3	S_1	S_2	S_3	S_4	S_5	
S_1	0	0	0	1	−1	−1	0	−1	3000
X_2	0	1	0	0	1	0	0	0	4000
X_3	0	0	1	0	0	1	0	0	2000
S_4	0	0	0	0	−1	0	1	0	1000
X_1	1	0	0	0	0	0	0	1	1000
	0	0	0	0	5/8	19/40	0	7/20	3800

On the basis of the final tableau, Mr. Uplift decided to follow the plan outlined and produce 4000 units of Moonview, 2000 units of Galaxy Delight, and 1000 units of Starkiss. He would have 1000 ounces of the old type solvent to destroy and his packaging machinery would have time left to package 3000 jars of additional facial creme. Following this strategy, he would make $3800 profit.

But, alas, Mr. Uplift made two errors in trying to solve his problem by a linear programming technique. The first was that simply because either the old chemicals or the new line of chemicals could be used to produce the respective brands there was no reason to limit his variables to three. Even though the old chemicals and the new chemicals could not be mixed, the possibility remains that batch processing the brands separately, with the old chemicals in one batch and the new chemicals in the other batch, could be used.

The second error was made in determining his true variable costs. The cost of the old chemicals was sunk; he had already purchased these chemicals and had them in inventory when the line was obsoleted and since they have no salvage value, these costs should not be included in the determination of the profit coefficients. The variables which will express the brands made with new chemicals should have these new costs inherent in their profit coefficients.

These variables would have been appropriate:

X_1 = number of jars of Starkiss to be made and sold using emulsifier on hand;
X_2 = number of jars of Starkiss to be made and sold using new emulsifier;
X_3 = number of jars of Moonview to be made and sold with solvent on hand;
X_4 = number of jars of Moonview to be made and sold with new solvent;
X_5 = number of jars of Galaxy Delight to be made and sold with resin on hand;
X_6 = number of jars of Galaxy Delight to be made and sold with new resin.

Objective function:

Maximize: $(13/20)X_1 + (7/20)X_2 + (31/40)X_3 + (5/8)X_4 + (27/40)X_5$
$$+ (19/40)X_6.$$

Constraints:

$X_1 + X_2 + X_3 + X_4 + X_5 + X_6 \leqslant 10{,}000$ jars that can be packaged;
$X_3 + X_4 \leqslant 4000$ jars of Moonview maximum that can be sold;
$X_5 \leqslant 2000$ ounces of old type resin available;
$X_3 \leqslant 5000$ ounces of old type solvent available;
$X_1 \leqslant 1000$ ounces of old type emulsifier available.

Final tableau:

	X_1	X_2	X_3	X_4	X_5	X_6	S_1	S_2	S_3	S_4	S_5	
X_6	0	1	0	0	0	1	1	-1	-1	0	-1	3000
X_3	0	0	1	1	0	0	0	1	0	0	0	4000
X_5	0	0	0	0	1	0	0	0	1	0	0	2000
S_4	0	0	0	-1	0	0	0	-1	0	1	0	1000
X_1	1	0	0	0	0	0	0	0	0	0	1	1000
	0	0.125	0	0.15	0	0	0.475	0.3	0.2	0	0.175	6525

The strategy outlined here calls for the production of 1000 jars of Starkiss made with the old emulsifier, 2000 jars of Galaxy Delight made with the old resin, 4000 jars of Moonview made with the old solvent, and 3000 jars of Galaxy Delight made with the new resin. All of the material on hand would be used with exception of 1000 ounces of the old type solvent which would have to be junked. Profits under this plan would be $6525.

Chapter 9

THE GREATER-THAN-OR-EQUAL-TO AND THE EXACTLY-EQUAL-TO CONSTRAINTS

Until now we have worked with inequalities expressed on a less-than-or-equal-to basis. The problem situations featured scarce resources. These resources established barriers beyond which we could not operate; they set up limits which we could not exceed.

There are other types of constraints, of course. In contrast to the "less-than" constraints which impose a maximum limit on an activity, the "greater-than" constraints require that we reach a certain minimum level of some activity and that we not fall below that level.

ADDING A GREATER-THAN-OR-EQUAL-TO CONSTRAINT TO THE MODEL

Assume that Furniture Manufacturing Company has entered into a contract with a furniture distributor and that this contract requires Furniture to supply the distributor with five tables and two benches each day. In other words, the company's freedom in making a decision about production is limited or constrained by the fact that five tables and two benches *must* be produced. Let us assume that no other aspects of the problem situation are changed. How will these new requirements affect the overall production decision?

Two new functional relationships are added to the model; these are

$$X_1 \geqslant 5 \quad \text{and} \quad X_2 \geqslant 2.$$

The model, stated in its entirety, is now

Maximize: $20X_1 + 24X_2 = P$ (profit contribution)

where

X_1 = total number of tables to produce each day,

X_2 = total number of benches to produce each day,

subject to these limiting constraints:

$$3X_1 + 6X_2 \leqslant 60 \quad \text{(Assembly Department constraint),}$$
$$4X_1 + 2X_2 \leqslant 32 \quad \text{(Finishing Department constraint),}$$
$$X_1 \geqslant 5 \quad \text{(contractual constraint for tables),}$$
$$X_2 \geqslant 2 \quad \text{(contractual constraint for benches),}$$

with the further requirement that all of the variables must be nonnegative.

Graphing the Constraints

When we graph the contractual constraints, we see that the points along the constraint lines, above and to the right of these lines, represent production possibilities that do not violate the constraints. Refer to Fig. 9–1.

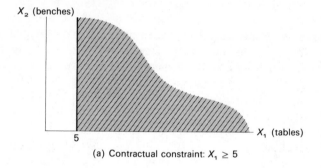

(a) Contractual constraint: $X_1 \geq 5$

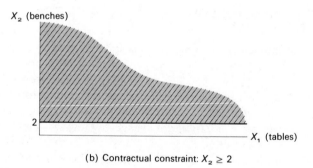

(b) Contractual constraint: $X_2 \geq 2$

FIG. 9–1 Greater-than-or-equal-to constraints

We can isolate the area of feasible solutions pictorially by graphing all of the constraints on the same chart. (See Fig. 9–2.) Notice that as more and more constraints are added to the model, the area of feasible solutions becomes smaller and smaller. (The observant reader may also notice that the Assembly Department constraint has now become redundant insofar as delineation of the area of feasible solutions is concerned. For the time being, however, let us ignore this fact. We shall return to the case of redundant constraints in a later chapter and our present treatment of the constraint will not be incorrect.)

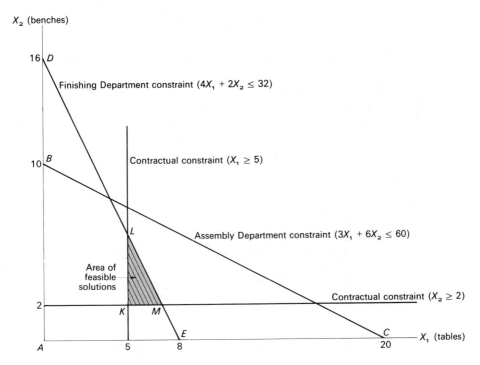

FIG. 9–2 *The area of feasible solutions*

CONVERTING THE "GREATER THANS" TO "LESS THANS"

So that all constraints—both the "less than" and the "greater than" varieties—may be treated in a consistent manner, we convert them all to a "less than" basis. Mathematically, the conversion is accomplished by multiplying a greater-than constraint by −1. This manipulation changes the direction of the inequality.*

---

* The sense of any inequality is reversed if both sides are multiplied by the same negative number. For illustration, consider the statement

$2 < 3$.

An equivalent statement is

$-2 > -3$.

We simply multiplied each term by −1 and changed the less-than inequality to a greater-than inequality.

The constraint inequalities for the Furniture Manufacturing Company product-mix problem, then, are restated as:

$$3X_1 + 6X_2 \leqslant 60 \quad \text{(Assembly Department constraint)},$$
$$4X_1 + 2X_2 \leqslant 32 \quad \text{(Finishing Department constraint)},$$
$$-X_1 \leqslant -5 \quad \text{(contractual constraint for tables)},$$
$$-X_2 \leqslant -2 \quad \text{(contractual constraint for benches)}.$$

CONVERTING THE INEQUALITIES TO EQUALITIES

With the simplex tableau, the inequalities must be converted to equalities. So we again invent variables for this purpose. For the Assembly Department constraint, we write, as before,

$$3X_1 + 6X_2 + S_1 = 60$$

where $S_1 =$ unused hours in the Assembly Department.

For the Finishing Department constraint, we write, as before,

$$4X_1 + 2X_2 + S_2 = 32$$

where $S_2 =$ unused hours in the Finishing Department..

We have termed variables such as S_1 and S_2 *slack variables*. They take up the "slack" between the available resources and the resources that are used.

For the two contractual constraints, we write

$$-X_1 + S_3 = -5$$

where $S_3 =$ the number of units of X_1 produced over and above the number required by the contract; then,

$$-X_2 + S_4 = -2$$

where $S_4 =$ the number of units of X_2 produced over and above the number required by the contract.

Variables of the same nature as S_3 and S_4 are termed *surplus variables*. These variables represent the amount by which we exceed a required minimum. Just as S_1 and S_2 are required to be nonnegative, so are S_3 and S_4 required to be nonnegative.

The mathematical difference between a slack and a surplus variable is illustrated in Fig. 9–3.

Surplus variables	*Slack variables*

Surplus variables

A surplus variable originates from a greater-than constraint; such as

$$X_1 \geqslant 10.$$

Here 10 represents a requirement that MUST be met.
We first convert the greater-than to a less-than constraint by multiplying through by -1. We obtain

$$-X_1 \leqslant -10.$$

A surplus variable is added to convert the inequality to an equality; that is

$$-X_1 + S_1 = -10.$$

Restated in terms of X_1 the equation is

$$-X_1 = -10 - S_1$$
$$X_1 = 10 + S_1$$

so that S_1 (the surplus variable) shows how far the solution value of X_1 is over and above the minimum requirement.

Slack variables

A slack variable originates from a less-than constraint; such as

$$X_2 \leqslant 10.$$

Here 10 represents a limit that cannot be exceeded.

A slack variable is added to convert the inequality to an equality; that is,

$$X_2 + S_2 = 10.$$

Restated in terms of X_2 the equation is

$$X_2 = 10 - S_2$$

so that S_2 (the slack variable) shows how far the solution value of X_2 is below the maximum limit.

FIG. 9–3 Comparison of the slack and surplus variables

THE TABLEAUS

The initial tableau for the model is shown in Fig. 9–4. There are several things worthy of note about the initial tableau. For one thing, it assumes the origin (where $X_1 = 0$ and $X_2 = 0$) as the starting point and, hence, does not represent a feasible solution.

Selecting the Pivot Row

For another thing, the negative numbers in the rightmost column must receive special attention. In the previous case where there were no negative numbers in the rightmost column of the initial tableau, we selected the pivot row and pivot column that would lead us in the most profitable direction. We now have to deal with a different type of constraint and we are, thus, forced to develop a new philosophy for selecting pivot rows and columns. Now we are dealing with constraints that tell us we *must* do something. These "musts" take priority over other considerations.

We see, then, that there are actually two reasons why we select a particular pivot-row–pivot-column combination:

1. this is the most profitable route; or

2. this is the required route.

The "-5" in the rightmost column of the tableau tells us we are five units below a requirement; the "-2" tells us we are two units below some other requirement. These units must be brought into solution before other items can be considered. Hence, *if there is a row (other than the objective-function row) which has a negative value in the rightmost column, that row must be selected as the pivot row.* If there are several rows with negative values in this column, any of these may be used as the pivot. All negative values must be cleared out of this column, however, before we can return to other considerations in selecting the pivot row.

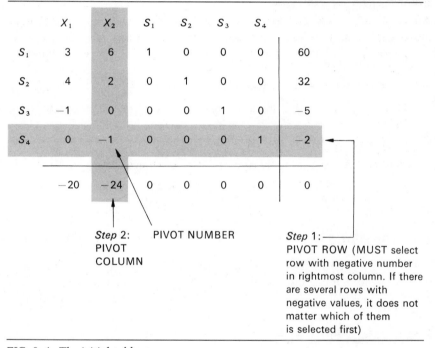

	X_1	X_2	S_1	S_2	S_3	S_4	
S_1	3	6	1	0	0	0	60
S_2	4	2	0	1	0	0	32
S_3	-1	0	0	0	1	0	-5
S_4	0	-1	0	0	0	1	-2
	-20	-24	0	0	0	0	0

Step 2:   PIVOT NUMBER   *Step* 1:
PIVOT   PIVOT ROW (MUST select
COLUMN   row with negative number
                                in rightmost column. If there
                                are several rows with
                                negative values, it does not
                                matter which of them
                                is selected first)

FIG. 9–4   The initial tableau

In tableaus where there are negative values in the rightmost column the pivot row is selected before the pivot column is chosen. The pivot row must be the row (or one of the rows) with the negative value in the right most column. In our illustration, we have selected the S_4 row although we might just as well have started with the S_3 row. (See Fig. 9–4.)

Selecting the Pivot Column

Having selected the pivot row, we would ordinarily use ratios between the numbers in the objective-function row and the numbers in the pivot row in order to determine which method of fulfilling the requirement would be most advantageous. In pivoting a tableau when setting up the ratios to determine which column will be the pivot column—having already chosen the pivot row by a minus value in the b vector—only *minus* a_{ij} values are considered. Then, the column producing the largest ratio becomes the pivot column.* However, in this problem, there is only one method of fulfilling the requirement outlined in the S_4 row and that is by introducing units of X_2 into solution. Thus, we must select the X_2 column as the pivot column.

Pivoting the Tableau

After the pivot row and pivot column have been chosen, the technique for moving to the next tableau is the same as previously outlined.

1. Divide the pivot row by the pivot number:

$$(0 \ -1 \ 0 \ 0 \ 0 \ 1 \ -2) \div (-1) = (0 \ 1 \ 0 \ 0 \ 0 \ -1 \ 2).$$

This becomes the new pivot row and is placed in the next tableau in the fourth row position, labeled with the pivot column label.

2. Multiply the new pivot row by the number in the first row, pivot column. Subtract the result from old row 1 to obtain row 1 for the new tableau:

$$(0 \ 1 \ 0 \ 0 \ 0 \ -1 \ 2) \times (6) = (0 \ 6 \ 0 \ 0 \ 0 \ -6 \ 12)$$

$$(3 \ 6 \ 1 \ 0 \ 0 \ 0 \ 60) - (0 \ 6 \ 0 \ 0 \ 0 \ -6 \ 12) = (3 \ 0 \ 1 \ 0 \ 0 \ 6 \ 48).$$

3. Move all other rows from the initial to the second tableau in this same manner:

a) Multiply the new pivot row by the number in the jth row, pivot column;

b) Subtract the result of step (a) from the old jth row to obtain the new jth row.

The completed second tableau is shown in Fig. 9–5.

	X_1	X_2	S_1	S_2	S_3	S_4	
S_1	3	0	1	0	0	6	48
S_2	4	0	0	1	0	2	28
S_3	−1	0	0	0	1	0	−5
X_2	0	1	0	0	0	−1	2
	−20	0	0	0	0	−24	48

FIG. 9–5 Second tableau

---

* This procedure will be illustrated in a later section of this chapter.

Second Tableau:

	X_1	X_2	S_1	S_2	S_3	S_4	
S_1	3	0	1	0	0	6	48
S_2	4	0	0	1	0	2	28
S_3	−1	0	0	0	1	0	−5
X_2	0	1	0	0	0	−1	2
	−20	0	0	0	0	−24	48

Step 1:
◄— PIVOT ROW
The negative row
must be chosen as
the pivot row!

Step 2:
PIVOT COLUMN

Third Tableau:

	X_1	X_2	S_1	S_2	S_3	S_4		Ratios:
S_1	0	0	1	0	3	6	33	33 ÷ 6 = 5.5
S_2	0	0	0	1	4	2	8	◄— 8 ÷ 2 = 4
X_1	1	0	0	0	−1	0	5	
X_2	0	1	0	0	0	−1	2	
	0	0	0	0	−20	−24	148	

Step 2:
PIVOT ROW
The smallest
ratio indicates
which row must
be the pivot
row

Step 1: PIVOT COLUMN
The column with the most
negative indicator is the pivot column

FIG. 9–6 Second and third tableaus

Fourth (and Final) Tableau:

	X_1	X_2	S_1	S_2	S_3	S_4	
S_1	0	0	1	-3	-9	0	9
S_4	0	0	0	1/2	2	1	4
X_1	1	0	0	0	-1	0	5
X_2	0	1		1/2	2	0	6
	0	0	0	12	28	0	244

FIG. 9–6 Final tableau

Moving from One Tableau to the Next

The second tableau, too, has a negative number in the rightmost column. The "-5" in the S_3 row warns us that we are five units below the contractual requirement for tables. This requirement must be fulfilled; this row must be chosen as the pivot row. The X_1 column must be selected as the pivot column because it is only by introducing units of X_1 into solution that this requirement can be met. The second tableau and the completed third tableau are shown in Fig. 9–6.

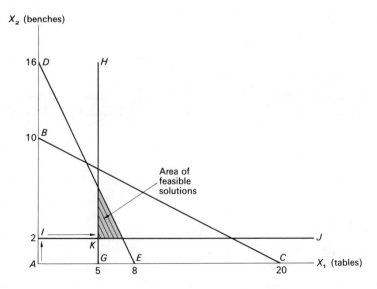

FIG. 9–7 *Moving from an infeasible to a feasible solution*

Notice that the third tableau is the first in this series of tableaus that represents a feasible solution. Graphically, we have moved from the origin (point A) to point K in Fig. 9–7. The first iteration carried us from point A to point I; the second iteration moved us from point I to point K.

There are no negative values in the rightmost column of the third tableau. There are, at this point, then, no unfulfilled requirements. We may return to a consideration of (1) the most negative indicator in selecting a pivot column and (2) the smallest ratio in selecting the pivot row. The completed fourth tableau is shown in Fig. 9–6.

The fourth tableau is the final tableau. There are no negative indicators and no unfulfilled requirements. Figure 9–8 shows graphically that the optimal solution is at the corner point L.

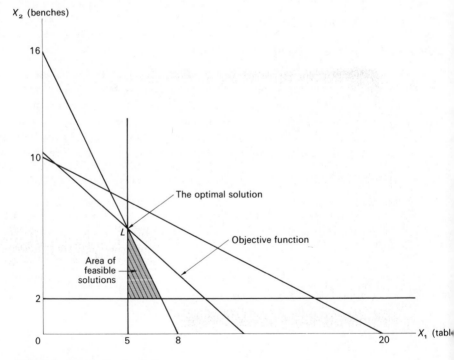

FIG. 9–8   The optimal solution

THE SOLUTION

Let us interpret this solution. First, we are told to produce five units of X_1 (five tables) and six units of X_2 (six benches) and that this production combination will yield the maximum possible profit contribution, which is $224.

Two other variables appear in the solution. There are nine units of S_1—

nine unused hours of Assembly Department time. We may check to see that this is the case by computing

$$3(5) + 6(6) + S_1 = 60$$
$$S_1 = 9.$$

The surplus variable S_4 has a solution value of four; we have produced four units of X_2 above the required number of units. We have produced six benches whereas the contract required only that we produce two. We can see that

$$-6 + S_4 = -2$$
$$S_4 = 4.$$

Let us distinguish carefully between the information given in the S_4 row and the X_2 row of the solution vector. The solution value for X_2 tells us that we should make six units of X_2 (six benches). The solution value of S_4 tells us that we have exceeded this requirement by four units. The contract requirement was that we make two benches; we will make six, four more than required.

A DIGRESSION:
DECIDING ON THE MOST ADVANTAGEOUS
METHOD OF MEETING A REQUIREMENT

Each of the contractual constraints of this problem could be met in only one way. Thus, when moving from one tableau to the next, once the pivot row (a row with a negative value in the rightmost column) was chosen, the pivot column was automatically specified; it was the column representing the variable which must be introduced into solution in order to meet the requirement.

Suppose, however, that a greater-than constraint could be met in a number of different ways. What should be given consideration in this situation when selecting a pivot column? Assume Furniture Manufacturing Company had entered into a contract that required that they produce either five tables *or* five benches or any combination of five of these each day. The constraint could be written

$$X_1 + X_2 \geqslant 5 \qquad \text{(contractual constraint).}$$

In the initial tableau, this constraint would appear as

	X_1	X_2	S_1	S_2	S_3	
S_1	–	–	–	–	–	–
S_2	–	–	–	–	–	–
S_3	-1	-1	0	0	1	$-5 \leftarrow$ Must be selected as pivot row
	-20	-24	0	0	0	0

The S_3 row must be selected as the pivot row because of the minus value in the b vector. Now let us determine which method of fulfilling the contract would be most profitable. We establish ratios between the numbers in the objective-function row and the negative numbers in the pivot row; that is,

For column X_1 For column X_2

$-20/-1 = 20$ $-24/-1 = 24$

These ratios give the profit contribution per unit of constraint per unit of product produced: \$20 for X_1's and \$24 for X_2's. We can move closer to our objective of maximizing total profit contribution by using units of X_2 to meet the contractual constraint than if we used units of X_1. Thus, we should select the X_2 column—the column with the largest ratio—as the pivot column.

EXACT EQUALITY CONSTRAINTS

We have considered constraints of both the "greater-than" and the "less-than" variety. We may also encounter from time to time constraints that must be expressed on an "exactly-equal-to" basis.

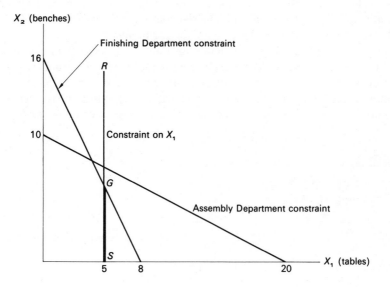

FIG. 9–9 An exact equality constraint

Let us consider, again, the model

Maximize $20X_1 + 24X_2$

subject to

$3X_1 + 6X_2 \leqslant 60$ (Assembly Department constraint),
$4X_1 + 2X_2 \leqslant 32$ (Finishing Department constraint),

when the exact-equality constraint

$X_1 = 5$

is added to the system. Let us assume that this constraint is required because a distributor has exclusive rights to this product and requires delivery of exactly five of the items each day.

We can see from Fig. 9–9 that the region of feasible solutions will not be a region at all but will simply be those points lying along the RS line between point G and point S.

While there are a number of different procedures by which the exact-equality constraint might be handled, the procedure described below is simple and uncomplicated and yields a correct solution.

First, multiply through the constraint by a "-1", as

$-X_1 = -5.$

This minus value in the b vector will force us to satisfy this constraint before we can consider any of the others in the system.

Then, when adding slack variables to the less-than inequalities to convert them to equations, add an "invented" variable to the exact-equality constraint as well, as

$-X_1 + S_3 = -5.$

So that we do not violate the equality condition, S_3 must have a solution value of zero; it must be a nonbasic variable. Hence, we must never select the S_3 column as a pivot column even though it might develop a negative indicator!

Now set up the tableaus as usual (see Fig. 9–10). On the first iteration the S_3 row must be selected as the pivot row because of the minus value in the rightmost column; the X_1 column must be selected as the pivot column since it is only by introducing units of X_1 that the minus b value can be cleared out. From this point onward, the pivoting of the tableaus is routine *except* that the S_3 column will never be selected as the pivot column.

Even the final tableau interpretation is conventional. The S_3 column tells us that the exact-equality constraint is presently costing us $28 per unit of the constraint. If the requirement could be reduced by one unit—so that $X_1 = 4$

Initial Tableau:

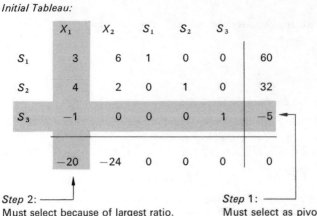

	X_1	X_2	S_1	S_2	S_3	
S_1	3	6	1	0	0	60
S_2	4	2	0	1	0	32
S_3	−1	0	0	0	1	−5
	−20	−24	0	0	0	0

Step 2: ———
Must select because of largest ratio.

Step 1: ———
Must select as pivot row
because of minus b value

Second Tableau:

	X_1	X_2	S_1	S_2	S_3		Ratios:
S_1	0	6	1	0	3	45	$45/6 = 7.5$
S_2	0	2	0	1	4	12	$12/2 = 6$
X_1	1	0	0	0	−1	5	$5/0 = \infty$
	0	−24	0	0	−20	100	

Step 1: ———
Most negative indicator. (Ignore indicator in S_3 column)

Step 2: ———
Must select
because of
smallest ratio

Third (and Final) Tableau:

	X_1	X_2	S_1	S_2	S_3	
S_1	0	0	1	−3	−9	9
X_2	0	1	0	1/2	2	6
X_1	1	0	0	0	−1	5
	0	0	0	12	28	244

FIG. 9–10 *The tableaus: exact-equality constraint*

and not 5—we would make one fewer units of X_1 and two units more of X_2 and increase profit contribution by

$$(-1)(\$20) + (2)(\$24) = \$28.$$

If the requirement were reduced by more than one unit, we would run out of assembly time; the exchange rates would change because we would begin moving along the Assembly Department constraint line rather than the Finishing Department constraint line. The requirement could be increased by only three units; we would then have used all the Assembly Department time.

EXERCISES

1. The Acme Axle Company produces both car and truck axles for national and international markets. Each axle must complete two manufacturing processes: molding and finishing. Each car axle requires 16 units of molding and 10 units of finishing, whereas a truck axle requires 24 units of molding and 20 units of finishing. Weekly, 480 units of molding and 360 units of finishing are available. The demand for Acme's axles is such that the firm may sell all it produces. Acme achieves a profit of $50 per car axle and $60 per truck axle.

Acme also has an agreement with the Spitz Motor Company to supply 12 car axles and 8 truck axles weekly.

Given the above constraints and requirements, Acme desires to know what amounts of car and truck axles to produce weekly in order to maximize profit.

Solve for the optimum production mix, using first the graphic and then the simplex methods.

2. A man who has $1000 to invest is considering two types of investments: bonds and stocks. After consultation with his broker, the investor has picked two stocks and two bonds that particularly appeal to him. The average yield he can expect from the investments is as follows:

Type investment:	Stock #1	Stock #2	Bond #1	Bond #2
Average yield:	5%	6%	$3\frac{1}{2}\%$	4%

Furthermore, his broker strongly recommends that he invest at least $400 in bonds and no more than $300 in Stock #2. This advice is in line with his financial goals and the risks he is willing to take so the investor agrees to these limitations and requirements.

His objective is to maximize his yield within these constraints. What is the optimal investment plan?

3. An assembly plant with 200,000 square feet of floor space is to be rearranged because one sales line has been discontinued. The significant information for the remaining products is as follows:

	Product			
	Card punch	Card sorter	Tape unit	Printing system
Minimum daily production	60	12	9	2
Maximum daily sales	120	30	40	15
Square feet of floor space required per unit produced daily	500	1200	1500	10,000
Labor hours required per unit produced daily	32	30	28	300
Profit contribution per unit produced	$25	$30	$40	$250

The labor available each day is 8000 hours.

Set up a linear programming model and solve for the optimum daily production schedule.

4. The Zingeria Vineyards produces a very select list of table wines. Two of their best sellers are Samaritan and Procrustian Wines, which have a profitability of $3 and $5 per case, respectively.

The bottles for Samaritan and Procrustian Wines are manufactured at the winery and are unique to the label. Bottles for Samaritan Wine take $1\frac{1}{2}$ hours per case to produce while those for Procrustian Wine take but one hour to produce. The bottle production operation has a capacity of 9000 hours a week.

The crushing, blending, and bottling operation takes one hour per case for Samaritan Wine and two hours per case for Procrustian Wine. Total weekly capacity for this operation is 12,000 hours.

The Zingeria brothers have set aside warehouse space for up to 7000 square feet for the two wines. Each type of wine takes one square foot of storage space per case stored.

The wholesaler who distributes the wines has insisted that the winery supply him with at least 4000 cases of Samaritan Wine each week.

Set up the linear programming constraints and the objective function. Solve the problem for the most profitable mix. Which constraints are limiting the solution?

If the wholesaler would reconsider and drop his insistance on at least 4000 cases of Samaritan Wine weekly, would this affect the product mix? If so, how would the mix change?

5. The Small Business Investment Company is considering the possibility of purchasing portions of two investments. Investment A is very risky but is expected to earn a 30% return. Investment B is less risky and is expected to earn a 10% return on investment.

A total of one million dollars is available for investment purposes. The company believes that investment in B should be no more than $200,000 because of the lower rate of return offered by this investment. In order to provide some diversification of risk, however, a minimum investment in B of $100,000 is required.

The company wishes to maximize return on investment subject to the above restrictions.

6. The advertising manager of a large department store is concerned with the weekly television advertising mix to be used during the next quarter. Two types of television ads are used by the store: a color ad for general advertising and a black-and-white ad for special sale advertising. Each ad is of 30 seconds duration and is "aired" exactly 20 times during the quarter. The color ads cost $3200 per prime time minute and the black and white special ads cost $2000 per minute. There is a limit of $32,000 per week during this quarter which can be spent for television advertising. In addition, the manager has been allotted $18,200 which can be spent for ad design and layout during the quarter. Historically, it has cost $1300 per minute of color ad for design and layout and $1400 per minute for black-and-white ads. The color ads are less expensive in this respect because of the various color effects which can be obtained inexpensively.

Every minute of color advertising is believed to increase sales revenues by $6130 and each minute of black and white advertising is believed to increase sales revenue by $5260. In addition, the president of the firm has said that there will be at least two different color ads each week and six different black and white ads.

What is the optimum mix of color and black and white advertising per week in minutes?

7. The manager of the Red-E-Mix Paint Company is considering projects to either replace or to modernize equipment in two departments of his plant. The projects involve dissimilar mixing tanks which produce the same paint products but would require differing amounts of labor per unit produced depending on the piece of equipment, the department in which it is located and whether it is to be modernized or replaced. Expected profit contributions will also differ depending on modernization or replacement because of materials.

If equipment in Department #1 is replaced, each unit of production will require 8 man-hours of time. If the equipment is only modernized, it will require 6 man-hours per unit of production. There are 48 man-hours available in Department #1 each day.

In Department #2 there are 40 man-hours of time available daily. If the equipment in this department is replaced, each unit of production will require 4 man-hours of labor. If the equipment is modernized, each unit of production will require 8 man-hours of labor.

There is a contractual requirement to produce at least 6 units per day.

What is the optimum production from replaced and modernized equipment if expected profit margins are $6 per unit and $8 per unit, respectively?

8. Saul, the sales manager, is an advocate of "Participative Management." He sees a value to the organization emanating from opportunities for all people in a group to face one another and to communicate with one another. In Saul's sales department there are 30 salesmen. What types of contacts between people should Saul provide in order to maximize the benefit to the firm?

He has made these estimates:

Type of Contact	Code	Maximum number	Cost to provide	Estimated benefit units	Minimum allowable
Manager→Salesman	M	30	$3.00	20	20
Salesman→Salesman	S	970	1.50	14	100
Salesman→Manager	F	30	4.50	22	—

The funds allocated to this project are $850.

9. A firm manufacturing plastic items now has a product line which consists of plastic reels for home and business recording tape, a plastic part used in the manufacture of mechanical pencils, and a letter opener with the customer's name stamped in gold which is used as a specialty advertising item.

A contract has been obtained from a large manufacturer of tape for 10,000 seven-inch reels, 1000 six-inch reels and 2500 five-inch reels per day. Sales surveys indicate that in addition to the tape reels on contract, probably not more than an additional 5000 seven-inch reels, 3000 six-inch reels and 2500 five-inch reels could be sold per day. The maximum number of pencil parts that could be sold each day was estimated at 20,000 and the maximum number of letter openers was estimated to be 15,000 each day.

Contribution to overhead for the five items is as follows:

7-in. reel: $13 per thousand   Pencil part: $2 per thousand
6-in. reel: $8 per thousand   Letter opener: $3 per thousand.
5-in. reel: $6 per thousand

The plant works an 8-hour day. There is one molding machine available that could produce one thousand of each item in the following times:

7-in. reel: 0.4 hours   Pencil part: 0.04 hours
6-in. reel: 0.28 hours   Letter opener: 0.06 hours
5-in. reel: 0.2 hours

There is also one stamping machine which is used for stamping the customers name in gold on the letter openers and stamping the tape manufacturer's name in gold on the tape reels. The machine can stamp one thousand of each item in the following times:

7-in. reel: 0.25 hours   5-in. reel: 0.25 hours
6-in. reel: 0.25 hours   Letter opener: 0.15 hours

There are only 8 hours of packing and shipping time available each day. The packing and shipping operations take the following times for one thousand of each of the items:

7-in. reel: 0.2 hours   Pencil part: 0.02 hours
6-in. reel: 0.2 hours   Letter opener: 0.12 hours
5-in. reel: 0.2 hours

The machine that mixes the raw plastic pellets and prepares the plastic for the molding machine has a capacity of 25,000 pounds per 8-hour day. The plastic needed for the five items (per one thousand items) is as follows:

7-in. reel: 1500 pounds   Pencil part: 100 pounds
6-in. reel: 1100 pounds   Letter opener: 150 pounds
5-in. reel: 900 pounds

What production strategy should the manufacturer follow?

Chapter 10

THE GREATER-THAN CONSTRAINTS: INTERPRETING THE FINAL TABLEAU

Let us return to the model whose tableaus were given in Figs 9–4 and 9–6. The optimal strategy—make five tables and six benches—is only one bit of information available from the final tableau of this model. Let us continue with our interpretation of the final tableau.

COLUMN INTERPRETATION AND RIGHT HAND-SIDE-RANGING FOR THE SLACK VARIABLES

In the final tableau (which is shown again in Fig. 10–1) the X_1, X_2, S_1, and S_4 columns are control columns; they represent the basic variables. Control columns are subject to a very simplistic interpretation. For example, the X_1 column would be read: to gain a unit of X_1 we would have to give up one unit of X_1; none of the other variables nor the objective-function value would be affected.

	X_1	X_2	S_1	S_2	S_3	S_4	
S_1	0	0	1	−3	−9	0	9
S_4	0	0	0	1/2	2	1	4
X_1	1	0	0	0	−1	0	5
X_2	0	1	0	1/2	2	0	6
	0	0	0	12	28	0	244

FIG. 10–1   The S_2 column from the final tableau

Column S_2 represents a slack variable that is not basic. (See Fig. 10–1.) This column is interpreted: to gain one unit of S_2 we should give up -3 units of S_1, give up $1/2$ unit of S_4, give up $1/2$ unit of X_2, and give up 12 units toward the objective function. The practical interpretation would be: if we had one fewer hour of finishing time available for use, the minimum this would cost us insofar as the total profit contribution is concerned is \$12. We should free up this hour of finishing time by making $1/2$ fewer benches, thus reducing our excess over the contractual requirement for benches by $1/2$ unit. With this change we would use three fewer hours of assembly time.

It is a simple matter to check, mathematically, these statements. The values of the variables become:

$$X_1 = 5 \qquad \text{(number of tables to produce)},$$
$$X_2 = 6 - (1/2) = 5\tfrac{1}{2} \quad \text{(number of benches to produce)},$$
$$S_1 = 9 - (-3) = 12 \quad \text{(unused hours of assembly time)},$$
$$S_2 = 0 + 1 = 1 \quad \text{(unused hours of finishing time)},$$
$$S_3 = 0 \qquad \text{(excess above requirement for tables)},$$
$$S_4 = 4 - (1/2) = 3\tfrac{1}{2} \quad \text{(excess above requirement for benches)}.$$

The slack variables, representing unused scarce resources, would become:

Assembly Department time:
$$3(5) + 6(5\tfrac{1}{2}) + S_1 = 60$$
$$S_1 = 12$$

Finishing Department time:
$$4(5) + 2(5\tfrac{1}{2}) + S_2 = 32$$
$$S_2 = 1.$$

The surplus variables, representing number of units by which the contractual requirements were exceeded, take on these values:

Number of tables produced above the minimum requirement:
$$-5 + S_3 = -5$$
$$S_3 = 0.$$

Number of benches produced above the minimum requirement:
$$-5\tfrac{1}{2} + S_4 = -2$$
$$S_4 = 3\tfrac{1}{2}.$$

The value of the objective function becomes:

$$\$20(5) + \$24(5\tfrac{1}{2}) = \$244 - \$12$$
$$\$232 = \$232.$$

Likewise, the effects column tells us that if we could increase the number of finishing hours available—if we had 33 hours to use rather than only 32—we could increase total profit contribution by $12. We could accomplish this by making 1/2 units more of X_2 (benches). We would, by this action, increase the excess over the required number of benches by 1/2 unit and have three hours fewer unused assembly hours (that is, we would use three hours more of assembly time).

Right-Hand-Side Ranging for the Slack Variable

The variable S_2 is a slack variable; interpretation of this column should have presented no new problems. Nor should the right-hand-side ranging for the resource finishing time present any difficulties.

The S_2 effects column outlines applicable exchange rates for the variable. Let us find the range over which this effects vector can be used. Recall that we range in terms of the resource, finishing hours, rather than in terms of the variable, unused finishing hours. A decrease in the amount of resource available to us has the effect of decreasing S_4 and X_2. After eight units of decrease in the resource, S_4 becomes zero. Further decreases would bring about an infeasible solution.

$$
\begin{array}{l}
\begin{array}{c} \text{Original} \\ \text{solution} \\ \text{vector} \end{array} \quad\quad \begin{array}{c} \text{Effects} \\ \text{vector} \\ S_2 \end{array} \quad\quad \begin{array}{c} \text{Adjusted} \\ \text{solution} \\ \text{vector} \end{array} \\[2mm]
\begin{matrix} S_1 \\ S_4 \\ X_1 \\ X_2 \\ {} \end{matrix}
\begin{pmatrix} 9 \\ 4 \\ 5 \\ 6 \\ 244 \end{pmatrix}
- (8)
\begin{pmatrix} -3 \\ 1/2 \\ 0 \\ 1/2 \\ 12 \end{pmatrix}
=
\begin{pmatrix} 33 \\ 0 \\ 5 \\ 2 \\ 148 \end{pmatrix}
\begin{matrix} {} \\ \leftarrow \text{Outgoing variable} \\ {} \\ {} \\ {} \end{matrix}
\end{array}
$$

The lower limit for the range of values for the quantity of the resource, finishing hours, available for use over which this S_2 effects vector is applicable is, then,

$$32 - 8 = 24$$

available hours of finishing time.

Increases in the number of units of the resource finishing time have the effect of increasing S_4 and X_2 but decreasing S_1. For each additional unit of finishing time, the effects vector indicates a 3-unit decrease in S_1. After three such increases, S_1 assumes a zero value. Additional increases in the resource result in an infeasible solution.

$$
\begin{array}{c}
S_1 \\
S_4 \\
X_1 \\
X_2 \\
\end{array}
\begin{array}{c}
\text{Original} \\
\text{solution} \\
\text{vector} \\
\begin{pmatrix}
9 \\
4 \\
5 \\
6 \\
244
\end{pmatrix}
\end{array}
+ (3)
\begin{array}{c}
\text{Effects} \\
\text{vector} \\
S_2 \\
\begin{pmatrix}
-3 \\
1/2 \\
0 \\
1/2 \\
12
\end{pmatrix}
\end{array}
=
\begin{array}{c}
\text{Adjusted} \\
\text{solution} \\
\text{vector} \\
\begin{pmatrix}
0 \\
5\frac{1}{2} \\
5 \\
7\frac{1}{2} \\
280
\end{pmatrix}
\end{array}
\leftarrow \text{Outgoing variable}
$$

The upper limit for the range over which this effects vector is applicable is, thus,

$$32 + 3 = 35$$

available hours of finishing time.

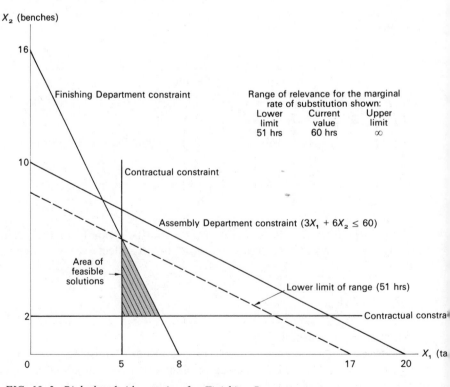

FIG. 10–2 Right-hand-side ranging for Finishing Department time

The resource—Assembly Department time—can be ranged in this same way. There are, with the optimum solution, nine unused hours of Assembly Department time. Because we already have more units of this resource than we can optimally use, the upper limit of the range of applicability for the effects vector S_1 is plus infinity. However, if the available supply of assembly hours were decreased by nine hours, the variable S_1 would assume a zero value. Further decreases would bring about a solution vector which represented an impossible solution.

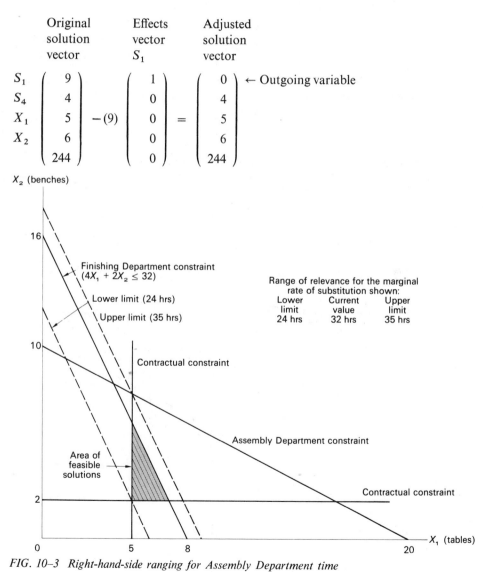

FIG. 10–3 Right-hand-side ranging for Assembly Department time

TABLE 10–1 *Right-hand-side ranging*

Resource	Current value	Lower limit	Upper limit	Outgoing variable Lower	Outgoing variable Upper
Assembly Department time (in hours)	60	51	∞	S_1	—
Finishing Department time (in hours)	32	24	35	S_4	S_1

The ranges for the resource supplies are shown in Table 10–1. Let us emphasize again that these are the ranges over which the effects vectors shown in the final tableau are applicable. Over this range the marginal rate of substitution outlined in the effects vector is appropriate and the shadow price shown in the effects vector can be considered to be the "worth" of a unit of the resource. These ranges are shown graphically in Figs 10–2 and 10–3.

COLUMN INTERPRETATION AND RIGHT-HAND-SIDE RANGING FOR THE SURPLUS VARIABLES

Columns S_3 and S_4 in the final tableau represent surplus variables. Recall that

S_3 = number of units of X_1 produced over and above the number required by the contract,

S_4 = number of units of X_2 produced over and above the number required by the contract.

The variable S_3 does not appear in solution. We are making no units of X_1 in excess of the minimum requirement. The contract states that five units of X_1 be made; the optimal solution calls for only five units of X_1.

	X_1	X_2	S_1	S_2	S_3	S_4	
S_1	0	0	1	-3	-9	0	9
S_4	0	0	0	$1/2$	2	1	4
X_1	1	0	0	0	-1	0	5
X_2	0	1	0	$1/2$	2	0	6
	0	0	0	12	28	0	244

FIG. 10–4 *The S_3 column from the final tableau*

To increase S_3 is to build up a surplus of tables (to build up a number in excess of the contractual requirement). To increase S_3, then, is to increase X_1; and to decrease S_3 is to decrease X_1. We may read from the S_3 column (see Fig. 10–4): to gain a unit of S_3 we would gain a unit of X_1 and nine units of S_1 and thereby decrease total profit contribution by \$28. We would have to give up two units of X_2 and two units of S_4.

With this exchange, the variable take on these values:

$X_1 = 5 - (-1) = 6$ (number of tables to produce),

$X_2 = 6 - 2 = 4$ (number of benches to produce),

$S_1 = 9 - (-9) = 18$ (unused hours of assembly time),

$S_2 = 0$ (unused hours of finishing time),

$S_3 = 0 + 1 = 1$ (excess above requirement for tables),

$S_4 = 4 - 2 = 2$ (excess above requirement for benches).

Also, the solution value of the objective function becomes

$$\$20(6) + \$24(4) = \$244 - \$28$$
$$\$216 = \$216.$$

We can see that the slack variables, representing unused scarce resources, would assume the values:

Assembly Department time:

$$3(6) + 6(4) + S_1 = 60$$
$$S_1 = 18.$$

Finishing Department time:

$$4(6) + 2(4) + S_2 = 32$$
$$S_2 = 0.$$

The surplus variables, representing the number of units by which we exceed the minimum contractual requirements, take on these values:

Number of tables produced above the minimum requirement:

$$-6 + S_3 = -5$$
$$S_3 = 1.$$

Number of benches produced above the minimum requirement:

$$-4 + S_4 = -2$$
$$S_4 = 2.$$

We may also read the column as an effects vector for decreases in S_3. In decreasing S_3 (and also X_1) by one unit, we may increase profit contribution by

$28—if we effect the decrease in S_3 by making two units more of X_2 and thereby increasing S_4 by two units. We would decrease S_1 by nine units, which means we would use the nine hours of assembly time which were previously unused.

For reassurance, let us mathematically verify these statements. We want to effect the change of decreasing S_3 by one unit; that is, we wish to accomplish

$$S_3 = 0 - 1 = -1.$$

We are really saying that we wish to reduce the minimum requirement for X_1 by one unit so that we are required to make only four, not five, tables each day. The other variables are changed in this way:

$X_1 = 5 + (-1) = 4$ (number of tables to produce),
$X_2 = 6 + 2 = 8$ (number of benches to produce),
$S_1 \ = 9 + (-9) = 0$ (unused hours of assembly time),
$S_2 \ = 0$ (unused hours of finishing time),
$S_4 \ = 4 + 2 = 6$ (excess above requirement for benches).

The profit contribution becomes

$$\$20(4) + \$24(8) = \$244 + \$28$$
$$\$272 = \$272.$$

The constraints are affected as follows:

Assembly Department time:
$$3(4) + 6(8) + S_1 = 60$$
$$S_1 = 0.$$

Finishing Department time:
$$4(4) + 2(8) + S_2 = 32$$
$$S_2 = 0.$$

Contractual requirement for X_1:
$$-4 + S_3 = -5$$
$$S_3 = -1.$$

Contractual requirement for X_2:
$$-8 + S_4 = -2$$
$$S_4 = 6.$$

Column S_4, representing the other surplus variable, is a control column in the final tableau; its interpretation should be evident.

**Right-Hand-Side Ranging
for the Surplus Variable**

Now for the ranging for the S_3 and S_4 columns. Let us think in terms of the *requirements* rather than in terms of the surplus variables. We want to think along the lines of (1) relaxing the requirement (reducing the number of units we are required by contract to make) or of (2) making the requirement more stringent (increasing the number of units we are required by contract to make).

Consider, first, the S_3 column and think in terms of relaxing the requirement for tables (which would be evidenced by an increase in the surplus variable). If we relax the requirement, the effects vector tells us to reduce the value of X_1 and the value of S_1. Only a one-unit decrease is possible. At this point, S_1 assumes a zero value and goes out of solution.

	Original solution vector		Effects vector S_3		Adjusted solution vector	
S_1	9		-9		0	← Outgoing variable
S_4	4		2		6	
X_1	5	$+(1)$	-1	$=$	4	
X_2	6		2		8	
	244		28		272	

Let us make certain, before we proceed, that we understand this manipulation. The requirement was originally stated

$$X_1 \geqslant 5.$$

The variable S_3 represents the number of units in excess of the requirement; that is,

$$X_1 = 5 + S_3.$$

A reduction in the requirement calls for an increase in the excess, in the surplus variable S_3. Hence, *we see the result of reducing the requirement by adding the effects vector.*

It follows that we find the upper limit for the range of applicability of the S_3 change vector by subtracting.

	Original solution vector		Effects vector S_3		Adjusted solution vector	
S_1	9		-9		27	
S_4	4		2		0	← Outgoing variable
X_1	5	$-(2)$	-1	$=$	7	
X_2	6		2		2	
	244		28		188	

Figure 10–5 illustrates this range graphically. We see that the same marginal rate of substitution would apply from the lower limit (a contractual requirement for four tables) to the upper limit (a contractual requirement for seven tables). This trade-off rate is established by the Finishing Department constraint. Beyond these limits, other constraints would cor   into play; hence, other trade-off rates would be applicable.

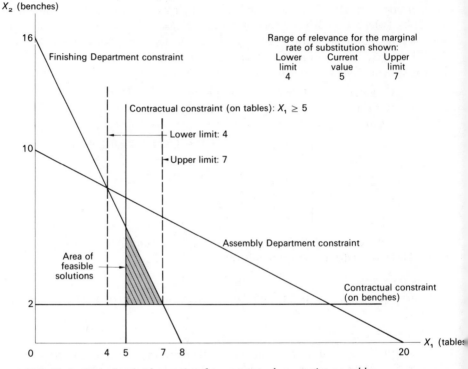

FIG. 10–5   Right-hand-side ranging for contractual constraint on tables

Now to find the range of applicability for column S_4 as an effects vector. The variable S_4 represents the number of benches produced in excess of the minimum required for benches. Again let us think in terms of the requirement for benches rather than in terms of the surplus variable S_4. The requirement currently is that we produce two benches each day.

Decreasing the requirement has the effect of increasing the surplus. We see from the final tableau that the effects vector S_4 could be added to the solution vector an infinite number of times and all of the values in the solution vector would remain positive (see Fig. 10–6). Thus, the lower limit for the range is minus infinity. For practical purposes, we will consider it to be zero.

	X_1	X_2	S_1	S_2	S_3	S_4	
S_1	0	0	1	-3	-9	0	9
S_4	0	0	0	1/2	2	1	4
X_1	1	0	0	0	-1	0	5
X_2	0	1	0	1/2	2	0	6
	0	0	0	12	28	0	244

FIG. 10-6   The S_4 column from the final tableau

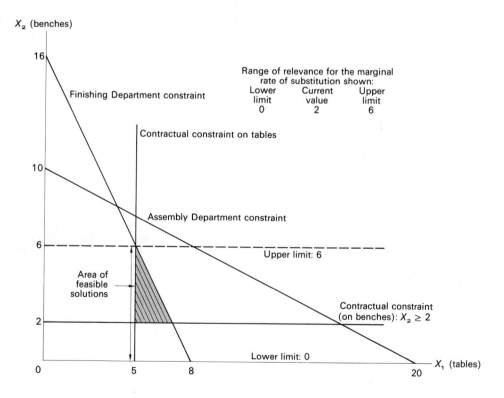

FIG. 10-7   Right-hand-side ranging for contractual constraint on benches

To increase the contractual requirement is to decrease the surplus variable S_4. We see that four one-unit reductions could be made.

$$
\begin{array}{c}
\text{Original} \\
\text{solution} \\
\text{vector}
\end{array}
\qquad
\begin{array}{c}
\text{Effects} \\
\text{vector} \\
S_4
\end{array}
\qquad
\begin{array}{c}
\text{Adjusted} \\
\text{solution} \\
\text{vector}
\end{array}
$$

$$
\begin{array}{c}
S_1 \\
S_4 \\
X_1 \\
X_2 \\
\end{array}
\begin{pmatrix}
9 \\
4 \\
5 \\
6 \\
244
\end{pmatrix}
- (4)
\begin{pmatrix}
0 \\
1 \\
0 \\
0 \\
0
\end{pmatrix}
=
\begin{pmatrix}
9 \\
0 \\
5 \\
6 \\
244
\end{pmatrix}
\quad \leftarrow \text{Outgoing variable}
$$

We can increase the requirement for benches by four units—from two benches to six and still be working with the exchange rates shown in the S_4 vector. Figure 10–7 shows that the constraint outlining the requirement for benches could be shifted from zero units to six units and over this entire range the same trade-off rate between benches and tables would be applicable. This trade-off rate is determined by the Finishing Department constraint. At the lower limit of this range, the restriction

$$X_1 \geqslant 0$$

would come into play. At the upper limit of this range, the contractual constraint

$$X_1 \geqslant 5$$

would become the intervening factor.

Complete right-hand-side ranging for this model is shown in Table 10–2.

TABLE 10–2 Right-hand-side ranging

	Current value	Lower limit	Upper limit	Outgoing variable Lower	Upper
Resource					
Assembly Department time (in hours)	60	51	∞	S_1	—
Finishing Department time (in hours)	32	24	35	S_4	S_1
Requirement					
Contractual requirement for tables (in units)	5	4	7	S_1	S_4
Contractual requirement for benches (in units)	2	0	6	—	S_4

OBJECTIVE-FUNCTION-COEFFICIENT RANGING: THE ACTIVITY VARIABLES

The optimal solution—make five units of X_1 and six units of X_2—was predicated on the profit contributions of $20 for each X_1 and $24 for each X_2. Over what range of values for these objective-function coefficients will this solution be the optimal solution?

The objective-function row in the final tableau is

X_1	X_2	S_1	S_2	S_3	S_4	
(0	0	0	12	28	0	244).

Note that the value of the objective function at this optimal solution is

$20(5) + $24(6) = $244.

Note also that the variable S_2 has a shadow price of $12. S_2 represents unused units of the scarce resource, finishing time. We have learned that this shadow price denotes the "worth" of an additional unit of the resource. We read from the S_2 column in the final tableau (see Fig. 10–1) that if we could obtain one additional hour of finishing time, we could increase total profit contribution by $12 if we used this additional hour of finishing time to make 1/2 units more of X_2. We substantiate this statement by the computation

$(1/2) \times (\$24) = \$12.$

The shadow price in the S_3 column is $28. S_3 is a surplus variable associated with the contractual requirement for tables. To increase the surplus variable is to decrease the minimum requirement. A one-unit decrease in the number of units of X_1 (tables) that the Furniture Manufacturing Company is required to make would result in a $28 increase in the total profit contribution. We read from the S_3 column (see Fig. 10–4) that if the requirement for tables were relaxed by one unit (reduced from five to four), we should produce one fewer units of X_1 and make two units more of X_2. That the effect on total profit contribution is $28 can be verified by

$$(-1) \times (\$20) = -\$20$$
$$(+2) \times (\$24) = \quad 48$$
$$\overline{\qquad\qquad \$28}$$

An increase in the minimum requirement for tables would have an opposite effect. If the minimum requirement were increased by one unit (increased from five to six), we would make one unit more of X_1 (table) and two fewer units of X_2 (benches) with a $28 decrease in the solution value of the objective function.

The numbers in the row vectors outline the effects of changes in the objective-function coefficient for the variable labeling that row. For example, a $1 increase in the profit contribution of benches (X_2) would change the objective function row in this way:

	S_2	S_3	
Objective-function row:	(12	28	244)
Effect of a $1 increase in the objective-function coefficient of X_2:	+1(1/2	2	6)
Adjusted objective-function row:	$12\frac{1}{2}$	30	250

Now the S_2 column shows a shadow price of $12.5. Let us see. The column vector tells us to use an additional hour of finishing time to make 1/2 units more of X_2. The variable X_2 now makes a profit contribution of

$$\$24 + \$1 = \$25.$$

The ability to make 1/2 units more of X_2 would, indeed, increase total profit contribution by

$$(1/2) \times \$25 = \$12.5.$$

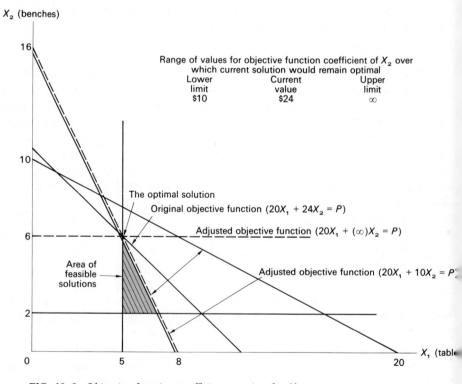

X_2 (benches)

Range of values for objective function coefficient of X_2 over which current solution would remain optimal

Lower limit	Current value	Upper limit
$10	$24	∞

The optimal solution

Original objective function $(20X_1 + 24X_2 = P)$

Adjusted objective function $(20X_1 + (∞)X_2 = P)$

Adjusted objective function $(20X_1 + 10X_2 = P)$

Area of feasible solutions

X_1 (table

FIG. 10–8 *Objective-function-coefficient ranging for X_2*

Thus, the shadow price of S_2 fluctuates with changes in the objective-function coefficient of X_2. We have learned that negative shadow prices (negative indicators) require another iteration of the tableau which, in turn, brings another optimal solution to the problem. Hence, changes can be made in the objective-function coefficients. For so long as such changes do not result in negative shadow prices, the optimal solution will not be altered.

Let us examine the objective-function row in the final tableau (ignoring columns that are control columns)

S_2 S_3
(12 28 244)

and the X_2 (benches) row

S_2 S_3
(1/2 2 226)

and determine the range of values for the profit contribution of benches which would still result in the optimal solution outlined by the final tableau. We can readily see that increases in the profit contribution of X_2 could never result in a negative shadow price. Thus the upper limit of the range is plus infinity. Refer to Fig. 10–8 and note that we are making as many units of X_2 as the prevailing constraints will allow us to make. No matter how high the profit contribution of X_2, the problem environment is such that we cannot make more than the six units we are presently planning to produce.

Decreases in the profit contribution of X_2 result in decreases in the shadow prices of both S_2 and S_3. A \$14 decrease would result in a zero shadow price for S_3 and additional decreases would call for a new solution.

	S_2	S_3	
Objective-function row:	(12	28	244)
Effect of 14 \$1-decreases in objective-function coefficient of X_2:	$-14(1/2$	2	6)
Adjusted objective-function row:	(5	0	160)

↑
Incoming variable

Insofar as the profit contribution of X_2 is concerned, only if the contribution were less than

$$\$24 - \$14 = \$10$$

would a new solution become optimal.

The X_1 row in the final tableau reads (ignoring control columns)

$$\begin{array}{ccc} & S_2 & S_3 \\ X_1 & (0 & -1 \qquad 5) \end{array}$$

Increases in the objective-function coefficient of X_1 result in decreases in the shadow price of S_3. Twenty-eight $1-increases could be made without altering the basic solution. The upper limit of this range, then, is

$20 + $28 = $48.

The objective-function coefficient for X_1 could decrease indefinitely without altering the solution. For practical purposes the lower limit is zero. (Note that the solution calls for only the minimum number of units of X_1 required by the contract; so we cannot make fewer than this number no matter how small the profit contribution.)

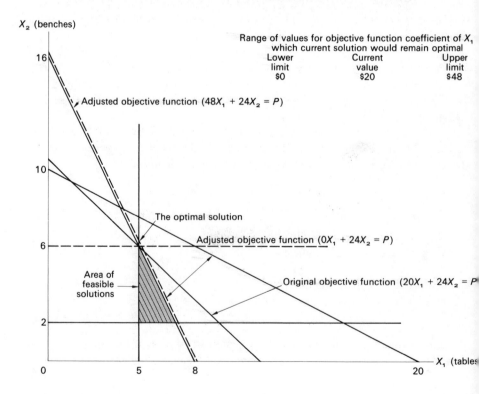

FIG. 10–9 Objective-function-coefficient ranging for X_1

These ranges are outlined in Table 10–3 and are shown graphically in Fig. 10–9.

TABLE 10–3 Objective-function coefficient ranging: the activity variables

Variable	Current value	Lower limit	Upper limit	Incoming variable Lower	Upper
X_1 (tables)	$20	$0	$48	—	S_3
X_2 (benches)	$24	$10	∞	S_3	—

OBJECTIVE-FUNCTION-COEFFICIENT RANGING: THE SLACK VARIABLES

Although the variable S_1 (unused assembly hours) was included in the objective function with a coefficient of zero, the assumption that unused assembly time has no cost, or has no worth, may not be strictly defensible. It may be helpful, then, to find a range of indifference for the costs or premiums associated with unused units of this resource.

Note in Fig. 10–10 the effect on the shadow prices of S_2 and S_3 and on the solution value of the objective function when "−$1" is used as the objective-function coefficient of the slack variable S_1. A −$1 objective-function coefficient of S_1 would indicate that there is a $1 cost associated with each unused hour of Assembly Department time.

Or we can see the effect of attaching an objective-function coefficient of −$1 to the variable S_1 by considering the row vectors; that is,

	S_2	S_3	
Objective-function row:	(12	28	244)
Effect of using −1 as the objective-function coefficient of S_1:	−1(−3	−9	9)
Adjusted objective-function row:	(15	37	235)

We see that a negative coefficient for S_1 could never result in a negative indicator. Hence, no matter how large the *cost* associated with having *unused* assembly hours, the optimal solution will not change. Intuitively, we can agree. The constraints that characterize the problem situation are such that we are forced to have unused assembly time. Within the framework of these constraints, there just isn't any way that we can use all available assembly hours. (Please refer again to Fig. 9–2.) The lower limit of the objective-function coefficient range for S_1 is, thus, minus infinity.

	Effects vector S_2		Objective function coefficient		
S_1	-3	$\times$	-1	$=$	3
S_4	$1/2$	$\times$	0	$=$	0
X_1	0	$\times$	20	$=$	0
X_2	$1/2$	$\times$	24	$=$	12
	12				15

The net effect on S_2 (unused finishing time) is $15 - \$12 = \$3$

	Effects vector S_3		Objective function coefficient		
S_1	-9	$\times$	-1	$=$	9
S_4	2	$\times$	0	$=$	0
X_1	-1	$\times$	20	$=$	-20
X_2	2	$\times$	24	$=$	48
	28				37

The net effect on S_3 (excess of X_1 over contractual requirement) is $\$37 - \$28 = \$9$

	Solution vector		Objective function coefficient		
S_1	9	$\times$	-1	$=$	-9
S_4	4	$\times$	0	$=$	0
X_1	5	$\times$	20	$=$	100
X_2	6	$\times$	24	$=$	144
	244				235

The net effect is $\$235 - \$244 = -\$9$.

FIG. 10–10 Effect of $1 decrease in objective function coefficient of S_1

A positive coefficient attached to S_1 in the objective function indicates that there is a premium associated with having unused assembly hours. The maximum positive value is $3\frac{1}{9}$; that is,

	S_2	S_3	
Objective-function row:	(12	28	244)
Effect of using $+3\frac{1}{9}$ as the objective function coefficient of S_1:	$+3\frac{1}{9}(-3$	-9	9)
Adjusted objective-function row:	$(2\frac{2}{3}$	0	272)

↑
Incoming variable

If unused assembly hours are more valuable than $+\$3\frac{1}{9}$, it would be advantageous for us to move from the corner point where the optimal solution is presently located down the finishing time constraint line and make more units of X_1 and fewer units of X_2. The variable S_3 (units of X_1 produced in excess of the contractual constraint) would be the new variable entering into the solution. Refer again to the original statement of the problem and note that units of X_1

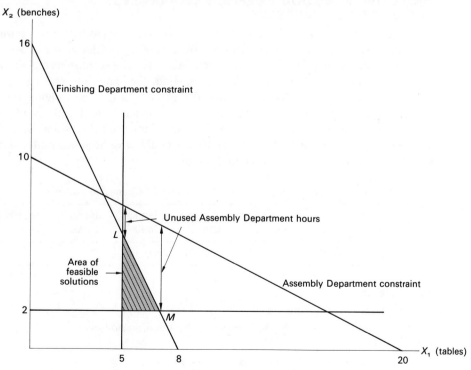

FIG. 10–11 Moving down the Finishing Department constraint line from point L toward point M. (More hours of assembly time are released for alternative uses.)

(whose production we would increase) use fewer assembly hours than do units of X_2 (whose production we would decrease as we moved down the Finishing Department constraint line). In fact, on Fig. 10–11 we see that movement down the Finishing Department constraint line would leave more and more unused assembly hours.

We see, then, that the objective-function coefficient for the variable S_1 (unused assembly hours) could range from minus infinity to $3\frac{1}{9}$ and this solution—make five units of X_1 and six units of X_2—would still be the optimal strategy. (This range is shown in Table 10–4.)

TABLE 10–4 *Objective-function-coefficient ranging: the slack variable*

Variable	Current value	Lower limit	Upper limit	Incoming variable Lower	Upper
S_1 (unused assembly hours)	0	$-\infty$	$3\frac{1}{9}$	—	S_3

OBJECTIVE-FUNCTION-COEFFICIENT RANGING: THE SURPLUS VARIABLES

The surplus variable S_4 is the last of the variables represented by a row vector in the final tableau. S_4 represents the number of units of X_2 produced in excess of the minimum number required by the contract. Although the surplus variable can be subjected to objective-function-coefficient ranging, the same information can be obtained by reference to the ranging of the variable X_2. The ranging for the surplus variable S_4 is shown in Table 10–5. The coefficient used in the model was zero. If the coefficient had been $14 less, another optimal solution would have been forthcoming; on the other hand, the coefficient could have been indefinitely large, and this same solution would remain optimal.

TABLE 10–5 *Objective-function-coefficient ranging: the surplus variable*

Variable	Current value	Lower limit	Upper limit	Incoming variable Lower	Upper
S_4 (excess units of X_2)	0	$-\$14$	∞	S_3	—

EXERCISES

1. The linear programming model

Maximize: $5X_1 + 4X_2 + 6X_3$ (profit contribution, in dollars)

subject to

$$2X_1 + 5X_2 + 10X_3 \leqslant 1500 \quad \text{(Resource \#1)}$$
$$4X_1 + 1X_2 + 8X_3 \leqslant 1000 \quad \text{(Resource \#2)}$$
$$2X_1 + 4X_2 + 3X_3 \geqslant 1200 \quad \text{(Restriction)}$$

where X_1 = number of units of Product #1 to produce
X_2 = number of units of Product #2 to produce
X_3 = number of units of Product #3 to produce

yields the following final tableau:

	X_1	X_2	X_3	S_1	S_2	S_3	
X_2	0	1	1.33	0.22	−0.11	0	222.22
S_3	0	0	5.67	0.78	0.11	1	77.78
X_1	1	0	1.67	−0.06	0.28	0	194.44
	0	0	7.67	0.61	0.94	0	1861.11

Interpret the final tableau. Find the right-hand-side and the objective-function-coefficient ranges. Explain the significance of these ranges.

2. The linear programming model

Maximize: $5X_1 + 4X_2 + 15X_3$ (profit contribution, in dollars)

subject to

$2X_1 + 5X_2 + 10X_3 \leqslant 1500$ (Resource #1)
$4X + X_2 + 8X_3 \leqslant 1000$ (Resource #2)
$2X_1 + 4X_2 + 3X_3 \geqslant 1200$ (Restriction)

where X_1 = number of units of Product #1 to produce
X_2 = number of units of Product #2 to produce
X_3 = number of units of Product #3 to produce

yields the following final tableau:

	X_1	X_2	X_3	S_1	S_2	S_3	
X_2	0	1	0	0.039	−0.137	−0.235	203.922
X_3	0	0	1	0.137	0.019	0.176	13.725
X_1	1	0	0	−0.284	0.245	−0.294	171.569
	0	0	0	0.794	0.971	0.235	1879.412

Interpret this tableau. Find the right-hand-side and the objective-function-coefficient ranges and explain the significance of these ranges.

3. A developer is making plans for a new apartment building he will construct. He is particularly interested in the number of efficiencies, one-, two-, and three-bedroom units to include in the building. The planned size of the building will not exceed 24,000 square feet. Each efficiency requires 400 square feet; each one-bedroom unit requires 600 square feet; each two-bedroom unit requires 700 square feet; and each three-bedroom unit 800 square feet.

A market research study of apartment rentals in the area leads the developer to believe that he should not include more than 12 efficiencies in the building, not more than 20 two-bedroom units, and not more than 6 three-bedroom units. Local building codes will not allow him to have more than a total of 40 units (of whatever type) in the one building. He has already leased four one-bedroom units and six two-bedroom units through an advance rental office.

The developer believes he will realize a monthly profit contribution of $35 from each efficiency built, $50 from each one-bedroom unit, $65 from each two-bedroom unit, and $75 from each three-bedroom unit.

Use a linear programming model to determine how many of each type of unit the developer should construct. Fully interpret the final tableau, including the right-hand-side and the objective-function-coefficient ranges.

4. The Sure-Fire Cartridge Company, manufacturer of 38- and 45-caliber cartridges, has an agreement with the local police force to supply shells for training and practice purposes by police officers. Sure-Fire has agreed to supply 50 boxes of 38-caliber and 100 boxes of 45-caliber cartridges to the police force each week.

Each cartridge must go through two manufacturing processes: loading (where the gunpowder is placed into the empty shell) and fusing (where the loaded shell and lead point are fused together). A box of fifty 38-caliber shells requires 6 units of loading and 4 units of fusing, whereas the same size box of 45-caliber shells requires 10 units of loading and 2 units of fusing. Sure-Fire has available each week 2400 units of loading and 1200 units of fusing.

Sure-Fire realizes a profit of $2 on each box of 38-caliber shells and $3 on each box of 45-caliber shells. They would like to know, given the requirements and the constraints involved, how many boxes of each type should be produced each week in order to maximize profits. Sure-Fire notes that the demand for shells allows the firm to sell all of whatever it produces.

Use a linear programming model to help Sure-Fire determine its production strategy. Fully interpret the final tableau, including the right-hand-side and the objective-function-coefficient ranges.

5. A commercial water-testing laboratory is able to process no more than 1000 water samples each day because of clerical limitations in the sample-receiving and reporting area. The laboratory is committed to test each day 300 samples from city water sources as called for in a contract with the mayor's office.

The laboratory realizes $0.20 profit per sample of city water. Water samples are also received from private swimming pools and from wells from surrounding rural areas. The profit contribution for these two types of samples is $0.24 and $0.22 per sample, respectively.

There are available 1500 units of laboratory technician and equipment time each day. While the pool samples require only one unit of technician and equipment time, the city-water and well samples require two units of time.

The firm believes that for public goodwill reasons, it should not test more pool samples than well samples on any day.

What combinations of samples will maximize profit for the laboratory? Interpret fully the information available from the model you build.

6. Golfco is a small manufacturer of a limited line of imitation leather golf bags. The recent boom in golfing activity has resulted in mushrooming sales, with demand easily keeping pace with production. To this point, Mr. Golf, owner and manager of the company, has been content to produce merchandise in a somewhat haphazard manner. Of the four styles of bags Golfco produces, production has roughly been divided equally among all four. The recent surge in sales has convinced Mr. Golf that he can sell almost

unlimited numbers of each of the four bags. He is, therefore, planning to limit production to that product mix which will maximize his profits. The only exception to this will be that at least 20% of total production will be "Golfco's Best" bag, the original company product and one which is closely tied to the company name through extensive magazine advertisements. Mr. Golf feels this model should get good distribution if only to keep the company image in front of the public.

The only real differences in the four bags are slight styling and coloring modifications in order to meet different style tastes. All bags are produced using varying amounts of imitation leather, zipper-strap units, and are treated with a chemical called "No-Crack," which prevents cracking, tearing, or leaking of Golfco bags for a guaranteed period of time. It is common knowledge that the success of Golfco is due in large part to this unique guarantee.

Golfco is able to purchase unlimited supplies of imitation leather and zipper-strap units. "No-Crack," however, is a patented product available from only one source. Golfco has contracted with the producer to purchase 500 pints of "No-Crack" each week. The cost of these raw materials is as follows:

Imitation leather (per yard)	$4.00
"No-Crack" (per pint)	3.50
Zipper-strap units (each)	3.90

"Golfco's Best," Model X_1, uses two yards of leather, two pints of No-Crack, and a single zipper unit. Model X_2 uses three yards of leather, two pints of No-Crack, and two zipper units. Model X_3 uses two yards of leather, two pints of No-Crack, and three zipper units. Model X_4 uses one yard of leather, three pints of No-Crack, and three zipper units. Model X_1 sells for $36, Model X_2 for $43, Model X_3 for $44.50, and Model X_4 for $42.50.

Production is also limited by the labor and machine hours available each week. Each Model X_1 requires 1.5 machine and 2.5 man hours. Each Model X_2 requires 1.7 machine and 2.4 man hours. Model X_3's take 1.5 machine and 2.5 man hours. Model X_4's require 1.6 machine and 2.6 man hours. There are 270 machine hours and 390 man hours available each week.

Use a linear programming model to help Mr. Golf analyze his production situation. Extract as much information from the model as you can.

7. The That's Where It's At Corporation is a producer of solar batteries for industrial use. There are six types of batteries being produced—A, B, C, D, E, and F. Each type of battery undergoes three machining processes—X, Y, and Z. Although many aspects of the manufacturing processes are automatic, labor is utilized in each to some extent. The number of hours of processes X, Y, and Z and the labor required to produce each type of battery is as follows:

Battery	Machining process			Labor
	X	Y	Z	
A	0.03	0.04	0.01	0.07
B	0.05	0.02	0.06	0.09
C	0.02	0.06	0.05	0.20
D	0.07	0.05	0.02	0.01
E	0.11	0.02	0.03	0.02
F	0.09	0.03	0.05	0.07

TWIA can sell all the batteries they can produce at a profit contribution per unit of 0.42 for *A*, 0.30 for *B*, 0.24 for *C*, 0.26 for *D*, 0.25 for *E*, and 0.31 for *F*. They are, however, currently operating at near plant capacity and expansion plans cannot go into effect for several years. TWIA wishes to maximize profit contribution for the coming year by determining the optimal product mix for production.

The company has contracts whereby it must produce the following quantities of batteries each month: 100,000 units of *A*; 20,000 units of *B*; 25,000 units of *C*; 10,000 units of *D*; 10,000 units of *E*; and 10,000 units of *F*. There are available 37,800 hours of labor each month, 34,000 hours of process *X*, 24,000 hours of *Y*, and 14,000 hours of *Z*.

The company would like to determine the optimal production strategy.

8. A company manufactures loving cups in two sizes. The production process is such that either of the types of cups can be produced with the same facilities. Maximum combined output per month, however, is 15,000 units. Because of marketing limitations, 1000 units of the larger cup is considered the maximum output desirable.

In order to prevent the company's credit rating from declining, a total of $120,000 in cash must be gengrarated from the cups during the next month. The net cash inflows during the coming month are expected to be $5 and $10 per unit for the larger and smaller size cup. Profit per unit is $14 and $12, respectively.

The company wishes to maximize profits subject to the above restrictions. The company is also considering a price change on these two products and would like information concerning the range over which per unit profits may vary without affecting the production strategy indicated earlier to be optimal.

If the marketing limitation on the larger sized cup could be lifted, what changes should be made in the strategy?

9. The Soupy Cement Company has the opportunity to supply various concrete mixes to a nearby construction project. The company, because it is a low-cost operation, has the option of selecting the mixes it finds most profitable to itself, subject only to the restriction that it supply a minimum of 600 cubic yards of 3-4-2 (3 parts cement to 4 parts gravel and 2 parts sand) each day at one site and 200 cubic yards of 3-0-2 each day at another site.

The concrete company will realize a profit contribution of $3.00 per cubic yard from the 3-4-2 mixture and $5.00 per cubic yard from the 3-0-2 mixture.

The plant can obtain for each day's operation a total of 3600 cubic yards of cement, 4000 cubic yards of gravel, and 3000 cubic yards of sand. The plant is situated on a fine flowing stream so that water is no problem.

The plant manager needs to know what proportion of his production should be the 3-4-2 mix and what proportion the 3-0-2 mix in order to realize the highest possible profit.

Set up a linear programming model to help the manager determine the optimal production strategy. Explain to the manager all of the information that is made available by this model.

10. Laura Lindsay, who lives in Virginia's Shenandoah Valley, is engaged part-time in the production of a very popular hand-crafted product, a stuffed terry cloth frog. These frogs seem to have several uses, such as doorstops, knicknacks, or as children's playthings.

Two sizes are currently in production: small and large. There are three operations in the production process: (1) pattern layout and cutting, (2) sewing, and (3) filling and closing. Workers generally specialize in one operation; and since these workers are housewives working part-time, they have a limited amount of time available.

There is also a raw material limitation on stuffing material, which is composed of small plastic pellets. These pellets are a by-product from a plastics plant where one of the workers' husband is employed. Because of limited availability, he is able to purchase only 500 pounds of this stuffing material each week.

Contracts have been signed with several of the local craft shops and souvenir stores to furnish a minimum of 100 frogs per week, size unspecified. In addition, direct sales are often made and it is estimated that demand will exceed the supply for the forseeable future.

The restrictions on skilled labor can be summarized as follows

	Available resources per week	Requirements per unit	
		Small frog	Large frog
Layout and cutting	690 minutes	4 minutes	7 minutes
Sewing	960 minutes	6 minutes	10 minutes
Filling and closing	360 minutes	3 minutes	4 minutes

The large frog requires 3.0 pounds of stuffing material while the small frog requires 1.5 pounds.

How many frogs should Laura Lindsay and her friends produce each week in order to maximize profits if the profit is $2.00 for the small frog and $3.25 for the large frog?

Set up a linear programming model to aid in the decision. Interpret fully the information available from this model and make any suggestions you feel appropriate concerning the venture.

11. The Yamatsu Electronic Company is a small manufacturer of miniature television sets. It produces only two models of sets, one color and one a black-and-white version. The company realizes a $50 profit from each color set and a $80 profit from each black-and-white set and seeks to maximize weekly profits.

There are essentially only two major steps in the production of the sets, the assembly and the alignment-and-checkout. The time requirements for each step are as shown:

Product	Man-hours required for each unit	
	Assembly	Alignment-and-checkout
Color set	20	10
Black-and-white set	8	15

The shorter time requirement for alignment and checkout of the color sets is the result of greater use of printed circuitry and more sophisticated equipment in the checkout phase.

The plant manager has a minimum quota of at least four color sets and six black-and-white sets each week. There are a total of 160 man-hours available each week in the assembly department and 150 man-hours in the alignment-and-checkout department.

How many of each type of set should the production manager try to produce on a weekly basis?

If five of the alignment and checkout man-hours presently devoted to the production of television sets could be transferred to another process where they have an imputed value of $10 each, what adjustment would you recommend in the production strategy?

If the selling price on the black-and-white sets had to be reduced so that the profit contribution of this item was only $55 rather than $80, what adjustments would you recommend in the production strategy? If the profit contribution of both types of sets decreased by 10%, what adjustments would you recommend in the production strategy?

12. Slim Stillwater produces and sells leisure-time spirits in the rural north Georgia community of Stark. Employing facilities salvaged from an old automobile, he has a weekly production capacity of 275 gallons and an established minimum weekly demand of 200 gallons. He is certain that with only moderately aggressive selling, there is no limit to his sales potential.

His two products, Lightning and Blue Lightning, sell for $4.00 per gallon and $5.00 per gallon, respectively. These products are interchangeable from a demand point of view in that if one is sold out the other simply replaces the sale that would have gone to it.

In formulating his beverages, Slim uses only three principal ingredients. These are water, grain, and sugar. The beverages are formulated as follows:

Lightning (*per gallon*)	Blue Lightning (*per gallon*)
12 pounds of grain	14.4 pounds of grain
sugar quantity dependent upon type of grain used	sugar quantity dependent upon type of grain used
8 gallons of water	8 gallons of water

The grains can be either corn or rye, in any percentage so long as the total weight equals that specified for the particular beverage. For each pound of corn, 0.1 pounds of sugar is required; and for each pound of rye, 0.15 pounds of sugar is required.

Slim can purchase 1600 pounds of corn, 2000 pounds of rye, and 100 pounds of sugar each week. These are the quantities of supplies to which he has found he must limit himself, so as not to draw attention to his activities. His supply costs are as follows:

corn: 8¢ a pound
rye: 10¢ a pound
sugar: 3¢ a pound

Since his water is obtained from a nearby brook, it has no cost.

If Slim's only costs are those of his supplies, what mix of grains and products will provide his greatest profit?

Chapter 11

THE MATTER OF MINIMIZATION

The cases considered thus far have dealt with situations where the goal was the maximization of some function. Linear programming can also be useful in the reverse situation, where the goal is the minimization of a function. For instance, a product may be of such a nature that several different combinations of raw material might be used in its manufacture and the decision-maker may be interested in determining which combination of raw material to use in order to minimize the cost of the product. The production manager may wish to evaluate alternative production methods in order to find that process which will yield the lowest cost of producing an item. An advertising agency may wish to plan a publicity campaign which utilizes various media in such a way as to reach the desired audience and yet keep the advertising budget at a minimum.

AN ILLUSTRATIVE SITUATION

Let us consider a simple example. A mill mixes feed for farm animals, using two different types of grain as the primary ingredients in its feed mix. These grains are mixed together in various proportions to produce a feed that meets certain nutritional requirements.

Suppose that each unit of grain #1 contains one unit of nutrient A while each unit of grain #2 contains just 1/2 unit of this nutrient. Now if an order is received for a feed mix which must contain at least ten units of nutrient A the order might be filled by a mix containing ten units of grain #1; or the order might be filled by a mix containing twenty units of grain #2; or the two grains might be combined in such a way that the mixture contains the required quantity of the nutrient.

If X_1 represents the quantity of grain #1 used to make up the required feed and X_2 represents the quantity of grain #2 used, the combinations of the two grains that would meet these specifications could be expressed as

$$X_1 + \tfrac{1}{2}X_2 \geqslant 10.$$

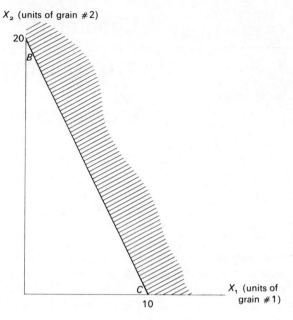

FIG. 11–1 *Requirement for nutrient A*

Figure 11–1 depicts, in the shaded area, the feasible combinations of the two grains. The line *BC* represents those combinations of the two grains that would furnish exactly ten units of nutrient *A*. The points above and to the left of the *BC* line represent feasible combinations of the grains; "feasible" in the sense that they

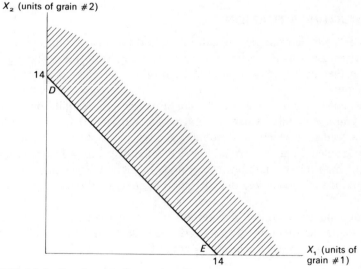

FIG. 11–2 *Requirement for nutrient B*

would furnish more, not less, than the required ten units of A. Any point below and to the left of the BC line represents an infeasible combination of the grains because it would not provide the required amount of A. Notice that the non-negativity requirement—the requirement that $X_1 \geqslant 0$ and $X_2 \geqslant 0$—excludes negative quantities of either of the grains.

Suppose that the order for the feed also specifies that the mix contains not fewer than 14 units of nutrient B and not fewer than six units of nutrient C. Each unit of grain #1 contains one unit of nutrient B and 1/3 unit of nutrient C. Each unit of grain #2 contains one unit of nutrient B as well as one unit of nutrient C.

All combinations of the grains that will meet the requirement for nutrient B can be expressed as

$$X_1 + X_2 \geqslant 14.$$

Figure 11–2 depicts the feasible region when only this specification is considered.

Then those combinations of the grains that meet the specifications for nutrient C can be expressed mathematically as

$$\tfrac{1}{3}X_1 + X_2 \geqslant 6.$$

These grain combinations are depicted in Fig. 11–3.

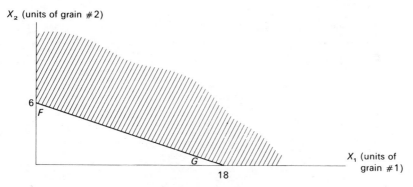

FIG. 11–3 Requirement for nutrient C

Of course, the feed mix must be such that all of the nutritional specifications are satisfied simultaneously. Any combination of grain #1 and grain #2, then, will be feasible for this order for the feed only if it is consistent with each of these constraints:

$X_1 + \tfrac{1}{2}X_2 \geqslant 10$ (requirement for nutrient A),

$X_1 + \ \ X_2 \geqslant 14$ (requirement for nutrient B),

$\tfrac{1}{3}X_1 + \ \ X_2 \geqslant 6$ (requirement for nutrient C), and

$$X_1 \geqslant 0 \quad \text{and} \quad X_2 \geqslant 0$$

where

X_1 = number of units of grain #1 used in the mix,

X_2 = number of units of grain #2 used in the mix.

The area of feasible solutions is shown as the shaded area, the area bounded on its lower side by $KBHJGL$, in Fig. 11–4. The fact that the area of feasible solutions is unbounded upward and to the right creates no difficulty since, as we shall discover when we explore the matter of the objective function, the area is bounded in the direction of optimality. The optimal solution must be at one of the corner points B, H, J, or G.

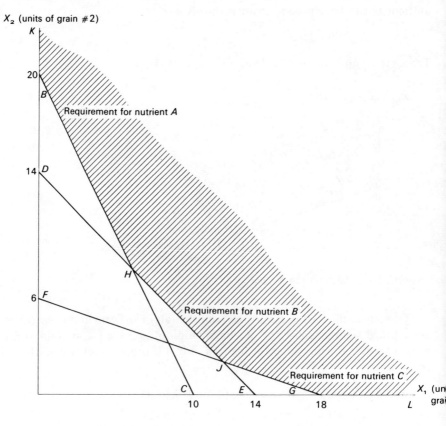

FIG. 11–4 Area of feasible solutions

MINIMUM-COST COMBINATION AS THE OBJECTIVE

Given the minimum specifications for the feed mix, the mill wishes to choose that combination of grains that will keep the cost as low as possible. Suppose that grain #1 can be purchased for $10 a unit and grain #2 for $6 a unit. Total cost for the mixture consisting of X_1 units of grain #1 and X_2 units of grain #2 would be

$$10X_1 + 6X_2 = Z.$$

Figure 11–5 shows a series of cost lines corresponding to a series of total costs. The closer the cost line to the origin, the lower the total cost. As the cost line moves farther from the origin, the total cost increases. Since the objective is to minimize cost, the goal will be that cost line as near the origin as possible but with at least one point in common with the area of feasible solutions. We can read from Fig. 11–5 that the mixture represented by point H will yield a lesser cost than any of the other possible combinations of grains.

Note that the optimal corner point lies on the constraint line for nutrient A and on the constraint line for nutrient B but lies above the constraint line for

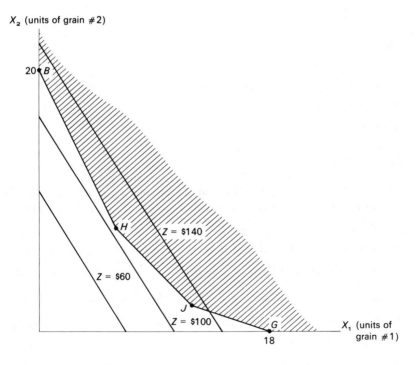

FIG. 11–5 Isocost lines

nutrient C. This means that this particular combination of grains exactly meets the minimum requirements for nutrients A and B but exceeds the minimum requirement for nutrient C.

A FORMAL MATHEMATICAL
APPROACH TO A SOLUTION

Let us make a formal statement of the feed-mix problem.

Minimize: $10X_1 + 6X_2 = Z$ (total cost of grain used)

subject to

$$X_1 + \tfrac{1}{2}X_2 \geqslant 10 \qquad \text{(requirement for nutrient } A\text{)},$$
$$X_1 + X_2 \geqslant 14 \qquad \text{(requirement for nutrient } B\text{)},$$
$$\tfrac{1}{3}X_1 + X_2 \geqslant 6 \qquad \text{(requirement for nutrient } C\text{)},$$

where

X_1 = number of units of grain #1 used in mix,

X_2 = number of units of grain #2 used in mix,

and

$$X_1 \geqslant 0,$$
$$X_2 \geqslant 0.$$

As before, the greater-than inequations must be converted to less-than inequations. This transformation is accomplished by multiplying the inequation by -1 and changing the sense of the inequality. The constraints are rewritten as

$$-X_1 - \tfrac{1}{2}X_2 \leqslant -10,$$
$$-X_1 - X_2 \leqslant -14,$$
$$-\tfrac{1}{3}X_1 - X_2 \leqslant -6.$$

Next, variables must be invented that will enable us to express the above statements as equations rather than inequations. Let us define these variables:

S_1 = number of units of nutrient A in excess of the minimum requirement,

S_2 = number of units of nutrient B in excess of the minimum requirement,

S_3 = number of units of nutrient C in excess of the minimum requirement.

These are "surplus" variables, aren't they? Their use will allow us to write:

$$-X_1 - \tfrac{1}{2}X_2 + S_1 + 0S_2 + 0S_3 = -10 \qquad \text{(requirement for nutrient } A\text{)},$$
$$-X_1 - X_2 + 0S_1 + S_2 + 0S_3 = -14 \qquad \text{(requirement for nutrient } B\text{)},$$
$$-\tfrac{1}{3}X_1 - X_2 + 0S_1 + 0S_2 + S_3 = -6 \qquad \text{(requirement for nutrient } C\text{)}.$$

Now any linear minimization problem can be viewed as the equivalent of a linear maximization problem if we utilize the principle that to maximize the negative of a function is to minimize that function. That is,

Minimize: $\sum_{j=1}^{n} c_j X_j$

can be treated as

Maximize: $\sum_{j=1}^{n} (-c_j) X_j.$

If the objective function is to be minimized, then, we merely multiply that objective function by -1 and proceed with the usual maximizing algorithm.

Thus, we shall alter the objective function

Minimize: $10X_1 + 6X_2 = Z$

so that it reads

Maximize: $-10X_1 - 6X_2 = Z'.$

THE TABLEAU OPERATIONS

The simplex tableau is set up just as if this were an ordinary maximization problem (see Fig. 11–6). Please notice that the bottom row is still "$-c$" where c is the objective-function-coefficient vector. So we have

$(-1) \times (-10 \ -6 \ 0 \ 0 \ 0 \ 0) = (10 \ 6 \ 0 \ 0 \ 0 \ 0)$

as the objective-function row in the initial tableau.

The pivoting of the tableau can be accomplished following the rules discussed previously. There will usually be more minus numbers in the b vector for the situation that is basically a minimization situation than there will be for the situation that is a maximization situation. These arise because the minimization model is ordinarily characterized by a predominance of greater-than inequalities. Hence, we must begin by clearing out these minus b values.

Refer to Fig. 11–6 and notice that in the initial tableau we have selected the S_2 row as the pivot row. Recall that whenever a row has a negative value in the b vector that row must be selected as the pivot row, but whenever more than one row has a negative value in the b vector, any of them may be selected as the pivot. We have selected the second row simply because, given that all nutritional specifications must be met, it seemed logical to fulfill the largest requirement first.

Initial Tableau:

	X_1	X_2	S_1	S_2	S_3	
S_1	-1	$-1/2$	1	0	0	-10
S_2	-1	-1	0	1	0	-14
S_3	$-1/3$	-1	0	0	1	-6
	10	6	0	0	0	0

Step 1: Pivot row ← (S_2 row)

Ratios: $\dfrac{10}{-1} = -10 \qquad \dfrac{6}{-1} = -6$

Step 2:
Pivot column

Second Tableau:

	X_1	X_2	S_1	S_2	S_3	
S_1	$-1/2$	0	1	$-1/2$	0	-3
X_2	1	1	0	-1	0	14
S_3	2/3	0	0	-1	1	8
	4	0	0	6	0	-84

Step 1: Pivot row ← (S_1 row)

Ratios: $\dfrac{4}{-1/2} = -8 \qquad \dfrac{6}{-1/2} = -12$

Step 2:
Pivot column

Third (and Final) Tableau:

	X_1	X_2	S_1	S_2	S_3	
X_1	1	0	-2	1	0	6
X_2	0	1	2	-2	0	8
S_3	0	0	4/3	$-5/3$	1	4
	0	0	8	2	0	-108

FIG. 11–6 *Pivoting the tableau*

Having decided to fulfill the requirement for nutrient B, we establish ratios between values in the objective-function row and values in the pivot row. These ratios are:

For X_1: $10/-1 = -10$

which is to say that each unit of X_1 costs $10 and furnishes one unit toward the requirement for nutrient B. Hence, the cost per unit of contribution to the requirement is $10.

For X_2: $6/-1 = -6$

which is to say that each unit of X_2 costs $6 and furnishes one unit toward the requirement for nutrient B. Thus, the cost per unit of contribution toward the requirement is $6.

The least costly way to fulfill the requirement is by using X_2. This is evidenced by the *largest* ratio. (Note: -6 is larger than -10.) The X_2 column must be selected as the pivot column.

Let us reemphasize the procedure for selecting the pivot row and pivot column. If there is a negative value in the b vector, we must select as the pivot row that row with the negative value. This negative number will represent a requirement that *must* be met. The numbers in the columns will tell us how this requirement can be met; the numbers in the objective-function row will relate the costs involved. Ratios established for each column between the objective-function row values and the negative values in the pivot row will tell us, for each method of meeting the requirement, the cost per unit of contribution to the requirement. The minimum-cost method of fulfilling the requirement must be used. Thus, *the column with the largest ratio must be selected as the pivot column.* This choice is critical so these ratios should be carefully considered.

Other steps followed in pivoting the tableau are the same as those we followed previously. The second and third tableaus for the feed-mix problem are shown in Fig. 11–6.

READING THE FINAL TABLEAU

We read from the final tableau that the variables in the optimal solution are:

$X_1 = 6$ (number of units of grain #1 to use in the mix),
$X_2 = 8$ (number of units of grain #2 to use in the mix),
$S_3 = 4$ (number of units of nutrient C in excess of the minimum requirement).

The minimum cost is shown to be $108. The requirements for nutrients A and B have been exactly met; the requirement for nutrient C has been exceeded by four units.

This, of course, is the answer to the specific question: How many units of each of grain #1 and grain #2 should be used in fulfilling an order for a feed mix which specifies that the feed mix must contain at least ten units of nutrient A, fourteen units of nutrient B, and six units of nutrient C, when it is desirable to keep the cost of the grain used at a minimum?

The answers to many other vital questions may also be found in the final tableau. We are interested in knowing whether or not the optimal mix will change if the prices of either of the grains change. What would happen to the cost of the mix if the nutritional requirements were altered?

RIGHT-HAND-SIDE RANGING FOR NUTRITIONAL REQUIREMENTS

We can read that the requirement for nutrient A presently has a shadow price of $8 per unit of requirement; the requirement for nutrient B presently has a shadow price of $2 per unit; the requirement for nutrient C has a shadow price of zero.

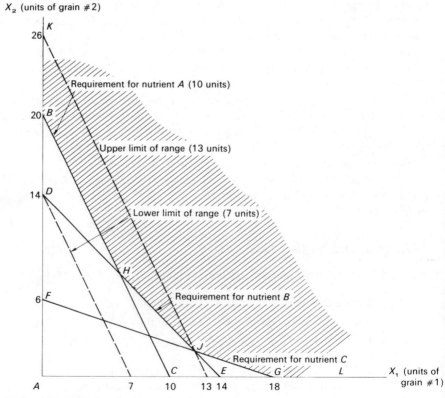

FIG. 11–7　Right-hand-side ranging for requirement for nutrient A

To increase the requirement for nutrient A by one unit would mean that total cost would increase by \$8. To meet the increased requirement we would add to the mix two units of X_1 (grain #1) and delete two units of X_2 (grain #2). If the requirement for nutrient A were increased by three units, the optimal mix would be 12 units of grain #1 and two units of grain #2, and the variable S_3 (representing units of nutrient C above the minimum requirement) would assume a zero value. The total cost at this point would be \$132. If the requirement for nutrient A were increased by more than three units, the S_1 column in this final tableau would no longer reflect the appropriate marginal rates of substitution nor the prevailing shadow price. Graphically (see Fig. 11-7) we would no longer be traversing the constraint line for nutrient B but would have moved from point H to point J and would be ready to move along the constraint line for nutrient C from point J toward point G.

The lower limit of the range of values for the requirement for nutrient A over which the S_1 change vector from the final tableau is applicable is shown in Fig. 11-7 to be seven units.

For each one-unit increase in the requirement for nutrient B, total cost would be increased by \$2. Likewise, if the requirement could be decreased by one unit,

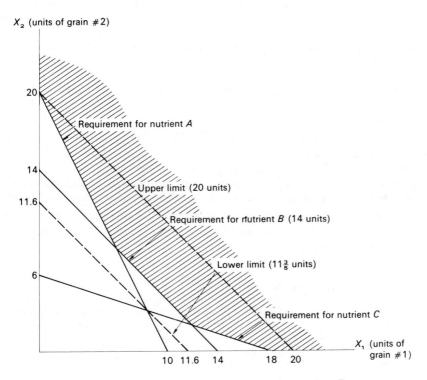

FIG. 11-8 Right-hand-side ranging for requirement for nutrient B

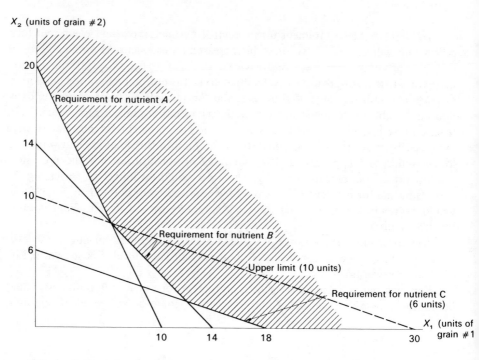

FIG. 11–9 Right-hand-side ranging for requirement for nutrient C

total cost would decrease by $2. Reading the exchange rates from the S_2 column, we see that if the requirement for nutrient B were increased by one unit, the most efficient way of effecting the increase would be to eliminate one unit of grain #1 from the mix and add two units of grain #2. The amount of nutrient C in the mix would increase by 5/3 units. This same plan of substitution should be used for an increase of up to six units in the requirement for nutrient B.

Decreases in the requirement for B should be handled in just the opposite manner—by adding one unit of grain #1 and deleting two units of grain #2.

Requirements for nutrient C would be decreased indefinitely without altering the optimal strategy; but if they were increased by more than four units, another solution would become optimal.

TABLE 11–1 Right-hand-side ranging

Requirement	Current level	Lower limit	Upper limit	Outgoing variable Lower	Upper
Nutrient A	10	7	13	X_1	S_3
Nutrient B	14	11.6	20	S_3	X_1
Nutrient C	6	0	10	—	S_3

Complete right-hand-side ranging for all three nutritional requirements is outlined in Table 11–1. The ranges for nutrients B and C are shown graphically in Figs 11–8 and 11–9.

We can see, then, how the optimal solution would be altered by changes in the requirements for the three nutrients. Now let us determine what would happen if the costs associated with each of the two types of grain were increased or decreased.

OBJECTIVE-FUNCTION-COEFFICIENT RANGING

Table 11–2 shows the objective-function-coefficient ranging for the two grains. We read from this table that should the price of grain #1 fall anywhere between $6 and $12 (while the price of grain #2 remains at $6), the present solution—use six units of X_1 and eight units of X_2—would still be optimal. However, if the cost of grain #1 were to go below $6, grain #1 would be so economical relative to grain #2 when their individual contributions towards the restraints are considered that more units of grain #1 and fewer units of grain #2 should be used in the optimal feed mix. The optimal corner point would move from point H to point J in Fig. 11–10.

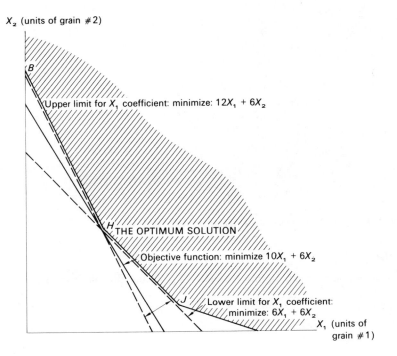

X_2 (units of grain #2)

B

Upper limit for X_1 coefficient: minimize: $12X_1 + 6X_2$

H THE OPTIMUM SOLUTION

Objective function: minimize $10X_1 + 6X_2$

J Lower limit for X_1 coefficient:
minimize: $6X_1 + 6X_2$

X_1 (units of grain #1)

FIG. 11–10 Objective-function-coefficient ranging for X_1

TABLE 11–2 Objective-function-coefficient ranging

Variable	Current value	Lower limit	Upper limit	Incoming variable Lower	Upper
X_1 (grain #1)	$10	$6	$12	S_1	S_2
X_2 (grain #2)	$6	$5	$10	S_2	S_1

If the cost of grain #1 were to go above $12, fewer units of grain #1 and more units of grain #2 should be used. The optimal corner point would shift from point H toward point B. (Refer again to Fig. 11–10.)

Figure 11–11 shows graphically what happens to the optimal solution point with increases or decreases in the cost of grain #2.

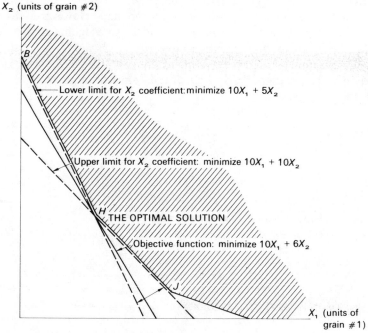

X_2 (units of grain #2)

B

Lower limit for X_2 coefficient: minimize $10X_1 + 5X_2$

Upper limit for X_2 coefficient: minimize $10X_1 + 10X_2$

H THE OPTIMAL SOLUTION

Objective function: minimize $10X_1 + 6X_2$

J

X_1 (units of grain #1)

FIG. 11–11 Objective-function-coefficient ranging for X_2

EXERCISES

1. Using the graphical method, find the values of X_1 and X_2 that minimize

$$6X_1 + 2X_2$$

subject to

$$X_1 + X_2 \geqslant 5$$
$$X_1 \leqslant 4$$
$$2X_1 + X_2 \geqslant 6.$$

2. Using the graphical method, find the nonnegative values of X_1 and X_2 that minimize

$$15 X_1 + 25 X_2,$$

subject to

$$5 X_1 + 2 X_2 \geqslant 20,$$
$$X_1 + X_2 \geqslant 5,$$
$$X_2 \leqslant 10.$$

3. Given the following model

Minimize: $4 X_1 + 3 X_2$ (cost in dollars),

where $X_1 =$ number of units of product 1 to produce,

$X_2 =$ number of units of product 2 to produce,

subject to

$$5 X_1 + X_2 \geqslant 1001 \quad (\text{requirement} \#1),$$
$$2 X_1 + 4 X_2 \geqslant 800 \quad (\text{requirement} \#2),$$

and the following *final* tableau:

	X_1	X_2	S_1	S_2	
X_1	1	0	-0.22	0.06	178
X_2	0	1	0.11	-0.28	111
	0	0	0.55	0.61	-1045

find the right-hand-side ranges and the objective-function-coefficient ranges. Explain the significance of these ranges.

4. The Pep Pill Company, producers of pep pills, sleeping pills, and tranquilizers, is considering marketing an inexpensive pill called Vita-Power which will supply the user with the daily minimum adult requirement of vitamins A and B. A bottle of 100 Vita-Power tablets requires a minimum of 10 units of vitamin A and 40 units of vitamin B.

After considerable research, the Pep Pill people found that a unit of calf-liver extract contains 1/4 units of vitamin A while a unit of soybean oil contains one unit of vitamin A. Conversely, a unit of calf-liver extract contains 2 units of vitamin B while a unit of soybean oil contains 1/2 unit of vitamin B.

The Pep Pill Company also notes that a unit of calf-liver extract costs $2.00 and a unit of soybean oil costs $3.00 a unit.

Given this information, the firm wishes to know what amounts of calf-liver extract and soybean oil to use per bottle of Vita-Power in order to minimize the cost of supplying the minimum requirements of vitamins A and B.

5. A company is considering the purchase of new automobiles for the next year and is interested in minimizing its cash outflows for that year. It will need ten vehicles which must be either Fords, Chevrolets, or Plymouths, in any combination. Research has indicated the following statistics:

Vehicle	Cost	Estimated maintenance hours per year	Estimated cost per maintenance hour	Other operating costs per year
Ford	$3150	30	$7.50	$225
Chevrolet	3175	28	7.50	375
Plymouth	3075	22	9.50	485

The company's maintenance capacity for the year is 250 hours and the total cash available for the initial purchase price of the cars is limited to $31,000.

The objective is to minimize cash outflows, which is the sum of the initial cost, the maintenance cost and the other operating costs.

6. The State Health Department blood chemistry laboratory receives several hundred blood specimens every month which must be analyzed on one or the other of two blood chemical autoanalyzer machines. The problem is to find a schedule which will allocate the autoanalyzers to the blood specimens in such a way as to minimize the costly hours of the laboratory machine time.

There are two different types of blood specimens (X_1 and X_2) and two types of machines: a single-channel autoanalyzer (A) and a dual-channel autoanalyzer (B). Each of the types of blood specimens can be run on either machine, but the analysis will be done at different speeds, as shown below:

Machine used	Machine hours required per specimen		Hours available each month
	Type of specimen		
	X_1	X_2	
Autoanalyzer A	10 hrs	3 hrs	1700 hrs
Autoanalyzer B	5 hrs	2 hrs	400 hrs
Required monthly specimen volume	120 specimens	380 specimens	

Because of other work demands, the number of machine hours available on the autoanalyzers for the month is restricted to 1700 on the single-channel machine and 400 hours on the dual-channel machine. The objective is to minimize the total hours required to process the two types of specimens, assuring that at least 120 specimens of type X_1 and 380 specimens of type X_2 are processed.

7. A chemical company blends coal for the purpose of obtaining certain by-products. The company purchases the coal from two different sources. An analysis of the coal from one source indicates a yield of 1400 pounds of coke per ton of coal, 400 pounds of tar, and 120 pounds of other tar derivatives. This coal costs $15.00 per ton. The coal from the other source is priced at $10.00 per ton and this raw product's analysis runs 1000 pounds of coke, 100 pounds of coal tar, and 80 pounds of derivative products per ton of coal.

The chemical company wishes to blend this raw material in such a manner that a resulting blend will contain not less than 2000 pounds of coke, 300 pounds of coal tar, and 200 pounds of derivative product.

Set up a linear programming model that will help the company decide how much raw material should be purchased from each of the two sources. Range the constraints and the coefficients and interpret the results.

If the coal from the second source increased in price from $10 to $12 per ton, would you recommend a change in strategy? If so, what would you recommend?

8. The Acme Engineering Company has two copying machines in its office. The Dupli-Kat has been in use for some time. The Kopy-Kat has just recently been purchased. Prior to the purchase of the Kopy-Kat, Acme sent about half its copying work out for overnight copying service. Now, with the new machine, they believe that they can do all their own copying.

A problem has arisen in deciding how to allocate copying to the two machines. Current requirements call for at least 2500 copies each day. The new Kopy-Kat can turn out 1600 copies each day based on the normal eight-hour working day. Under normal operating levels the cost of electricity and copying fluid for the Kopy-Kat runs at 10¢ a copy. However, a special paper is used in the Kopy-Kat and this paper costs 2¢ more per copy than the paper used in the other machine.

The Dupli-Kat is capable of two printing speeds. Under normal conditions it can copy 100 pages an hour for a cost of 2¢ a copy. At its high-speed setting, the Dupli-Kat can copy 150 pages per hour at a cost of 5¢ per copy. The print quality of the Dupli-Kat is not as good as that of the Kopy-Kat, but for most of the work which Acme has, the quality is sufficient. Acme does require that 400 copies be run on the Kopy-Kat each day because of the higher print quality.

How should Acme Engineering utilize the two copiers in order to minimize the cost of copying each day?

9. The Low-Bid Construction Company is preparing a bid on the construction of a jet airport runway. They want to determine the minimum cost of placement of fill in order to meet the minimum design California Bearing Ratio (CBR). The design has been converted to a minimum number of cubic yards of material meeting the CBR requirement.

Four supplies of material have been located to meet the requirements. Specifications concerning these materials are as follows:

Material	Cubic yards available (in 1000's)	Cost of Placement (per 1000 cu. yds)	Haul– miles required	Compaction hours required (per 1000 cu. yds)
CBR 60	35	$2.80	3	200
CBR 50	25	3.00	2	100
CBR 40	35	3.20	1	133
CBR 8	60	2.00	3	33

The minimum design specifications call for not less than 25,000 cubic yards of CBR 60, 32,000 cubic yards of CBR 40, and 56,000 cubic yards of CBR 8.

Because of imposed time constraints, earth-moving equipment and compaction equipment are of limited availability. Vehicles which can accommodate 300,000 cubic-yard-miles will be available. Compaction equipment will be available for 11,000 compaction hours of work.

The company would like to know the optimum mix of fill materials. Build a linear programming model that will help to determine this mix. Interpret, carefully, all of the information available from the model.

10. Trans-Atlantic pilot Al Airways is performing his preflight planning for a run from New York to Paris. Meteorology has advised him of the expected weather en route. Al knows that his enroute speeds and altitudes depend of several factors, including air temperature, wind, air-traffic control and international control procedures plus time and fuel considerations. Control procedures restrict him to odd thousand altitudes east-bound and he may not exceed 28,000 feet until reaching the Air Defense Identification Zone (ADIZ) 380 miles out. Given the temperature and winds aloft, Al has computed his aircraft's maximum continuous and normal cruising speeds for the available altitudes below his ship's service ceiling and for which there are favorable winds.

	25,000 *feet*		31,000 *feet*	
	Speed	*Fuel consumption*	*Speed*	*Fuel consumption*
Maximum continuous	460 kts	2000 lbs/hr	440 kts	1750 lbs/hr
Normal cruise	430 kts	1600 lbs/hr	420 kts	1440 lbs/hr

Standard operating procedure at Trans-Atlantic permits engine cruise operations at either max continuous or normal cruise. The pilot may select a speed between these but only in unusual circumstances. Normally max continuous is flown only as necessary to make the scheduled time, and normal cruise is flown for the remainder of time. The purpose of this is to minimize wear and fuel consumption. For planning purposes, then, Al feels he should treat the speeds as discrete and make any adjustments necessary enroute. He also knows that for proper reception of navigation aid, he should be above 28,000 feet for the middle third of the 3000-mile $6\frac{3}{4}$-hour scheduled run.

What should Al's mix of speeds and altitudes be for minimum fuel consumption? Use a linear programming model to learn as much about the flight strategy as possible.

Chapter 12

THE
BLENDING PROBLEMS

In this chapter we shall discuss an additional type of problem situation where linear programming models are extensively used. This is the *blending* problem.

THE BLENDING PROBLEMS

One general class of problem situations where linear programming has been extensively utilized might be called the "blending" problems. These situations are characterized by the need to find the optimal blend of available ingredients which will meet prescribed standards in respect to the properties of the finished products. In the blending of petroleum, for example, there is a need to find a blend of basic ingredients which will have certain properties with respect to factors such as octane, viscosity, additives, and so forth. The same type of purpose is a part of the process of blending crude oil, molten metals, and certain chemicals. A manufacturer of some types of food products may seek a blend of basic ingredients to achieve a prescribed result in terms of protein, carbohydrates, minerals, fats, vitamins, and so forth.

Often the objective in these blending processes is to meet the set of standards at a minimum cost, although this is not always the case.

A SAMPLE PROBLEM

Let us discuss a simplified version of a typical blending problem. Chocolate-Covered-Candy Company markets a Deluxe Mix that sells for $1.00 a pound and a Party Mix selling for $0.90 a pound. These mixes consist of chocolate-covered peanuts, chocolate-covered raisins, and chocolate-covered caramel balls. While the composition of the two mixes may vary to some extent, there are standards which each pound of each of the mixes must meet. The specifications governing the two types of mix are:

Ingredient	Deluxe Mix	Party Mix
Chocolate-covered peanuts	Not less than 40%	(no restriction)
Chocolate-covered raisins	Not more than 50%	Not less than 30%
Chocolate-covered caramel balls	(no restriction)	Not more than the proportion of raisins

Each day C–C–C Company can obtain for use 80 pounds of chocolate-covered peanuts which cost them $0.50 per pound, 120 pounds of chocolate-covered raisins costing $0.40 per pound, and 100 pounds of chocolate-covered caramels costing $0.30 per pound. C–C–C Company believes that it can sell all of either of the mixes it can produce and would like to use the available candies in such a way as to realize the greatest profit contribution possible.

THE VARIABLES

We quickly recognize, then, that the problem facing C–C–C Company is one of allocating scarce resources in such a way as to maximize an objective. And we would probably begin confidently by defining the activity variables as:

X_1 = number of pounds of Deluxe Mix to prepare each day,

X_2 = number of pounds of Party Mix to prepare each day.

But stop and think for a moment. We have discussed properties which the activity variables in a linear programming model must possess. We have said that *these variables must be controllable within a range*. Well, the variables we have just defined do meet this criterion; they are controllable within a range. But this is not, in itself, enough. The other prerequisite was that *the variables must provide a plan for action*. If the model tells C–C–C to make X_1 pounds of Deluxe Mix and X_2 pounds of Party Mix each day, would they know what to do? The answer is "No!" Because, although they would know the total number of pounds of Deluxe Mix to prepare, they wouldn't know exactly what to put into each pound of the mix. Should the pound of Deluxe consist of 1/2 pound of chocolate-covered peanuts and 1/2 pound of chocolate-covered raisins; or should it be composed of 0.4 pounds of peanuts, 0.3 pounds of raisins, and 0.3 pounds of caramels; or . . . We could think of countless other combinations which would meet the specifications outlined for the mix. And the same dilemma would prevail concerning the proportion of each of the ingredients to include in the Party Mix.

C–C–C Company needs a model that will tell it *how to blend* each pound of the two candy mixes. Let us, then, consider these variables:

X_1 = pounds of chocolate-covered peanuts to include in Deluxe Mix,

X_2 = pounds of chocolate-covered raisins to include in Deluxe Mix,

X_3 = pounds of chocolate-covered caramel balls to include in Deluxe Mix,

X_4 = pounds of chocolate-covered peanuts to include in Party Mix,

X_5 = pounds of chocolate-covered raisins to include in Party Mix,

X_6 = pounds of chocolate-covered caramel balls to include in Party Mix.

If the model furnishes numerical values for each of these variables, would C–C–C Company have sufficient information to proceed? With this information, C–C–C would not only know how many pounds of Deluxe and Party Mix to prepare but also the proportions of each of the ingredients to be included in each mix.

It is this feature of the blending models—the definition of the activity variables—that often presents a real challenge. This is the key to the successful use of the linear programming model in this type of decision situation.

THE BLENDING CONSTRAINTS

Now let us turn our attention to the restraints on the mixes. The total amount of Deluxe Mix prepared each day is

$$X_1 + X_2 + X_3.$$

One requirement that must be met is that the chocolate-covered peanuts in Deluxe Mix must not be less than 40% of the total Deluxe Mix. (Observe that the requirement is stated, not as an absolute quantity, but as a *proportion*. While this presents no stumbling block when formulating the constraint equations, it does introduce a certain flavor of intrigue into the interpretation of the solution.) We can express this requirement as

$$X_1 \geqslant 0.4(X_1 + X_2 + X_3).$$

Also, product specifications dictate that the chocolate-covered raisins in the Deluxe Mix must not be more than 50% of the total Deluxe Mix; that is,

$$X_2 \leqslant 0.5(X_1 + X_2 + X_3).$$

The total amount of Party Mix prepared each day is

$$X_4 + X_5 + X_6.$$

The chocolate-covered raisins in Party Mix must not be less than 30% of the total mix, or

$$X_5 \geqslant 0.3(X_4 + X_5 + X_6).$$

The amount of chocolate-covered caramel balls in the Party Mix must not be more than the amount of chocolate covered raisins in the mix; that is

$$X_6 \leqslant X_5.$$

There are also three constraints imposed by the quantities of the ingredients that are available for use each day. Each day 80 pounds of peanuts are available. X_1 represents the number of pounds of peanuts used in Deluxe Mix and X_4 represents the number of pounds of peanuts used in Party Mix; then,

$$X_1 + X_4 \leqslant 80.$$

There are available for use each day 120 pounds of raisins and 100 pounds of caramel balls. Hence, these two constraints are required for the model:

$$X_2 + X_5 \leqslant 120,$$
$$X_3 + X_6 \leqslant 100.$$

A few manipulations must be performed on certain of these constraints to transform them into a format suitable for the simplex tableau. Let us begin with this constraint:

$$X_1 \geqslant 0.4(X_1 + X_2 + X_3).$$

We can remove the parentheses in the usual manner; that is,

$$X_1 \geqslant 0.4X_1 + 0.4X_2 + 0.4X_3.$$

Next, we can move terms from one side of an inequality symbol to the other side by changing the algebraic sign of the term, just as we can move terms across an equality symbol. So we can rewrite the above expression as

$$0.6X_1 - 0.4X_2 - 0.4X_3 \geqslant 0.$$

Notice that this is a greater-than inequality. Therefore, let us multiply through by -1 and change the direction of the inequality. We obtain the expression

$$-0.6X_1 + 0.4X_2 + 0.4X_3 \leqslant 0.$$

And by inventing a variable S_1—this will be a surplus variable—we can finally write

$$-0.6X_1 + 0.4X_2 + 0.4X_3 + S_1 = 0.$$

The reader should verify that the other constraints can be rewritten as shown below:

The inequality	*The equation*
$X_2 \leqslant 0.5(X_1 + X_2 + X_3)$	$-0.5X_1 + 0.5X_2 - 0.5X_3 + S_2 = 0$
$X_5 \geqslant 0.3(X_4 + X_5 + X_6)$	$0.3X_4 - 0.7X_5 + 0.3X_6 + S_3 = 0$
$X_6 \leqslant X_5$	$-X_5 + X_6 + S_4 = 0$
$X_1 + X_4 \leqslant 80$	$X_1 + X_4 + S_5 = 80$
$X_2 + X_5 \leqslant 120$	$X_2 + X_5 + S_6 = 120$
$X_3 + X_6 \leqslant 100$	$X_3 + X_6 + S_7 = 100$

THE OBJECTIVE FUNCTION

C–C–C would like to use the available ingredients in such a way as to maximize the profit contribution of the mixes, where profit contribution is deemed to be the sales revenue minus the cost of the ingredients of the mixes.

Each pound of Deluxe Mix sells for $1.00 so that the revenue from the sales of Deluxe Mix is

$$\$1(X_1 + X_2 + X_3).$$

Each pound of Party Mix sells for $0.90 so that the revenue from sales of Party Mix is

$$\$0.90(X_4 + X_5 + X_6).$$

Total sales revenue would be

$$X_1 + X_2 + X_3 + 0.90X_4 + 0.90X_5 + 0.90X_6.$$

The company pays $0.50 a pound for each pound of chocolate-covered peanuts used. This ingredient would, then, cost

$$\$0.50(X_1 + X_4).$$

The chocolate-covered raisins cost $0.40 a pound and the chocolate-covered caramels cost $0.30 a pound. The cost of these ingredients is

$$\$0.40(X_2 + X_5)$$

and

$$\$0.30(X_3 + X_6).$$

Total cost for all ingredients used would be

$$0.5X_1 + 0.4X_2 + 0.3X_3 + 0.5X_4 + 0.4X_5 + 0.3X_6.$$

Sales revenue minus cost of ingredients would be

$$0.5X_1 + 0.6X_2 + 0.7X_3 + 0.4X_4 + 0.5X_5 + 0.6X_6.$$

This is the function that C–C–C Company wishes to maximize.

THE TABLEAUS AND THE OPTIMAL SOLUTION

The initial tableau and the final tableau are shown in Fig. 12–1.

We are able to read from the final tableau these values for the variables:

$X_1 = 80$, pounds of chocolate-covered peanuts in Delux Mix,

$X_2 = 20$, pounds of chocolate-covered raisins in Deluxe Mix,

$X_3 = 100$, pounds of chocolate-covered caramel balls in Deluxe Mix.

The Initial Tableau:

	X_1	X_2	X_3	X_4	X_5	X_6	S_1	S_2	S_3	S_4	S_5	S_6	S_7	
S_1	−0.6	0.4	0.4	0	0	0	1	0	0	0	0	0	0	0
S_2	−0.5	0.5	−0.5	0	0	0	0	1	0	0	0	0	0	0
S_3	0	0	0	0.3	−0.7	0.3	0	0	1	0	0	0	0	0
S_4	0	0	0	0	−1	1	0	0	0	1	0	0	0	0
S_5	1	0	0	1	0	0	0	0	0	0	1	0	0	80
S_6	0	1	0	0	1	0	0	0	0	0	0	1	0	120
S_7	0	0	1	0	0	1	0	0	0	0	0	0	1	100
	−0.5	−0.6	−0.7	−0.4	−0.5	−0.6	0	0	0	0	0	0	0	0

The Final Tableau:

	X_1	X_2	X_3	X_4	X_5	X_6	S_1	S_2	S_3	S_4	S_5	S_6	S_7	
X_2	0	1	0	3/2	0	−1	5/2	0	0	0	3/2	0	−1	20
S_2	0	0	0	−1/4	0	1	−5/4	1	0	0	−1/4	0	1	80
S_3	0	0	0	−3/4	0	1	−7/4	0	1	0	−21/20	7/10	7/10	70
S_4	0	0	0	−3/2	0	2	−5/2	0	0	1	−3/2	1	1	100
X_1	1	0	0	1	0	0	0	0	0	0	1	0	0	80
X_5	0	0	0	−3/2	1	1	−5/2	0	0	0	−3/2	1	1	100
X_3	0	0	1	0	0	1	0	0	0	0	0	0	1	100
	0	0	0	1/4	0	0	1/4	0	0	0	13/20	1/2	3/5	172

FIG. 12–1   The tableaus

Therefore, 200 pounds of Deluxe Mix should be prepared each day.

$X_4 = 0$, pounds of chocolate-covered peanuts in Party Mix,
$X_5 = 100$, pounds of chocolate-covered raisins in Party Mix,
$X_6 = 0$, pounds of chocolate-covered caramel balls in Party Mix.

Therefore, 100 pounds of Party Mix should be prepared each day.

We can check to ascertain that none of the mix specifications were violated. We see that

$(X_1 = 80) \geqslant 0.4(200)$ or $80 \geqslant 80$; therefore, $S_1 = 0.$
$(X_2 = 20) \leqslant 0.5(300)$ or $20 \leqslant 100$; therefore, $S_2 = 80.$
$(X_5 = 100) \geqslant 0.3(100)$ or $100 \geqslant 30$; therefore, $S_3 = 70.$
$(X_6 = 0) \leqslant (X_5 = 100)$ or $0 \leqslant 100$; therefore, $S_4 = 100.$
$[(X_1 = 80) + (X_4 = 0)] \leqslant 80$ or $80 \leqslant 80$; therefore, $S_5 = 0.$
$[(X_2 = 20) + (X_5 = 100)] \leqslant 120$ or $120 \leqslant 120$; therefore, $S_6 = 0.$
$[(X_3 = 100) + (X_6 = 0)] \leqslant 100$ or $100 \leqslant 100$; therefore, $S_7 = 0.$

All of the available resources are used. They are purchased at a total cost of

$80(\$0.50) + 120(\$0.40) + 100(\$0.30) \doteq \$118.$

Two hundred pounds of Deluxe Mix are prepared, each pound composed of 40% peanuts, 10% raisins, and 50% caramels. One hundred pounds of Party Mix are prepared, each pound consisting solely of raisins. The candy sells for a total of

$200(\$1) + 100(\$0.90) = \$290.$

The profit contribution totals, then,

$\$290 - \$118 = \$172.$

RIGHT-HAND-SIDE
RANGING FOR THE RESOURCES

The final tableau is the source of an abundance of additional information. We read from the S_5, S_6, and S_7 columns that an extra pound of peanuts could be used to increase profit by $13/20, an extra pound of raisins could be used to increase profit by $1/2, and an extra pound of caramels by $3/5.

Let us take a closer look at these columns. The S_5 column tells us that one additional pound of chocolate-covered peanuts could be used to increase profit contribution by $13/20 if these changes were made in the blending strategy:

Deluxe Mix	*Party Mix*
increase by 1 lb peanuts	—
increase by 1.5 lb raisins	decrease by 1.5 lb raisins

The basic variables would assume these values when these changes are effected:

$X_1 = 80 + 1 = 81$ $S_2 = 80 - 1/4 = 78\frac{3}{4}$

$X_2 = 20 + 3/2 = 21.5$ $S_3 = 70 - 21/20 = 68\frac{19}{20}$

$X_3 = 100$ $S_4 = 100 - 3/2 = 98.5$

$X_5 = 100 - 3/2 = 98.5.$

The total quantity of Deluxe Mix produced would become

$81 + 21.5 + 100 = 202.5$ pounds

and would yield a gross revenue of $202.50.

The total quantity of Party mix produced would become 98.5 pounds and would yield a gross revenue of $88.65. Total revenue for both mixes would be

$202.50 + $88.65 = $291.15.

Direct ingredient cost (which would increase by $0.50, the cost of the additional pound of chocolate-covered peanuts) would be $118.50. Profit contribution would now be

$291.15 - $118.50 = $172.65

which is $0.65 greater than it was with the previous solution. (This $0.65 is the shadow price of peanuts.)

We should ascertain that, with these changes in the blends, the product specifications have not been breached. First, we see that

$81 \geqslant 0.4(81 + 21.5 + 100)$

$81 \geqslant 81.$

Then,

$21.5 \leqslant 0.5(81 + 21.5 + 100)$

$21.5 \leqslant 101.25.$

The variable representing the amount by which the raisins-in-Deluxe specification is exceeded takes on the value

$S_2 = 79.75.$

Lastly, the constraint

$X_6 \leqslant X_5$

$0 \leqslant 98.5$

remains inviolate; and $S_4 = 98.5.$

A unit decrease in the quantity of chocolate-covered peanuts available for use should have a directly converse effect. These exchange strategies would be appropriate for as much as a $66\frac{2}{3}$ pound increase of a $13\frac{1}{3}$ pound decrease in the supply of chocolate-covered peanuts.

If an additional pound of chocolate-covered raisins could be obtained by C–C–C Company, the company should use the pound in this way:

Deluxe Mix	*Party Mix*
no change	increase by 1 lb raisins

This change in blends would increase profit contribution by $0.50, the contribution of a pound of raisins in Party Mix.

Only one activity variable would change in this case:

$$X_5 = 100 + 1 = 101.$$

The blend requirement that

$$X_5 \geqslant 0.3(X_4 + X_5 + X_6)$$
$$101 \geqslant 30.3$$

is still met satisfactorily, as is the requirement

$$X_6 \leqslant X_5$$
$$0 \leqslant 101.$$

A one-pound decrease in the quantity of raisins available for use would simply decrease by that one pound the quantity of Party Mix produced, and decrease the value of the objective function accordingly. These changes in blend would be appropriate for an indefinite increase in the quantity of raisins available for use and for as much as a 100-pound decrease in the quantity of raisins available.

The S_7 column tells us that an extra pound of caramels should be used in this way:

Deluxe Mix	*Party Mix*
increase by 1 lb caramel	—
decrease by 1 lb raisins	increase by 1 lb raisins

That is, the extra pound of caramel would go into the Deluxe Mix. Then, so that the specifications

$$X_1 \geqslant 0.4(X_1 + X_2 + X_3)$$

and

$$X_2 \leqslant 0.5(X_1 + X_2 + X_3)$$

are not violated, one pound of raisins is transferred from the Deluxe to the Party Mix. Notice that the activity variables now assume these values:

$$X_1 = 80 \qquad\qquad X_4 = 0$$
$$X_2 = 20 - 1 = 19 \qquad X_5 = 100 + 1$$
$$X_3 = 100 + 1 = 101 \qquad X_6 = 0.$$

Total Deluxe Mix prepared is still 200 pounds and the restrictions on composition of the mix are still inviolate; that is

$$(X_1 = 80) \geqslant 0.4(200) \qquad \text{or} \qquad 80 \geqslant 80;$$

therefore, $S_1 = 0$, and

$$X_3 = 19) \leqslant 0.5(200) \qquad \text{or} \qquad 19 \leqslant 100;$$

therefore, $S_2 = 80 + 1 = 81$.

The total Party Mix is 101 pounds and standards for this mix still are met; that is,

$$(X_5 = 101) \geqslant 0.3(101) \qquad \text{or} \qquad 101 \geqslant 30.3;$$

therefore, $S_3 = 70 + 0.7 = 70.7$ and

$$(X_6 = 0) \leqslant (X_5 = 101) \qquad \text{or} \qquad 0 \leqslant 101;$$

therefore, $S_4 = 100 + 1 = 101$.

The extra pound of caramels would, if used in this way, increase total profit contribution by $0.60.

The S_7 effects vector outlines the most efficient exchange rates for an increase of as much as 20 pounds of caramel, or a decrease of as much as 80 pounds of caramel.

Right-hand-side ranging for the three resources is shown in Table 12–1.

TABLE 12–1   Right-hand-side ranging for the resources

Resource	Current value	Lower limit	Upper limit	Outgoing variable Lower	Upper
Chocolate-covered peanuts	80 lbs	$66\frac{2}{3}$	$146\frac{2}{3}$	X_2	S_3, S_4, X_5
Chocolate-covered raisins	120 lbs	20	∞	S_3, S_4, X_5	—
Chocolate-covered caramel balls	100 lbs	20	120	S_2	X_2

RANGING A PROPORTION CONSTRAINT

Notice from the final tableau that the surplus variable S_1 (representing excess over the minimum requirement for peanuts in Deluxe Mix) has a shadow price of \$1/4. Lets see what this means.

The requirement for which S_1 is the surplus variable is stated

$$X_1 \geqslant 0.4(X_1 + X_2 + X_3)$$

In the optimal solution, we have

$$80 \geqslant 0.4(80 + 20 + 100)$$
$$80 \geqslant 80$$

so that there is no excess of peanuts in Deluxe Mix over the minimum requirement. When setting up the tableau, we reworded the inequality in this manner:

$$X_1 + 0.4(X_1 + X_2 + X_3) + S_1 = 0.$$

We can substitute the solution values for the activity variables and solve to obtain

$$-80 + 0.4(80 + 20 + 100) + S_1 = 0$$
$$S_1 = 0.$$

(S_1 has a solution value of zero.)

Now if we could relax the requirement by one unit, X_1 (pounds of peanuts in Deluxe Mix) could be one unit less than

$$0.4(X_1 + X_2 + X_3) \quad \text{or} \quad [0.4(X_1 + X_2 + X_3)] - 1.$$

This requirement is stated, not as an absolute number of pounds, but as a *proportion* of the total mix. When we think of adjusting the requirement, we must think of what the requirement in absolute numbers would be according to the proportion constraint, and then adjust this number. To decrease this requirement by one unit, we consider the quantity $[0.4(X_1 + X_2 + X_3)]$ and decrease it by one unit.

The S_1 change vector tells us that we should make these alterations in our strategy if we are able to relax the requirement for peanuts in Deluxe Mix by one unit:

$$X_1 = 80 + 0 = 80,$$
$$X_2 = 20 + 5/2 = 22.5,$$
$$X_3 = 100 + 0 = 100,$$
$$X_5 = 100 - 5/2 = 97.5.$$

We can check from the original equation by computing:

$$-80 + 0.4(80 + 22.5 + 100) + S_1 = 0$$
$$S_1 = -1.$$

Or

$$X_1 \geqslant [0.4(X_1 + X_2 + X_3)] - 1,$$

$$80 \geqslant 0.4(80 + 22.5 + 100) - 1,$$

$$80 \geqslant 80.$$

We are now allowed to make 202.5 pounds of Deluxe Mix which can be sold at $1 a pound and 97.5 pounds of Party Mix selling at $0.90 a pound, so that total revenue becomes

$$202.5(\$1) + 97.5(\$0.90) = \$290.25.$$

Cost does not change since in both situations all available ingredients are being used. Gross profit is

$$\$290.25 - \$118.00 = \$172.25$$

which is $1/4 = $0.25 greater than with the optimal solution outlined in the final tableau.

If the requirement for peanuts in Deluxe Mix were made more restrictive by one unit, we would have to meet the specification

$$X_1 \geqslant [0.4(X_1 + X_2 + X_3)] + 1.$$

For each unit by which the restriction is increased, C–C–C Company would lose $0.25 profit contribution. This particular restriction on the mixes is, then, currently costing C–C–C $0.25 per unit of restriction.

The proportion constraints demand careful interpretation since there are usually several ways in which changes in the restrictions can be effected. For example, in changing the requirement for peanuts in Deluxe Mix, we did not alter the amount of peanuts included in the mix. The adjustments were made through the quantity of raisins in Deluxe Mix and the quantity of raisins in Party Mix! And with a one-unit change in the specification for peanuts in Deluxe, the quantity was adjusted, not by one pound, but by 2.5 pounds!

If this particular requirement were increased by 8 units so that it read

$$X_1 \geqslant [0.4(X_1 + X_2 + X_3)] + 8$$

these changes would take place in the optimal strategy:

	Original solution vector		Effects vector S_1		Adjusted solution vector	
X_2	20		2.5		0	← Outgoing variable
S_2	80		−1.25		90	
S_3	70		−1.75		84	
S_4	100	−(8)	−2.5	=	120	
X_1	80		0		80	
X_5	100		−2.5		120	
X_3	100		0		100	
	172		0.25		170	

Or if the requirement were relaxed by 40 units so that it read

$$X_1 \geqslant [0.40(X_1 + X_2 + X_3)] - 40$$

these changes would be wrought in the strategy:

	Original solution vector		Effects vector S_1		Adjusted solution vector	
X_2	20		2.5		120	
S_2	80		−1.25		30	
S_3	70		−1.75		0	←
S_4	100	+(40)	−2.5	=	0	←
X_1	80		0		80	
X_5	100		−2.5		0	← Outgoing variables
X_3	100		0		100	
	172		0.25		162	

We can read from the S_2, S_3, and S_4 columns of the final tableau that the other restrictions upon the composition of the mixes have a zero shadow price; these product specifications are not currently preventing C–C–C Company from realizing the optimum revenue.

Complete right-hand-side ranging for the requirements is given in Table 12–2.

TABLE 12–2   Right-hand-side ranging for the requirements

	Current value	Lower limit	Upper limit	Outgoing variable Lower	Upper
Minimum requirements					
Peanuts in Deluxe	$X_1 \geqslant 0.4$ $(X_1 + X_2 + X_3)$	down 40 units	up 8 units	S_3, S_4, X_5	X_2
Raisins in Party	$X_5 \geqslant 0.3$ $(X_4 + X_5 + X_6)$	down to zero units	up 70 units	—	S_3
Maximum requirements					
Raisins in Deluxe	$X_2 \leqslant 0.5$ $(X_1 + X_2 + X_3)$	down 80 units	∞	S_2	—
Caramel in Party	$X_6 \leqslant X_5$	down 100 units	∞	S_4	—

OBJECTIVE-FUNCTION-COEFFICIENT RANGING

The objective-function-coefficient ranging in the blending problem is complicated by the fact that changes in one coefficient are likely to be accompanied by changes in the other coefficients. The coefficient for X_1 (peanuts in Deluxe Mix) could change because the price of the Deluxe Mix has changed, in which case the coefficients for X_2 (raisins in Deluxe Mix) and X_3 (caramels in Deluxe Mix) would also change; or the coefficient of X_1 (peanuts in Deluxe Mix) could change because the cost of peanuts changes, in which case the coefficient for X_4 (peanuts in Party Mix) would also be altered. The other coefficients are interrelated in much the same manner. Because the contribution coefficients of the variables are interrelated, let us consider some of the types of interactions that could take place.

The contribution of X_1 (peanuts in Deluxe) could increase by \$1 because the selling price of Deluxe Mix increased by \$1.00. If this happened, the contribution of X_2 (raisins in Deluxe) and X_3 (caramel in Deluxe) would each increase by \$1.00, as well. The effect on the objective-function row would be the sum of the X_1 row vector and the X_2 row vector and the X_3 row vector. That is, if the selling price of Deluxe Mix increased by \$1, the effect on the objective-function row would be:

	X_4	X_6	S_1	S_5	S_6	S_7	
Effect of							
change in X_1:	(1	0	0	1	0	0	80)
plus			+				
Effect of							
change in X_2:	(3/2	−1	5/2	3/2	0	−1	20)
plus			+				
Effect of							
change in X_3:	(0	1	0	0	0	1	100)
equals							
combined effect:	(5/2	0	5/2	5/2	0	0	200)

Compare this aggregate effect of a $1 increase in the selling price of Deluxe Mix to the objective-function row

Objective-							
function row:	(1/4	0	1/4	13/20	1/2	3/5	172)

and note that the selling price of Deluxe Mix could go up indefinitely without altering the product blends. However, since the aggregate effect of a $1 decrease in the selling price of a pound of Deluxe Mix would be

$$(-5/2 \quad 0 \quad -5/2 \quad -5/2 \quad 0 \quad 0 \quad -200)$$

a decrease in the selling price of only $0.10 would call for a new solution strategy. A decrease of more than $0.10 would result in a negative value in the objective-function row in both the X_4 and S_1 columns. S_1 or X_4 would be the variable coming into solution; X_2 would go out of solution.

An increase in the selling price of Party Mix would cause an increase in the contribution coefficients for X_4, X_5, and X_6. The aggregate effect of a $1 increase in the selling price of Party Mix would be:

	X_4	X_6	S_1	S_5	S_6	S_7	
Effect of							
change in X_4:	(−1	0	0	0	0	0	0)
plus			+				
Effect of							
change in X_5:	(−3/2	1	−5/2	−3/2	1	1	100)
plus			+				
Effect of							
change in X_6:	(0	−1	0	0	0	0	0)
equals							
Combined							
effect	(−5/2	0	−5/2	−3/2	1	1	100)

Thus, if the price of Party Mix increased by more than $0.10, S_1 or X_4 would come into solution and X_2 would go out of solution. If the selling price of Party Mix decreased by more than $0.50, S_6 would come into solution.

Changes could take place, not just because the selling prices of the mixes are changed, but also because the cost of the ingredients are changed. Suppose that the cost of chocolate-covered peanuts decreased by $1 so that the contribution of X_1 (peanuts in Deluxe Mix) and of X_4 (peanuts in Party Mix) both increase by $1. The net effect of this change would be:

	X_4	X_6	S_1	S_5	S_6	S_7	
Effect of							
change in X_1:	(1	0	0	1	0	0	80)
plus			+				
Effect of							
change in X_4:	(−1	0	0	0	0	0	0)
equals							
Combined							
effect:	(0	0	0	1	0	0	80)

The cost of peanuts could decrease, and thus the contribution increase, indefinitely without bringing about a new strategy. But the cost of peanuts could increase, thereby decreasing the contribution of X_1 and X_4, by only $0.65 before a new strategy would be called for. S_5 would be the variable coming into solution.

If the cost of chocolate-covered raisins decreased by $1, the contribution of X_2 (raisins in Deluxe) and X_5 (raisins in Party) would each increase by $1. The combined effect would be

	X_4	X_6	S_1	S_5	S_6	S_7	
Effect of							
change in X_2:	(3/2	−1	5/2	3/2	0	−1	20)
plus			+				
Effect of							
change in X_5:	(−3/2	1	−5/2	−3/2	1	1	100)
equals							
Combined							
effect:	(0	0	0	0	1	0	120)

We see that the cost could decrease indefinitely. But if the cost of the raisins increased, the contributions of X_2 and X_5 would decrease. The effect of a $1 increase in the cost of raisins would be

$$(0 \quad 0 \quad 0 \quad 0 \quad -1 \quad 0 \quad -120)$$

Referring again to the objective-function row in the final tableau, we see that an increase in the cost of more than 1/2 unit (or \$0.50) would cause a change in blends with S_6 coming into solution.

Changes in the cost of chocolate-covered caramels would result in changes in the contribution coefficients of both X_3 and X_6. By combining the individual effects vectors, we see that the cost of this ingredient could range from minus infinity (or zero as a practical lower limit) to \$0.90 a pound without altering the optimal solution mix.

The effects of changes in the selling prices of the mixes or in the costs of the ingredients are outlined in Table 12–3.

TABLE 12–3 *Ranging for the selling price of the mixes and the cost of the ingredients*

	Current value	Lower limit	Upper limit	Incoming variable Lower	Upper
Selling price of					
Deluxe Mix	\$1.00	\$0.90	∞	S_1, X_4	—
Party Mix	\$0.90	\$0.85	\$1.00	S_6	S_1, X_4
Cost of					
Chocolate-covered peanuts	\$0.50	0	\$1.15	—	S_5
Chocolate-covered raisins	\$0.40	0	\$0.90	—	S_6
Chocolate-covered caramels	\$0.30	0	\$0.90	—	S_7

EXERCISES

1. A pharmaceutical company makes, among other products, two types of vitamins, a therapeutic (Type A) and a pre-natal (Type B). USP standards require certain percentage content of the two critical ingredients, calcium and iron. The final absolute chemical content of each tablet is determined by its particular size, but the percentages of calcium and iron must be within limits. Specifically, Type A must contain not more than $\frac{1}{3}$ calcium nor less than $\frac{1}{3}$ iron. Type B must contain not less than 50% calcium nor more than 50% iron. Further, the calcium content of the therapeutic vitamins cannot contain less than 10% of the calcium in the pre-natals if the firm intends to use the technical description "therapeutic" in their labeling.

Neither calcium nor iron are available in daily amounts exceeding 100 kilograms.

If calcium carbonate costs \$13 per kilogram, iron costs \$8 per kilogram, Type A vitamins sell for \$18 per kilogram and Type B for \$20 per kilogram, what amounts of each chemical should enter the process for each vitamin type if profits are to be maximized?

Compute the objective-function-coefficient and the right-hand-side ranges and interpret these ranges.

2. An exotic food firm has been experimenting for many years to develop some new and unique types of salad dressing. In developing these new products they felt it essential to minimize the cost to the consumer since they realized the problem of overcoming people's established tastes would be difficult without some special inducement to try the products. Finally, success, they felt, was attained and the products were accepted with great enthusiasm.

One dressing, Golden Venus, consisted of at least 50% soybean oil, not over 30% banana oil, and the remainder was olive oil. The other salad oil, King Lear, contained similar ingredients except in different proportions. This product required at least 20% banana oil, not over 40% olive oil and the remainder soybean oil. Of course, selected spices were added to the basic ingredients in both products.

The purchasing department of the firm had obtained the following quantities of oil at the stated prices: 500 gallons of soybean oil at a cost of $0.30 a gallon, 300 gallons of banana oil at $0.40 a gallon, and 400 gallons of olive oil at $0.35 a gallon. These quantities of the ingredients could be purchased each week at these prices.

The selling prices of the salad oils would be $0.40 a gallon for the Golden Venus and $0.50 a gallon for the King Lear.

Given the weekly supply of basic ingredients, the firm would like to know how to blend the products in order to maximize its profits.

Use a linear programming model to aid the firm in this decision. Interpret carefully all of the information available from the model and make whatever suggestions you feel appropriate.

3. Galaxy Foods, Inc., manufactures two high-protein food supplements: Kids' Stuff and Adults Only. Both Kids' Stuff and Adults Only contain specified amounts of two basic resources: cod liver oil and wheat germ extract. As Kids' Stuff is intended only for children six to twelve, the requirements for these basic ingredients will vary somewhat from that of Adults Only. The required amounts are listed below:

Unit of Kids' Stuff: not more than 40% cod liver oil
                        not less than 50% wheat germ extract

Unit of Adults Only: not less than 30% cod liver oil
                        not more than 60% wheat germ extract

The revenue per unit of Kids' Stuff and Adults Only is $6.50 and $8.00, respectively. Direct costs other than the basic ingredients listed above are $1.00 for each unit of both products. The cost of a unit of cod liver oil is $3.50; wheat germ may be obtained for $2.75 a unit. Daily, 700 units of cod liver oil and 900 units of wheat germ extract are available.

Galaxy is in the enjoyable position of being able to sell all of whatever it produces. Hence, the firm desires to know what amounts of Kids' Stuff and Adults Only to sell and the corresponding proportion of resources to use in each product in order to maximize profit.

From the linear programming model used to determine the optimum product blend, compute the right-hand-side and the objective-function-coefficient ranges and explain their significance. If an extra unit of cod liver oil were to become available, how should it be used and what effect would it have on profits? If an extra unit of wheat germ extract were to become available, how should it be used and what effect would it have on profits?

4. The Davidson Dairy Farm would like to expand their operation and market butter-milk and/or whipping cream. They have done a market analysis and are confident that they can sell all of either or both products that they can make. They could sell buttermilk at $2.50 a gallon and whipping cream at $3.00 a gallon. Davidson's must meet certain standards in the composition of the milk products, however. These requirements are as follows:

Ingredient	Buttermilk	Whipping cream
Whole milk	not more than 60%	not more than 40%
Butter	not less than 30%	not less than 50%

The availability and cost of the ingredients are:

Ingredient	Gallons available each day	Cost per gallon
Whole milk	150	$1.00
Butter	100	$1.50

The problem is to determine how to blend the ingredients for the two products in order to maximize profits. Use a linear programming model to aid in this decision.

According to the model, what is the optimal number of gallons of buttermilk and whipping cream to produce each day? Of what ingredients would each be composed? What would be the profit for this strategy?

If one additional gallon of butter were available, how should it be used? What effect would this have on profit? Find the right-hand-side ranges for the resources and explain their significance.

Find the right-hand-side ranges for the blending specifications and interpret these carefully.

If the selling price of buttermilk were to increase by 5¢ a gallon, what changes should be made in the production plan? If the selling price of whipping cream were to decrease by $0.25 per gallon, what changes should be made in the production strategy?

If the cost of whole milk were to increase by $0.10 per gallon, what changes should be made in the production strategy?

If the cost of butter were to decrease by $0.30 per gallon, what changes should be made in the production strategy?

Find the objective-function-coefficient ranges and interpret them carefully.

5. Friendly Feed Mills blends chicken feed. Depending on what stage of growth the chickens are in, different proportions of ingredients are required in their feed. Friendly has just received an order from Empire Farms for a minimum of 7100 pounds of feed which must contain at least 30% Gro-Chick, 20% Fast-Feed, and no less than 40% Profit-Builder ingredients. Friendly has on hand 2500, 2000, and 3500 pounds of each ingredient, respectively. How should the order for the feed be filled in order to minimize costs if Gro Chick costs $0.40 a pound, Fast-Feed costs $0.30 a pound, and Profit-Builder costs $0.20 a pound?

If Friendly could quickly obtain an additional 500 pounds of Profit-Builder for $0.35 a pound, should it purchase the ingredient? If so, how should Friendly use the additional Profit-Builder? If Friendly could quickly obtain an additional 500 pounds of Gro-Chick for $0.50 a pound, should it purchase the ingredient? If so, how should the Gro-Chick be used?

Friendly is particularly interested in the cost imputed to each unit of each of the blending restrictions as well as in the variations possible in these restrictions without altering the optimal solution blend. Compute the ranges for the blending requirements and explain their significance.

How much variation can be tolerated in the costs of the basic ingredients before the optimal blend will be altered?

6. A consulting team is designing a training program for employees at a government agency. There are two types of employees involved, middle-management and supervisors. The instruction requirements for the program are as follows:

Type of instruction	Value points	Requirements for the program (in hours)	
		Middle-management	Supervisors
Class with PhD instructor	15	$\geqslant 180$	$\leqslant 80$
Class with assistant instructor	10	$\geqslant 160$	$\geqslant 160$
Laboratory	5	$\frac{1}{3}$ of total	$\frac{1}{3}$ of total

The program is of ten-weeks duration. There are available only 360 PhD instruction-hours and 600 Assistant instruction-hours.

What should be the mix of PhD instruction-hours, Assistant instruction-hours, and laboratory hours in order to satisfy the requirements of the program and give the maximum value points?

If PhD instruction-hours cost $250 each, Assistant instruction-hours cost $200 each, and laboratory hours cost $150 each, and if the agency wanted to plan a program that would meet the requirements at the least possible cost, what program should be planned?

7. The Blending Company produces two products, First and Second. The products are closely related such that the properties of Second are stated in terms of First's weight.

Three basic ingredients are used in the production of the products. The specifications which must be met are:

a) The #1 ingredient in First must be less than 20% of First's total weight.

b) The #2 ingredient in First must be greater than 10% of First's total weight.

c) The #3 ingredient in First must be less than 50% of #1 ingredient's weight in First.

d) The #1 ingredient in Second must be greater than 30% of First's total weight.

e) The #2 ingredient in Second must be greater than 30% of First's total weight.

f) The #3 ingredient in Second must be less than 20% of the total of the #1 and the #2 ingredients in First.

The monthly supply of ingredients #1, #2, and #3 are 2000 pounds, 3000 pounds, and 2500 pounds, respectively. The cost of each of these ingredients is $1.00 per pound. The selling price of First is $4.00 per pound and of Second is $5.00 per pound.

The company wishes to maximize profit for the coming month by determining the proper mix in total pounds for each ingredient in the two products. Use a linear programming model to aid in this decision.

The possibility of a change in the supply of ingredients makes it necessary to know the range within which the column vectors will remain valid as the best plan for incorporating any such changes.

The company is also considering the possibility of price changes and will, therefore, need the ranges for the objective-function coefficients.

The company would also like as much information as they can get from the model about the specifications that have been established for the products such as the cost per unit of specification, variations that would be allowed in the specifications without altering the optimal product mix, and so forth.

8. The Elite Fastener Company employs hard-core workers to package fasteners for retail distribution. The fasteners are received in bulk shipments and put in the hoppers of weighing machines which fill plastic bags. The bags are then sealed and labeled. Additional equipment has recently been purchased from a bankrupt war-toy company and a new production plan is needed.

A lumber supply chain has been buying a combination package of screws and nails with a mix of at least 30% screws and at least 20% nails. The lumber company has stated that they will buy up to 2500 pounds of fasteners each week at the current price of 55¢ per pound.

Two other customers have been found. A hardware chain has stated that they will buy a mixture of nuts, bolts, and screws. The quantity of nuts (by weight) must be equal to that of bolts and together these should be at least 40% of the package; screws must be at least 20% of the package. They will pay 60¢ per one-pound package for as many packages as Elite can supply.

A discount chain will pay 50¢ per one-pound package for a fastener package with nails making no more than 50% of the package, screws at least 20%, and nuts and bolts together at least 10%. They also will purchase as many packages as Elite can supply.

The total packaging capacity at Elite is 5000 pounds per week. The weighing machines with bolt guides can process 1500 pounds a week. The capacity for nuts is 500 pounds a week. Up to 2000 pounds of screws and 3000 pounds of nails can be weighed each week. The packaged cost of bolts is 60¢ a pound, of nuts is 40¢ a pound, of screws is 45¢ a pound, and of nails is 20¢ a pound.

Use a linear programming model to help the company find the optimal blend of items.

9. The Ragout Spaghetti Sauce Company makes and markets two kinds of spaghetti sauce—sauce with meat and sauce with mushrooms. The specifications that govern the two sauces are as follows:

Ingredient	Sauce with meat	Sauce with mushrooms
Ground beef	not less than 50%	no specifications
Tomato sauce	not more than 35%	not less than 50%
Mushrooms	no specifications	not more than 40%

These proportion restrictions are necessary because of the taste characteristics which must be achieved by the two sauces.

There are available each hour 1000 pounds of ground beef at a cost of $0.35 a pound. There are 1500 pounds of tomato sauce which can be handled each hour at $0.20 a pound, and 800 pounds of mushrooms available each hour at $0.50 a pound.

Ragout can sell all of either type of sauce it produces and would like to maximize its profits. The selling price of the meat sauce is $0.65 per pound and the mushroom sauce sells for $0.75 a pound.

Use a linear programming model to help Ragout determine the optimal product blend. Extract as much information from the model as you can.

10. The Milquetoast Mutual Fund is a conservative in common stock and is concerned with maximizing the returns obtained through the purchase of various classes (according to risk) of equity. Although other objectives were open for consideration (such as maximizing dividends only, maximizing capital gains, or minimizing capital losses), the overall rate of return on both dividends and capital gains was selected.

After careful analysis of the large number of possible selections, the investor has categorized these into three groups according to risk and long-term growth potential—a "risky" group, a "less risky" group, and a "conservative" group. By study of past performance and other financial data, it was determined that the rate of return on these three groups of securities averaged 13%, 11%, and 8%, with the most risky having the highest rate of return.

The bank, in order to protect the position of its depositors, has indicated that the cost of borrowing will vary depending on the risk of the securities. These rates will be 8% for the risky group, 6% for the less risky group, and 5% for the conservative group. In addition, the bank also requires that not more than one-half of the total amount invested can be placed in the most risky stock and at least 25% of the total amount be invested in the conservative stock.

As with most purchases of securities, the investor is using not only his own funds but also but also money obtained from a bank. Milquetoast has $100,000 to invest and the margin requirements are 50%. Thus, it can borrow $1 from the bank for each $1 of its own funds. Milquetoast's bank is willing to lend this maximum amount.

If the objective is to maximize return, what should the investment plan be?

11. Bio-reagent Company sells biological reagents to area high schools for their biology classes. (A reagent is something added to a complex solution to determine, by the chemical action if any results, the presence or absence of a certain substance.)

The reagent that the company sells to the schools (hereafter referred to as School reagent) is one that is used in a standard experiment in all the biology laboratory demonstrations. The School reagent must have at least 30% of Kelly's media (K), at least 40% of treated horse serum (H), and no less than 30% but no more than 40% of monkey kidney cells (M) in solution.

Management of Bio-reagent has carefully estimated that in order to fill orders for the schools during the coming nine-month school term, they will need at least 500 ounces of School reagent. The company also receives some orders for this reagent from sources other than schools. Still they feel that they can afford to stock no more than a total of 750 ounces of the School reagent to take care of any orders they may receive, from whatever source. The School reagent has only a ten-month shelf-life and all that is not sold during that period will spoil and have to be discarded.

Bio-reagent Company buys its products from small local producers. Three local laboratories (X, Y, and Z) each produce a reagent with the three required ingredients. However, the ingredient proportions vary. These producers use automated methods and the cost is, therefore, quite low. If Bio-reagent Company ordered the School reagent made to its required specifications the cost would be prohibitive. The reagent from producer X costs \$1.00 per ounce and has 20% K, 60% H, and 20% M. The reagent from producer Y costs \$1.20 per ounce and has 40% K, 30% H, and 30%M. The reagent from producer Z costs \$1.50 per ounce and has 10% K, 40% H, and 50%M.

The reagents from the various producers can be combined linearly at the Bio-reagent Company laboratory in order to form the School reagent.

From which producers and in what quantities should Bio-reagent purchase the reagents in order to minimize their cost?

Chapter 13

SOME TECHNICAL VICISSITUDES OF THE MODEL

All the illustrative linear programming models we have examined thus far have behaved very nicely. They have not deviated from the routine pattern of technical operation. Irregularities can and do arise, however, in the application of linear programming to real-world situations. Moreover, we may make errors in the definition of the problem which could lead us astray. We must be able to recognize these anomalies when they occur and to deal with them effectively. In

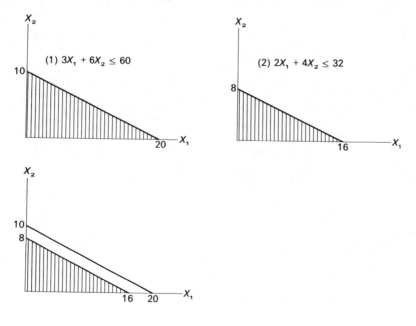

FIG. 13–1 A redundant constraint of the "less-than" type

this chapter we will explore some of the types of operational difficulties we may encounter in working with linear programming.

REDUNDANT CONSTRAINTS

In setting up a linear programming model, we may define a constraint in such a way that it lies entirely within a region that has been made infeasible because of other constraints on the problem situation. Consider this system of constraints, for example:

1. $3X_1 + 6X_2 \leqslant 60$,
2. $2X_1 + 4X_2 \leqslant 32$.

All nonnegative values that satisfy the second constraint satisfy the first as well. The reverse, however, is not true. See Fig. 13–1. The second constraint is clearly the more restrictive of the two. The first constraint is really ineffective because it is dominated by the second. The first constraint is said to be *redundant*.

A similar situation exists for these two constraints:

3. $3X_1 + 6X_2 \geqslant 60$,
4. $2X_1 + 4X_2 \geqslant 32$.

Here inequality (4) is redundant. Inequality (3) is the more restrictive of the two and the other is, indeed, of no consequence to the model. See Fig. 13–2.

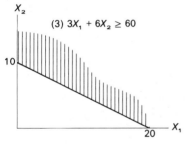

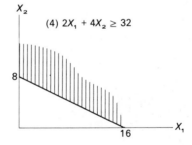

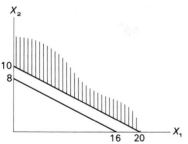

FIG. 13–2 A redundant constraint of the "greater-than" type

A redundant constraint plays no role in defining the area of feasible solutions; it cannot in any way affect the optimal solution. Therefore, these superfluous constraints may be omitted altogether from the model. Their effect, if they are not eliminated from the model, will simply be to compound the mathematical manipulations involved in arriving at the optimal solution. (Their presence in the system requires just as much manipulation as if they were necessary to the model.) Although they will not prevent the model from locating the optimal strategy, if these unnecessary constraints are detected and removed from the system, the resultant benefit will be a decrease in the amount of computational effort required for arriving at that optimal strategy.

It may not always be possible to determine simply by inspection that a given constraint is or is not redundant. The two rules listed below may be used in a more systematic search for redundant constraints.

Rule 1: If for any two constraints of the "less-than" variety,

$$\frac{b_r}{a_{rj}} \leqslant \frac{b_s}{a_{sj}} \qquad \text{for all } j$$

then the sth inequality is redundant with respect to the rth and may be removed from the system.

In the illustrative set of constraints, we compare

Constraint (2)		*Constraint (1)*
$32/2 = 16$	$\leqslant$	$60/3 = 20$
$32/4 = 8$	$\leqslant$	$60/6 = 10$

and see that the constraint (1) is redundant.

Rule 2: If for any two constraints of the "greater-than" variety,

$$\frac{b_r}{a_{rj}} \geqslant \frac{b_s}{a_{sj}} \qquad \text{for all } j$$

then the sth inequality is redundant with respect to the rth and may be removed from the system.

In the illustrative set of constraints, we compare

Constraint (3)		*Constraint (4)*
$60/3 = 20$	$\geqslant$	$32/2 = 16$
$60/6 = 10$	$\geqslant$	$32/4 = 8$

and see that constraint (4) is redundant.

If, in either case listed above, the ratios are equal for all j, the two constraints are identical and either, but not both, is redundant.

PROBLEMS HAVING NO FEASIBLE SOLUTION

Another important irregularity in problem definition is that situation where the model has no feasible solution. Consider the set of constraints

  1. $3X_1 + 6X_2 \geqslant 60$;
  2. $2X_1 + 4X_2 \leqslant 32$.

If we pictured these inequations, we could see immediately that there is no area of feasible solutions. See Fig. 13–3.

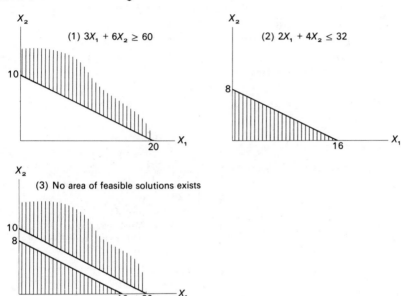

FIG. 13–3 *Problem having no feasible solution*

In the very simple cases it may be possible to ascertain just by inspection of the system of constraints that no feasible solution exists; in other cases this may not be possible. In either situation, the simplex algorithm will signal that a real problem exists.

Refer to Fig. 13–4 where the two constraints listed above, along with an accompanying objective function

Maximize: $20X_1 + 24X_2$

have been set up in a simplex tableau. The initial tableau is pivoted on the X_1 column and the S_1 row. The S_1 row is selected, first, as the pivot row because of the minus value in its b vector cell. The X_1 column is, then, selected because it provides the largest ratio. The pivoting takes place in the usual way. On the second iteration, it becomes apparent that some inconsistency exists in the definition of the problem.

Initial Tableau:

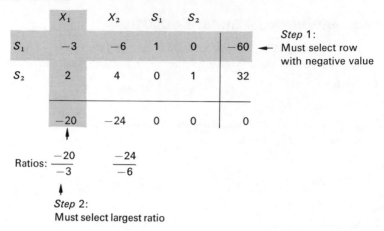

Step 1:
Must select row
with negative value

Step 2:
Must select largest ratio

Second Tableau:

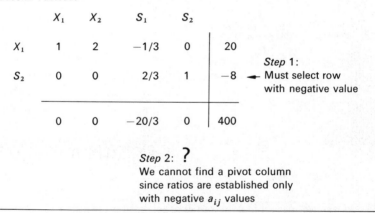

Step 1:
Must select row
with negative value

Step 2: **?**
We cannot find a pivot column
since ratios are established only
with negative a_{ij} values

FIG. 13–4   The tableaus: a problem having no feasible solution

PROBLEMS HAVING MORE THAN ONE OPTIMAL SOLUTION

We have noted previously that linear programming models may have more than one optimal solution. Graphically, when the objective function runs parallel to one of the constraints defining the area of feasible solutions, the two corner points which terminate the side of the feasible region, along with every point on the line segment joining these two corners, will all have the same value of the objective function and, thus, all will be optimal.

From the decision-maker's point of view, the identification of alternative optimal strategies may be important since he, then, has the opportunity to base his decision on factors which are not included in the mathematical formulation of the model.

The model

Maximize: $12X_1 + 24X_2$

subject to

$$3X_1 + 6X_2 \leqslant 60$$
$$4X_1 + 2X_2 \leqslant 32$$

provides an illustration of a system with more than one optimal strategy. The model is depicted graphically in Fig. 13–5. The tableaus required for moving to the optimal solution are shown in Fig. 13–6.

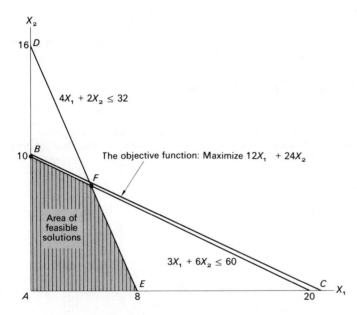

FIG. 13–5 Problem having more than one optimal solution

In order to be able to identify alternative optima we examine the objective function row of the final tableau. A zero in this row under a variable that is *not in solution* signals that an alternative optimal solution exists. Refer to Fig. 13–6 where the tableaus for the example model are displayed. Notice that the first tableau is conventional and is pivoted in the conventional manner. Notice that in the second tableau there are no negative indicators; this is an optimal solution. The variables in solution are X_2 and S_2 with solution values of $X_2 = 10$ and $S_2 = 12$. The value of the objective function is $240. Notice carefully that the shadow

The Initial Tableau:

	X_1	X_2	S_1	S_2		Ratios:
S_1	3	6	1	0	60	◄ 60/6 = 10 ◄—Smallest ratio
S_2	4	2	0	1	32	32/2 = 16
	−12	−24	0	0	0	

↑

The Second Tableau:

	X_1	X_2	S_1	S_2		
X_2	1/2	1	1/6	0	10	
S_2	3	0	−1/3	1	12	AN OPTIMAL SOLUTION
	0	0	4	0	240	

↑

(The zero shadow price for a nonbasic variable indicates that there is
an alternative optimal solution. To obtain that alternative optimal solution,
pivot on this column.)

The Third Tableau:

	X_1	X_2	S_1	S_2		
X_2	0	1	2/9	−1/6	8	AN ALTERNATIVE
X_1	1	0	−1/9	1/3	4	OPTIMAL SOLUTION
	0	0	4	0	240	

FIG. 13–6   The tableaus: problem having more than one optimal solution

prices for the two nonbasic variables are \$4 for S_1 and zero for X_1. The zero
shadow price for this nonbasic variable indicates that another optimal strategy
exists.

The alternative optimal solution may be obtained by pivoting the tableau on
the column which contains this nonbasic variable. Here it is the X_1 column.
X_1 becomes the incoming variable. The smallest ratio between the b_j *and* a_{ij} values

found in the S_2 row; thus, S_2 is the outgoing variable. The simplex computational steps are applied in the usual fashion.

Because of the zero in the objective-function row, pivot-column cell, the pivoting will not alter the values of the objective function row, including the optimal value of the objective function itself.

Graphically, the optimal solutions are at corner point B and corner point F of Fig. 13–5. Note that whenever there exist more than one optimal solution to a linear programming problem there will be an infinite number of optimal solutions. Only the corner points will be basic solutions, the points on the line segment connecting these corners will not be basic. They will, nonetheless, be optimal—all providing the same value for the objective function. The only differences among the solutions will be in the strategies.

PROBLEMS WHERE THE AREA OF FEASIBLE SOLUTIONS IS UNBOUNDED IN THE OPTIMIZING DIRECTION

Another troublesome situation arises when the constraints are defined in such a way that there is no boundary to the area of feasible solutions *in the optimizing direction*. In this case, one or more constraints have probably been omitted or misstated.

An unbounded area of feasible solutions is not always an error. For instance, we saw such an unbounded region in the minimization problems we worked. The

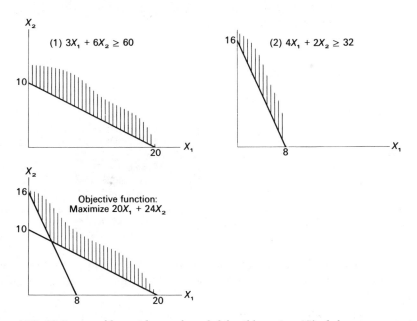

FIG. 13–7   A problem with an unbounded feasible region. (Shaded area represents area of feasible solutions.)

unbounded region is an incongruity only when it is unbounded in the direction of the optimality.

Assume that a model consists of these greater-than constraints

$$3X_1 + 6X_2 \geqslant 60$$
$$4X_1 + 2X_2 \geqslant 32$$

with the accompanying objective function

Maximize: $20X_1 + 24X_2$.

Initial Tableau:

	X_1	X_2	S_1	S_2	
S_1	-3	-6	1	0	-60
S_2	-4	-2	0	1	-32
	-20	-24	0	0	0

Step 1: — May select either negative row

Ratios: $\dfrac{-20}{-3}$ $\dfrac{-24}{-6}$

Step 2:
Must select largest ratio

The Second Tableau:

	X_1	X_2	S_1	S_2	
X_1	1	2	$-1/3$	0	20
S_2	0	0	$-4/3$	1	48
	0	16	$-20/3$	0	400

Step 2: **?**
We cannot find a
pivot row since
ratios are established
only for positive
a_{ij} values

Step 1:
Must select negative indicator

FIG. 13–8 *The tableaus: problem having unbounded feasible region*

Clearly, the optimum value for the objective function is obtained by setting both X_1 and X_2 at infinitely large values since there is no upper limit imposed on these variables. See Fig. 13–7.

Of course, we are not always able to depict graphically the model we are working with. Still, the condition of an unbounded feasible region which yields an infinite value for one or more of the variables will become evident in the simplex technique. It will become impossible to establish ratios between the pivot column elements and the b vector elements. Please refer to Fig. 13–8 where the tableaus for this model are displayed.

The initial tableau is pivoted on the X_1 column and the S_1 row following the usual rules for pivoting a tableau with a minus value in the b vector. In the second tableau, all the minus b values have disappeared so that we would ordinarily select a pivot column by reference to the negative indicators. Tentatively, we would choose the S_1 column. However, recall that the rule for pivoting states that ratios will be established between the b_j value and the *positive* a_{ij} values. There are no positive a_{ij} values in the S_1 column. We are, therefore, unable to find a pivot row.

Referring to the marginal rates of substitution for the S_1 column, we read that to increase S_1 would result in an increase in the other variables; so, theoretically, we can increase S_1 indefinitely. We know that this, for practical purposes, is not possible and we realize that something has gone wrong in building the model.

THE PROBLEM OF DEGENERATE SOLUTIONS

We have seen that when a basic solution, or basis, is formed for a particular set of constraints that basis will contain just as many variables as there are constraints in the system. Thus, for example, in a set consisting of nine variables—three of which are activity variables and six of which are either slack or surplus variables—a basic solution containing six variables, either activity, slack, and/or surplus, may be formed. The remaining three variables must be nonbasic; they must have zero values. A special problem arises when not only are the nonbasic variables equal to zero but also one or more of the basic variables have zero values. Any solution containing one or more basic variables—activity, slack, or surplus—at a zero value is called *degenerate*.

A degenerate solution may appear in the initial, or in a subsequent, tableau.

Initial Basis is Degenerate

Suppose that in formulating a problem we specify that

$$X_1 \leqslant X_2.$$

When the slack variable is added and X_2 is transferred to the left-hand side of the equation, we write

$$X_1 - X_2 + S_1 = 0.$$

Suppose now that we have one other constraint for the model; that is,

$$X_1 + X_2 \leqslant 10$$

which is rewritten as

$$X_1 + X_2 + S_2 = 10.$$

The constraint set contains two nonbasic variables, X_1 and X_2. The initial values of these variables are set equal to zero in the customary way; that is,

$$X_1 = 0 \quad \text{and} \quad X_2 = 0.$$

Then, we read the values of the two basic variables, S_1 and S_2, as

$$S_1 = 0 \quad \text{and} \quad S_2 = 10.$$

This initial basic solution provides an example of degeneracy since it contains a basic variable at a zero value.

Let us add the objective function

Maximize: $3X_1 + 2X_2$

to the model and see how this degeneracy can be resolved. From Fig. 13–9 we can

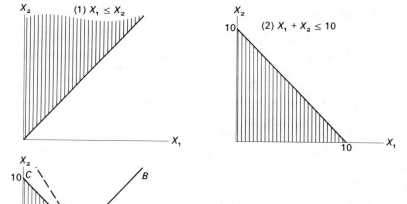

FIG. 13–9 An initial solution that is degenerate. (Shaded area represents area of feasible solutions.)

Initial Tableau:

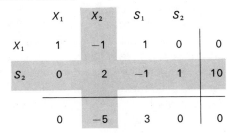

	X_1	X_2	S_1	S_2	
S_1	1	−1	1	0	0
S_2	1	1	0	1	10
	−3	−2	0	0	0

Step 1:
Select the most negative indicator

Ratios:

Step 2: Select
0/1 = 0   −   the smallest ratio

10/1 = 10

Second Tableau:

	X_1	X_2	S_1	S_2	
X_1	1	−1	1	0	0
S_2	0	2	−1	1	10
	0	−5	3	0	0

Step 1
Select the most negative indicator

Ratios:

Do not establish ratio because $a_{ij} \leqslant 0$.

10/2 = 5

Step 2:
Select the smallest ratio.

The Third (and Final) Tableau:

	X_1	X_2	S_1	S_2	
X_1	1	0	1/2	1/2	5
X_2	0	1	−1/2	1/2	5
	0	0	1/2	5/2	25

FIG. 13–10 The tableaus: an initial solution that is degenerate

see that the optimal solution will be at corner point E, where $X_1 = 5$ and $X_2 = 5$.
The simplex tableaus for this model are shown in Fig. 13–10.

The X_1 column is chosen as the pivot column in the initial tableau because it
has the most negative indicator. The S_1 row ratio is

$0/1 = 0$

and this is smaller than the S_2 row ratio which is

$10/1 = 10.$

S_1, thus, becomes the pivot row. The tableau is then pivoted in the customary way.

Notice, by comparing the first and second tableaus in Fig. 13–10, these effects of replacing a zero basic variable:

1. The value of the incoming variable—here it is X_1—is zero in the new basic solution.

2. The value of the other basic variable—here it is S_2—has not changed in value from the initial to the second tableau.

3. The value of the objective function has remained unchanged.

We see that the second tableau, too, represents a degenerate solution. On the next iteration, X_2 is the variable coming into solution. In setting up the ratios to determine which variable should be eliminated from solution, no ratio is established for the X_1 row since the value in the pivot column is negative. (Only when the value in the a_{ij} cell is greater than zero is that row considered as a candidate for the outgoing variable.) Hence, S_2 is the outgoing variable for the second iteration.

The new solution has these values for the variables:

Basic variables	Nonbasic variables
$X_1 = 5$	$S_1 = 0$
$X_2 = 5$	$S_2 = 0.$

This is the final solution. It clearly corresponds to point E in Fig. 13–9 which we found in our graphic analysis to be the optimal vertex.

Degenerate Solution Occurs After the Initial Basis

Degenerate solutions may also first occur in tableaus other than the initial tableau. To illustrate this phenomenon, let us look at the model

Maximize: $6X_1 + 5X_2$

subject to

$X_1 + 2X_2 \leqslant 8$
$3X_1 + X_2 \leqslant 15$
$X_1 + X_2 \leqslant 5.$

Figure 13–11 shows graphically that the area of feasible solutions is the area $ABHE$. The slope of the objective function is such that the optimal solution occurs at corner point E, where $X_1 = 5$ and $X_2 = 0$.

The initial tableau for the model is shown in Fig. 13–12. The reader should note particularly that in selecting the variable to leave the solution in proceeding from the initial tableau to the second tableau, two ratios are equal. Whenever this condition prevails, the solution will become degenerate. Replacing either one of the "tied" variables will automatically reduce its value to zero and will also reduce the other tied variable—which will remain basic—to zero.

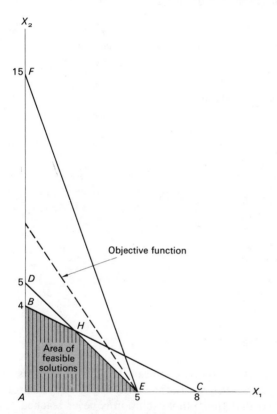

FIG. 13–11   A degenerate solution

In the case of equal ratios used to determine the outgoing variable, the degeneracy will ordinarily be resolved satisfactorily if we select one of these rows at random to be the pivot row. We selected the S_3 row in the example; and on pivoting obtained the optimal solution shown in Fig. 13–11. Although this solution has a zero-valued basic variable, it is the optimal solution.

Degeneracy ordinarily will not seriously affect the finding of an optimal solution. The optimal solution, if one exists, will eventually be reached although a degenerate solution has appeared. The greatest danger associated with degeneracy —and it is a very remote one—is the phenomenon known as *cycling*. Cycling occurs

Initial Tableau:

	X_1	X_2	S_1	S_2	S_3		Ratios:
S_1	1	2	1	0	0	8	$8/1 = 8$
S_2	3	1	0	1	0	15	$15/3 = 5$
S_3	1	1	0	0	0	5	$5/1 = 5$
	−6	−5	0	0	0	0	

Equal ratios

Step 2: If the smallest ratios are equal, may select either

Step 1:
Select the most negative indicator

The Second (and Final) Tableau:

	X_1	X_2	S_1	S_2	S_3	
S_1	0	1	1	0	−1	3
S_2	0	−2	0	1	−3	0
X_1	1	1	0	0	1	5
	0	1	0	0	6	30

FIG. 13–12 *The tableaus: A degenerate final solution*

when, after a series of iterations of the simplex tableau, the tableau returns to a previously encountered solution. In other words, the model begins to cycle around the same set of corner points so that the optimal solution is never reached. Although it sounds ominous, cycling can be virtually ignored since its probability of occurrence in actual practice is almost nil.

THE DUAL IN LINEAR PROGRAMMING

Every linear programming problem has two alternative forms, the *primal* and the *dual*. The solution obtained by working with the original statement of the problem, called the primal problem, can also be obtained by working with the dual problem.

Recall the Furniture Manufacturing Company product-mix problem. (See Chapter 2.) We shall use this case as a vehicle for illustrating the two alternative forms of a linear programming model. The objective in the original model was to

[handwritten margin notes: $X_1 \rightarrow$ table, $X_2 \rightarrow$ bench]

maximize total profit contribution of the items produced, where production was limited by processing hours available in the Assembly Department and by processing hours available in the Finishing Department. To be specific, the model was

Maximize: $20X_1 + 24X_2$ (total profit contribution)

subject to

$3X_1 + 6X_2 \leqslant 60$ (available hours in Assembly Department),

$4X_1 + 2X_2 \leqslant 32$ (available hours in Finishing Department),

where X_1 = number of tables to be produced each day, and

X_2 = number of benches to be produced each day.

The final tableau of the model is reproduced in Fig. 13–13.

[handwritten margin notes:
$P = 20X_1 + 24X_2$
$20X_1 + 24X_2 \leqslant 60$
$3X_1 + 6X_2 \leqslant 32$
$4X_1 + 2X_2$
$24 + 24$
$8 \quad 3 \quad 48$
72
60]*

	X_1	X_2	S_1	S_2	
X_2	0	1	2/9	−1/6	8
X_1	1	0	−1/9	1/3	4
	0	0	28/9	8/3	272

FIG. 13–13   Final tableau of primal (Furniture Manufacturing Company Case)

The optimum production strategy is to produce four tables and eight benches for a total daily profit contribution of $272. The shadow price of S_1 (where S_1 is defined as unused hours of assembly time) tells us that an additional hour of assembly time has an imputed worth of $28/9$; that is, an additonal hour of assembly time could be used to increase the value of the objective function by $28/9$. In a like manner, the shadow price of S_2 (where S_2 is defined as unused hours of finishing time) tells us that an additional hour of finishing time could be used to increase the total profit contribution by $8/3$.

This same formulation is available from the dual formulation of the model. Whereas the primal formulation approached the problem from the standpoint of maximizing the total profit contribution of the items produced, the dual will be concerned with minimizing the imputed costs of the scarce resources. More specifically, the objective of the dual will be to find the smallest total imputed cost for the hours of processing capacity in the Assembly Department and the hours of processing capacity in the Finishing Department that are given up in the manufacture of tables and benches. Note that we are not thinking about "standard" or "accounting" cost but rather of economic or implicit cost (or "opportunity cost" or marginal value). The economic cost of an available hour of processing time in either department is a "dual" variable which depends upon the solution values of the activity variables. The dual problem evaluates sets of solution values for these dual variables.

Let us, then, define

Y_1 = imputed cost of one hour of processing time in the Assembly Department,

Y_2 = imputed cost of one hour of processing time in the Finishing Department.

Total cost imputed to the production facilities that have been made available is

$60Y_1 + 32Y_2.$

The objective of the model is

Minimize: $60Y_1 + 32Y_2.$

The objective is to minimize the imputed value of the production facilities used in the manufacture of tables and benches subject to the restriction that the imputed value of the resources that go into each unit of output must not be less than the profit contribution realized from the unit of output. We know from the primal statement of the problem that each unit of X_1 (each table) will require three hours of processing time in the Assembly Department and four hours of processing time in the Finishing Department. The imputed cost associated with the production of one unit of X_1, or the total "value" of the scarce resources which are used in producing one table, will be

$3Y_1 + 4Y_2.$

This "cost" should be restrained to be not less than the profit contribution of one unit of X_1. (This idea complies with the microeconomic optimality condition that marginal cost equals marginal revenue. The dual problem approaches this condition from the position of a higher marginal cost.)

If the total imputed cost of resources used in one unit of output is greater than the profit margin per unit of output, the resources are not allocated optimally. Hence, we write this inequality for the dual model:

$3Y_1 + 4Y_2 \geqslant 20$ (imputed cost and profit contribution of one table).

We can reason similarly about the second product. One X_2 (one bench) requires six hours of processing time in the Assembly Department and two hours of processing time in the Finishing Department. Y_1 and Y_2 represent the cost imputed to one hour of processing in these two departments, respectively. The cost imputed to one unit of the product should not be less than the profit contribution of one unit of that product. Hence, the inequality

$6Y_1 + 2Y_2 \geqslant 24$ (imputed cost and profit contribution of one bench).

Next we solve the dual linear programming model to find the cost which must be imputed to one hour of processing time in each of the two departments, in order for the marginal cost of each product to be equal to the marginal revenue.

The inequalities are converted to equalities by adding the variables E_1 and E_2 where

E_1 = amount by which marginal cost exceeds marginal revenue for one table,

E_2 = amount by which marginal cost exceeds marginal revenue for one bench.

The tableaus for the model are shown in Fig. 13–14.

The model: Minimize $\quad 60Y_1 + 32Y_2$

subject to $\quad 3Y_1 + 4Y_2 \geqslant 20$

$\qquad\qquad\quad 6Y_1 + 2Y_2 \geqslant 24$

First Tableau:

	Y_1	Y_2	E_1	E_2	
E_1	-3	-4	1	0	-20
E_2	-6	-2	0	1	$-24 \leftarrow$
	60 $\uparrow$	32	0	0	0

Second Tableau:

	Y_1	Y_2	E_1	E_2	
E_1	0	-3	1	$-1/2$	$-8 \leftarrow$
Y_1	1	$1/3$	0	$-1/6$	4
	0	12 $\uparrow$	0	10	-240

Third (and Final) Tableau:

	Y_1	Y_2	E_1	E_2	
Y_2	0	1	$-1/3$	$1/6$	$8/3$
Y_1	1	0	$1/9$	$-2/9$	$28/9$
	0	0	4	8	-272

FIG. 13–14 Tableaus for the dual (Furniture Manufacturing Company case)

The optimal solution for the dual problem indicates that the cost imputed to an hour of processing time in the Assembly Department is $28/9. The cost imputed to an hour of processing time in the Finishing Department is $8/3. Compare these values to the shadow prices of S_1 and S_2 in the primal solution (see Fig. 13–13). The total value of the objective function is $272, the same as observed in the solution of the primal problem. Maximum total contribution to profit is equal to minimum total imputed cost of the resources utilized.

The values in the objective-function row and the E_1 and E_2 columns are the same as the solution values for the variables X_1 and X_2 in the primal. Recall that E_1 and E_2 represent the excess of imputed cost over marginal profit contribution for tables and benches. Both E_1 and E_2 are nonbasic variables—have a zero value—so this excess is zero for the production strategy outlined in the final tableau. If this marginal cost of a table were increased by one dollar per table, the value of the objective function—the total imputed cost of assembly time and finishing time required to produce this output—would be increased by $4. Consequently, four tables have been included in the production strategy. In a like manner, if the cost imputed to a bench were increased by one dollar, the total cost imputed to this production would be increased by $8. Hence, eight benches are included in the production plan.

The mathematical relationships between the primal problem and the dual problem are as follows:

1. If the primal objective function is to be maximized, the dual objective function is to be minimized.

2. A new set of variables, representing imputed costs, will be introduced in the dual. The dual will have as many variables as the primal has constraints and as many constraints as the primal had variables.

3. The coefficients in the dual objective function are the same as the constant terms on the right-hand-side of the primal constraint equations. The right-hand-side values of the constraint equations of the dual are the same as the objective-function coefficients of the primal. (That is, the b_i and the c_j are interchanged in the primal and the dual.)

4. If the restrictions in the primal were of the less-than variety, the restrictions of the dual will be of the greater-than variety, and vice versa.

5. The a_{ij} coefficients are the same except that the rows and columns are interchanged. The coefficient of the jth variable in the ith constraint of the primal problem becomes the coefficient of the ith variable in the jth constraint of the dual problem. (That is, each a_{ij} is moved to the a_{ji} cell.)

6. The nonnegativity requirement applies to all variables in either formulation.

7. If one of these models has an optimal solution, so does the other. Moreover, the two objective functions will have the same optimal value (but with opposite signs, using the algorithm outlined above).

All of the information available from the dual is available as well from the primal. On occasion, however, the solution to the dual can be obtained with less computational effort. Consider a linear programming model with 10 variables and 100 constraints. When the inequalities are converted to equalities, the model will will have 110 variables and 100 equations to manipulate. The dual, however, would have only 100 variables and 10 equations.

Still, the "computational efficiency" arguments for the dual are largely obsoleted by new generation computer systems.

Chapter 14

NONLINEAR OBJECTIVE FUNCTIONS

One of the great oversimplifications of the linear programming model is the assumption of linearity of the objective function. Product-mix problem situations are often encountered where the per unit cost of an item changes at different levels of production. One example of the occurrence of this situation is the use of over-time hours when production levels become high. During the regular-time hours (usually the first 40 hours worked in a week), the worker is paid a regular-time wage; but whenever the employee works in excess of 40 hours in a week, he is paid for these hours at an overtime wage which is usually 150% of the regular-time hourly wage. This increase in the cost of a man-hour of labor has a corresponding effect on the cost of the product and on its contribution to profit. Or if raw materials are purchased in larger quantities, quantity purchasing discounts may serve to decrease the unit cost of the raw materials. In some instances, the selling price of a product may change as different quantities of the item are offered for sale.

Admittedly, when these effects are minor we have a tendency to disregard them and proceed with the linear programming model on the assumption of linearity of the objective function. Even where this assumption is clearly untenable, however, the linear programming model may often still be used if a few minor modifications are made in the construction of the model and in the interpretation of its results.

SEGMENTED OBJECTIVE FUNCTIONS

Many of the nonlinear objective functions can be fairly well approximated by a series of piecewise-linear segments. If this is the case and the objective involves maximizing a function that is concave downward or minimizing a function that is concave upward (see Fig. 14–1), we may be able to approximate the objective function with linear segments and build a model using *multiple variables*. If the objective function is piecewise linear but is either concave upward in a maximizing situation or concave downward in a minimizing situation (see Fig. 14–2), we may build a model which utilizes *multiple tableaus*.

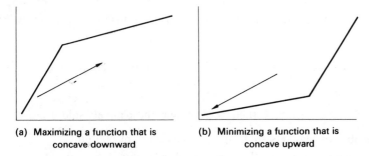

(a) Maximizing a function that is
    concave downward

(b) Minimizing a function that is
    concave upward

FIG. 14–1 Segmented objective functions where the use of multiple variables would be appropriate

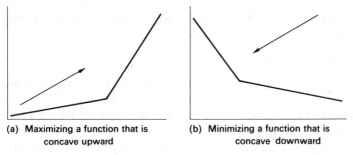

(a) Maximizing a function that is
    concave upward

(b) Minimizing a function that is
    concave downward

FIG. 14–2 Segmented objective functions where the use of multiple tableaus would be appropriate

PIECEWISE-LINEAR OBJECTIVE FUNCTION AND THE USE OF MULTIPLE VARIABLES

Let us suppose Sports Specialties is considering marketing two types of specialty products, synthetic cashmere stadium blankets and portable stadium seats. The owner of the firm believes he can sell all the blankets he can obtain for $10 each. However, he feels that selling expense for the first 500 units will be only $1 for each unit but will increase to $3 for each unit sold above the first 500 units. The increase in selling expense occurs because in order to sell in excess of 500 units, commission agents would have to be used and their commissions would cause the $2 increase in selling expense. Sports Specialties purchases the blankets directly from the manufacturer for $4 each.

The owner of the company believes that he can also sell all the stadium seats he can obtain for $8 each. Selling expense for the first 1000 seats will be $1 for each unit but will increase to $3 a unit for all units above the first 1000. This increase in the selling expense, again, takes place because commission agents would have to be used if more than 1000 seats are to be sold. Sports Specialties purchases the stadium seats for $3 each.

For the first 500 units of blankets sold, the profit contribution per unit will be

$10 − ($4 + $1) = $5.

For any units sold above 500, the profit contribution for each unit will be

$10 − ($4 + $3) = $3.

Let us define *two* variables, then, to represent the blankets sold:

X_1 = number of blankets sold, up to a maximum of 500 units,

X_2 = number of blankets sold in excess of 500 units.

We must immediately establish the constraint that

$X_1 \leqslant 500$.

The objective-function coefficients for these variables will be $5 and $3, respectively. That is, we will tell the model to

Maximize: $5X_1 + 3X_2 + \dots$.

The model will "prefer" X_1 to X_2 because the magnitude of its objective-function coefficient is larger. Therefore, the model will make as many units of X_1 as possible before making the first unit of X_2. The model will be stopped from attempting to make X_1 greater than 500 by the constraint we have written.

We shall also use two variables for the units of stadium seats sold. Let us define

X_3 = number of stadium seats sold, up to a maximum of 1000 units,

X_4 = number of stadium seats sold in excess of 1000 units.

The constraint

$X_3 \leqslant 1000$

must be written into the model.

The profit contribution associated with each X_3 is

$8 − ($3 + $1) = $4

and for each unit of X_4 is

$8 − ($3 + $3) = $2.

Again, because X_3 is more attractive than X_4 insofar as the objective function is concerned, the model will attempt to set the value of X_3 as high as possible but will be controlled by the constraint we have written. Only after X_3 takes on the value 1000 will X_4's come into solution.

The complete objective function is written

Maximize: $5X_1 + 3X_2 + 4X_3 + 2X_4$.

The company has only \$11,000 to invest in this venture. Each blanket would require an "investment" of \$4 while each stadium seat would require an "investment" of \$3. The limitation on funds available imposes this constraint on the model:

$$4X_1 + 4X_2 + 3X_3 + 3X_4 \leqslant 11,000.$$

The Tableaus

The tableaus for this model are shown in Fig. 14–3. The reader should follow these tableaus from the initial through to the final, noting carefully the sequence of incoming and outgoing variables.

Initial Tableau:

	X_1	X_2	X_3	X_4	S_1	S_2	S_3	
S_1	4	4	3	3	1	0	0	11000
S_2	1	0	0	0	0	1	0	500 ←
S_3	0	0	1	0	0	0	1	1000
	−5	−3	−4	−2	0	0	0	0

Second Tableau:

	X_1	X_2	X_3	X_4	S_1	S_2	S_3	
S_1	0	4	3	3	1	−4	0	9000
X_1	1	0	0	0	0	1	0	500
S_3	0	0	1	0	0	0	1	1000 ←
	0	−3	−4	−2	0	5	0	2500

Third Tableau:

	X_1	X_2	X_3	X_4	S_1	S_2	S_3	
S_1	0	4	0	3	1	−4	−3	6000 ←
X_1	1	0	0	0	0	1	0	500
X_3	0	0	1	0	0	0	1	1000
	0	−3	0	−2	0	5	4	6500

Fourth (and Final) Tableau:

	X_1	X_2	X_3	X_4	S_1	S_2	S_3	
X_2	0	1	0	3/4	1/4	−1	−3/4	1500
X_1	1	0	0	0	0	1	0	500
X_3	0	0	1	0	0	0	1	1000
	0	0	0	1/4	3/4	2	7/4	11000

FIG. 14–3 The tableaus, Sports Specialties Case

In the final analysis, the model tells us that under the conditions outlined it is most profitable to market 2000 blankets and 1000 portable stadium seats for a realized profit contribution of $11,000. All of the available funds would be invested.

The Ranging

The shadow price on the X_4 column tells us that to force another stadium seat (a unit of X_4) into solution would cost the company $0.25 per unit.

Each additional $1 available for investment in the venture would increase the profit contribution by $0.75; these additional funds would be invested in blankets (X_2). For each additional blanket that could be sold without the expense of the extra selling commission, profit contribution could be increased by $2 (which is the exact amount of the extra sales commission). In the same manner, for each stadium seat that could be sold without the expense of the extra selling commission, profit contribution could be increased by $1.75. The $1.75 results from the fact that in order to have another stadium seat to sell (at a profit of $4) we would lose 3/4 unit of a blanket (at a profit of (3/4) ($3) = $2.25); or $4 − $2.25 = $1.75.

The appropriate right-hand-side and objective-function-coefficient ranging for the Sports Specialties model is given in Table 14–1.

TABLE 14–1 Ranging, the Sports Specialties Case

	Current level	Lower limit	Upper limit	Outgoing variable Lower	Upper
Right-hand-side ranging					
Resource:					
Funds available for investment	$11,000	$5,000	∞	X_2	—
Restrictions: Blankets saleable without extra sales commission	500	0	2000	X_1	X_2
Stadium seats saleable without extra sales commission	1000	0	3000	X_3	X_2
Objective-function-coefficient ranging				Incoming variable	
Basic variables:					
Blankets (X_1)	$5	$3	∞	S_2	—
Blankets (X_2)	$3	$2.67	$5	X_4	S_2
Stadium seats (X_3)	$4	$2.25	∞	S_3	—
Nonbasic variables: Stadium seats (X_4)	$2	0	$2.25	—	X_4

USING MULTIPLE TABLEAUS

The use of multiple variables and segmented objective functions as illustrated in the previous example is feasible only when (1) maximizing a function that is concave downward or (2) minimizing a function that is concave upward. In these instances, the "first" units of a variable are preferred by the model over the "latter" units so that we encounter no special difficulty in moving from zero units upward in an orderly manner.

However, if the function to be maximized looks like the one shown in Fig. 14–2(a)—that is, it is concave upward—the model would prefer the latter units to the earlier ones and we have no simple way of forcing it to select the first units of the variable before it tries to select the latter ones. The same difficulty is encountered when attempting to minimize a function that is concave downward, as shown in Fig. 14–2(b). Here costs are becoming more favorable and the model will want to select the latter units of the product before it selects the first units. In cases such as these, *multiple tableaus*, rather than a single tableau, must be used.

For example, let us assume that the Two-Products Company manufactures two products. The manufacture of one product (lets be imaginative and call it Product #1) is such that economies of scale are realized after the first 400 units. The profit contribution is $1.00 for each unit for the first 400 units of Product #1, but it is $4.00 for each unit in excess of 400 units.

The other product (let's call it Product #2) makes a constant contribution to profit of $5.

Two scarce resources, materials A and B, are used in the manufacturing process. Each unit of Product #1 requires three units of A and one unit of B. Each unit of Product #2 requires two units of A and three units of B. There are 2000 units of material A and 600 units of material B available each day.

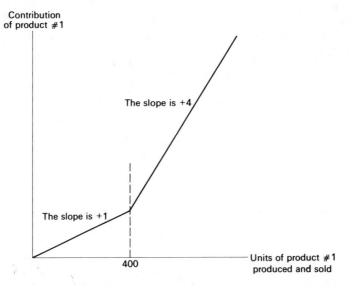

FIG. 14–4 Piecewise linear contribution function, the Two-Products Company Case

The function for the profit contribution of Product #1 is depicted in Fig. 14–4. The function has a slope of $+1$ over the range zero-to-400 units and a slope of $+4$ over the range above 400 units. If the objective is to maximize profit contribution, the model naturally prefers the segment of the function with the steeper slope. In reality, however, the first 400 units of the product must be produced before any units in excess of 400 can be considered.

We must, then, use two models. In the first model we define these variables:

$X_1 =$ number of units of Product #1 to produce each day,

$X_2 =$ number of units of Product #2 to produce each day,

and we include the constraint

$X_1 \leqslant 400.$

This constraint will keep us within that portion of the contribution function for Product #1 where its contribution is a constant $1.

The resource constraints would be:

$3X_1 + 2X_2 \leqslant 2000$ (material A),

$X_1 + 3X_2 \leqslant 600$ (material B).

We use an objective-function coefficient of $1.00 for X_1 and $5.00 for X_2. The tableaus for this model are shown in Fig. 14–5.

Initial Tableau:

	X_1	X_2	S_1	S_2	S_3	
S_1	3	2	1	0	0	2000
S_2	1	3	0	1	0	600 ◄ ◄
S_3	1	0	0	0	1	400
	−1	−5	0	0	0	0

Second (and Final) Tableau:

	X_1	X_2	S_1	S_2	S_3	
S_1	7/3	0	1	−2/3	0	1600
X_2	1/3	1	0	1/3	0	200
S_3	1	0	0	0	1	400
	2/3	0	0	5/3	0	1000

FIG. 14–5 *Tableaus for the Two-Products Company problem*

The model indicates that all the available units of resource B should be used in the production of units of Product #2. Two hundred units of the item can be produced with a total profit contribution of $1000. There will be 1600 unused units of material A.

Not any units of Product #1 will be produced when X_1 has an objective-function coefficient of \$1.00. However, we know that for all units of this product after the first 400, the contribution will become \$4.00. Note that the shadow price in the X_1 column is 2/3. This tells us that if the contribution of X_1 were any greater than \$1 + \$2/3 = \$1.67, X_1 would be included in the optimal strategy. Let us, then, reconstruct the model, assuming that we will produce more than 400 units of Product #1 and using as the objective-function-coefficient for X_1 the \$4.00 profit contribution (rather than the \$1.00). We will have to specify that

$$X_1 \geqslant 400.$$

The resource constraints will remain unchanged.

Realizing that on the first 400 units of X_1 the profit contribution will be overstated by the amount

$$400 (\$4 - \$1) = \$1200$$

we may, if we like, enter this value in the lower right-hand corner of the initial tableau as a negative initial value of the objective function. See Fig. 14–6 where the

Initial Tableau:

	X_1	X_2	S_1	S_2	S_3	
S_1	3	2	1	0	0	2000
S_2	1	3	0	1	0	600
S_3	−1	0	0	0	1	−400 ◄
	−4	−5	0	0	0	−1200

Second Tableau:

	X_1	X_2	S_1	S_2	S_3	
S_1	0	2	1	0	3	800
S_2	0	3	0	1	1	200 ◄
X_1	1	0	0	0	−1	400
	0	−5	0	0	−4	400

Third Tableau:

	X_1	X_2	S_1	S_2	S_3	
S_1	0	0	1	$-2/3$	7/3	2000/3
X_2	0	1	0	1/3	1/3	200/3 ←
X_1	1	0	0	0	-1	400
	0	0	0	5/3	$-7/3$	2200/3

↑

Fourth (and Final) Tableau:

	X_1	X_2	S_1	S_2	S_3	
S_1	0	-7	1	-3	0	200
S_3	0	3	0	1	1	200
X_1	1	3	0	1	0	600
	0	7	0	4	0	1200

FIG. 14–6 *The tableaus, the Two-Products Company Case*

tableaus for this model are displayed. While we must be mindful of the fact that use of a $4.00 objective-function coefficient overstates the contribution of Product #1, it is not necessary that we make this adjustment in the initial tableau. We may begin as usual with a zero objective-function value and make the correction in the final tableau. No other modifications of the model are required.

Again the reader should follow the sequence of incoming and outgoing variables. The final solution indicates that 600 units of Product #1 and zero units of Product #2 should be manufactured. The value of the objective function has been adjusted for the reduced profit contribution on the first 400 units of Product #1. We can check to see that:

First 400 units of Product #1	(400) ($1)	= $400
Units of Product #1 in excess of 400	(600–400) ($4)	= 800
		$1200

We should compare this objective-function value with that obtained in the first model of the problem situation to make certain that this strategy does give a higher objective-function value than did the first. When we do, we see that the $1200 of the second model is, indeed, more desirable than the $1000 of the first model, and we follow the strategy outlined in the second model.

The right-hand-side and the objective-function-coefficient ranging for the final tableau is shown in Table 14–2.

TABLE 14–2 Ranging, the Two-Products Company Case

	Current level	Lower limit	Upper limit	Outgoing variable Lower	Upper
Right-hand-side ranging					
Resource Material *B* (in units)	600	400	$666\frac{2}{3}$	S_3	S_1
Objective-function-coefficient ranging				Incoming variable	
Basic activity variable: Product #1 (X_1)	$4	$1.67	∞	X_2	—
Nonbasic activity variable: Product #2 (X_2)	$5	0	$12	—	X_2

ONE STEP BEYOND SEGMENTATION TO CURVILINEAR OBJECTIVE FUNCTIONS

Another approach to the treatment of a curvilinear objective function in adapting a problem situation to the linear programming model is to approximate the non-linear curve, over what is believed to be the most relevant range for the variable, by a linear function. After a solution is obtained based on this assumption, a comparison is made between the contribution at the specified value of the variable and the approximation of the contribution used as the objective-function coefficient in order to activate the model. Adjustments may be required because of the simplifying assumptions. These adjustments may require additional iterations of the tableau and another checking of the new solution for correspondence to the new assumptions. This cycle will continue until the assumptions are found to fall within acceptable limits.

We shall discuss two different situations: (1) maximizing an objective function that is increasing by a decreasing amount, and (2) maximizing an objective function that is increasing by an increasing amount. These two types of functions are shown in Fig. 14–7. These two curve types must be handled in a slightly different manner because of the relationships between total contribution, average contribution, and marginal contribution of each.

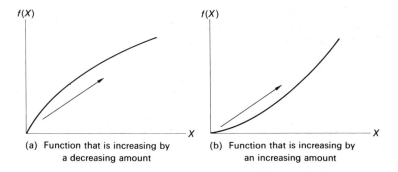

(a) Function that is increasing by a decreasing amount

(b) Function that is increasing by an increasing amount

FIG. 14–7 Functions that are increasing

The function

$$f(X) = -0.12X^2 + 2.4X \qquad 0 \leqslant X \leqslant 10$$

would have the general shape of that curve (a) in Fig. 14–7. Suppose this function represents the total contribution function for X. We can find the *total contribution* for ten units of X by substituting

$$f(10) = -0.12(10)^2 + 2.4(10)$$
$$= 12$$

or for six units by

$$f(6) = -0.12(6)^2 + 2.4(6)$$
$$= 10.08.$$

We find the *average contribution* of X over the range $a \leqslant X \leqslant b$ by fitting a straight line to the two points $f(a)$ and $f(b)$ and finding the slope of this straight line. That is, the average contribution of X over the range (a, b) can be found by

$$\frac{f(b) - f(a)}{b - a}.$$

We will ordinarily be concerned with a range whose lower limit is $X = 0$ and will be able to find the average contribution of X over the range $0 \leqslant X \leqslant b$ by finding

$$\frac{f(b)}{b}.$$

For example, the average contribution of ten units of X would be found by

$$\frac{f(10) - f(0)}{10 - 0} = \frac{12 - 0}{10} = 1.2.$$

Or the average may be computed by

$$\frac{f(X)}{X} = \frac{-0.12X^2 + 2.4X}{X} = -0.12X + 2.4,$$

and for ten units is found to be

$$-0.12(10) + 2.4 = 1.2.$$

(a) Total contribution $= -0.12X^2 + 2.4X$ $0 \leqslant X \leqslant 10$
    Average contribution $= -0.12X + 2.4$
    Marginal contribution $= -0.24X + 2.4$

X	Total	Average	Marginal	
1	2.28	2.28	2.16	This function is
2	4.32	2.16	1.92	increasing by a
3	6.12	2.04	1.68	decreasing amount.
4	7.68	1.92	1.44	
5	9.00	1.80	1.20	
6	10.08	1.68	0.96	
7	10.92	1.56	0.72	
8	11.52	1.44	0.48	
9	11.88	1.32	0.24	
10	12.00	1.20	—	

(b) Total contribution $= 0.12Y^2$ $0 \leqslant Y \leqslant 10$
    Average contribution $= 0.12Y$
    Marginal contribution $= 0.24Y$

X	Total	Average	Marginal	
1	0.12	0.12	0.24	This function is
2	0.48	0.24	0.48	increasing by an
3	1.08	0.36	0.72	increasing amount.
4	1.72	0.48	0.96	
5	3.00	0.60	1.20	
6	4.32	0.72	1.44	
7	5.88	0.84	1.68	
8	7.68	0.96	1.92	
9	9.72	1.08	2.16	
10	12.00	1.20	2.40	

FIG. 14–8 Total contribution, average contribution, and marginal contribution for two increasing functions

For six units the average contribution is

$$-0.12(6) + 2.4 = 1.68.$$

Now the *marginal contribution* is the slope of the curve at any one point. The marginal contribution is represented by the first derivative of the function, which in this case is

$$f'(X) = -0.24X + 2.4.$$

The marginal contribution indicates the amount by which the total contribution is changed with a slight movement along—from left to right—the X-axis. The slope of this function at $X = 6$ is given by

$$f'(6) = -0.24(6) + 2.4$$
$$= 0.96.$$

The slope at $X = 2$ is

$$f'(2) = -0.24(2) + 2.4$$
$$= 1.92.$$

(a) For a contribution function that is increasing by a decreasing amount

Total contribution = $f(X) = -0.12X^2 + 2.4X$

Average contribution = $\dfrac{f(X)}{X} = -0.12X + 2.4$

Marginal contribution = $f'(X) = -0.24X + 2.4$

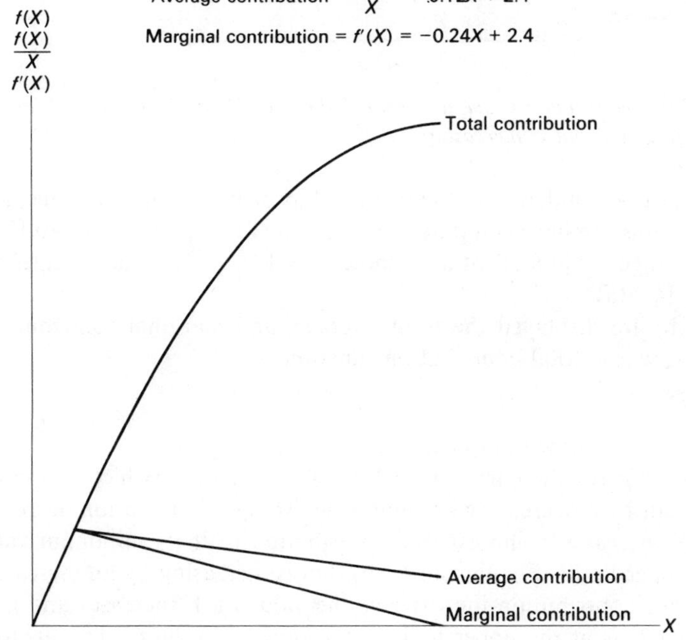

$f(X)$
$\dfrac{f(X)}{X}$
$f'(X)$

Total contribution

Average contribution

Marginal contribution

X

FIG. 14–9A   Total contribution, average contribution, and marginal contribution for two increasing functions

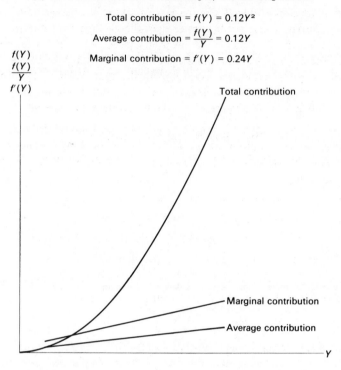

(b) For a contribution that is increasing by an increasing amount

Total contribution = $f(Y) = 0.12Y^2$

Average contribution $= \dfrac{f(Y)}{Y} = 0.12Y$

Marginal contribution $= f'(Y) = 0.24Y$

FIG. 14–9B Total contribution, average contribution, and marginal contribution for a contribution function that is increasing

Because we must be familiar with the relationships between total, average, and marginal contributions, we have computed these for the function $f(X) = -0.12X^2 + 2.4X$, over the range of values for the variable $X = 1, 2, ..., 10$. These values are displayed in Fig. 14–8(a).

In Fig. 14–8(b) are displayed the total, average, and marginal contributions for the variable Y, whose total contribution function is

$$f(Y) = 0.12Y^2.$$

These two functions are shown graphically in Fig. 14–9.

Note carefully that for the curve (a) in Fig. 14–8 and 14–9 (which is a curve that is increasing but by a decreasing amount), the average contribution decreases as the value of X increases. The average contribution is at its minimum value when X is at its upper limit. For the curve (b) that is increasing by an increasing amount, the average contribution increases as the value of Y increases and is at its maximum when Y is at the upper limit of the range of values it can assume.

When the total contribution function is increasing by a decreasing amount, the value of the marginal contribution is also decreasing as the value of X increases but the marginal contribution is always less than or equal to the average contribution. The marginal contribution is never greater than the average contribution for this shape function. (See Fig. 14–9(a).) On the other hand, when the total contribution function is increasing by an increasing amount, the marginal contribution is also increasing and is greater than the average contribution. (See Fig. 14–9(b).)

With this understanding of these features of these two simple curve types, let us look at a problem situation where the objective function is curvilinear.

Contribution is Increasing by a Decreasing Amount

For a very uncomplicated illustration, let us suppose that we are working with the constraints:

Machine time: $2X + 3Y \leqslant 30$

Raw material: $X + (5/4) Y \leqslant 14$

where X = number of units of product X to produce each day, and

Y = number of units of product Y to produce each day.

The contribution of X is believed to be a constant \$1.00 per unit produced and sold; but the contribution of Y is believed to follow the function

$$f(Y) = -0.12Y^2 + 2.4Y \qquad \text{for} \qquad 0 \leqslant Y \leqslant 10.$$

This is the function portrayed in Figs 14–8(a) and 14–9(a). We see, then, that the per unit contribution of Y will decrease as the total number of units of Y produced increases. For example, if four units of Y are produced, the average contribution is \$1.92; if six units of Y are produced, the average contribution decreases to \$1.68; and so on. The minimum average contribution is \$1.20 at the maximum value of Y, where $Y = 10$. Yet, in order to use the linear programming model we must have a constant value to represent the contribution of the variable.

We may overcome this dilemma by approximating the contribution of Y, using this approximation to obtain a tentative strategy, and then making the necessary adjustments to compensate for the crude approximation. The procedure will be simplified if you will determine the maximum number of units of Y that could be produced and use the average contribution over that range as the objective-function coefficient. Looking at the constraints, we see that the most limiting resource insofar as Y is concerned is machine time; it restricts the production to not more than ten units of Y. The average contribution for ten units is \$1.20. Let us use this as the contribution coefficient of Y in the objective function for the model.

Assuming maximization of contribution as the goal, the objective function is stated

Maximize: $X + 1.2Y$.

The tableaus for this model are shown in Fig. 14–10.

The model indicates that 14 units of X and zero units of Y should be produced. The value of the objective function can be calculated as:

Contribution of X: (14 units) ($1 per unit)   = $14.00
Contribution of Y: zero units   =   0

Total Contribution of X and Y $14.00

Initial Tableau:

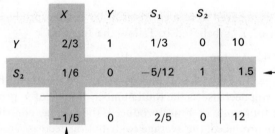

	X	Y	S_1	S_2	
S_1	2	3	1	0	30 ←
S_2	1	5/4	0	1	14
	−1	−1.2	0	0	0

Second Tableau:

	X	Y	S_1	S_2	
Y	2/3	1	1/3	0	10
S_2	1/6	0	−5/12	1	1.5 ←
	−1/5	0	2/5	0	12

Third Tableau:

	X	Y	S_1	S_2	
Y	0	1	2	−4	4 ←
X	1	0	−5/2	6	9
	0	0	−1/10	6/5	13.8

Fourth Tableau:

	X	Y	S_1	S_2	
S_1	0	1/2	1	−2	2
X	1	5/4	0	1	14
	0	1/20	0	1	14

FIG. 14–10   *The tableaus*

This strategy is predicted on a contribution of $1 for each X and $1.20 for each Y. We know (refer to Fig. 14–8(a)) that this is the average contribution of Y only if exactly 10 units of Y are produced. If fewer than 10 units are produced, the average contribution is greater than $1.20. The average contribution of zero units is, of course, zero. But for one unit of Y the average contribution is $2.28; and for two units the average contribution is $2.16. We see that we may have misled the model by understating the contribution of Y. We can look at the objective-function-coefficient ranging for Y to see whether or not this understatement is significant.

The objective-function-coefficient range for Y is

	Lower	Current	Upper
Y	0	$1.20	$1.25

Clearly, since the $1.20 is the minimum average contribution, the lower limit of the range will be of no consequence, but if one additional unit of Y will make a contribution that is greater than the upper limit of the objective-function-coefficient range, we can justify increasing the production of Y. The $2.28 contribution of the first unit is above this upper limit; hence, the solution presented is not really the optimal solution. In fact, we should add units of Y to the production plan for so long as the *marginal* contribution of the last Y added is greater than $1.25.

When working with a curve that has the shape of that of the contribution function of Y, we are primarily concerned with the marginal contribution rather than the average contribution of the units. We have seen that for the function that is increasing by a decreasing amount, the marginal contribution is always less than the average contribution. Thus, in the current example, although the average contribution of seven units of Y is $1.56, the seventh unit itself only adds $0.72 to the total profit. And although the average contribution of five units of Y is $1.80, the fifth unit itself only adds $1.20 to the total profit. We must justify the last unit produced; hence, its marginal contribution must exceed the objective-function-coefficient range limit. That is, we want to add units of Y to the production plan for so long as the marginal contribution of the last Y added is greater than $1.25. Let us pivot the tableau once more. We can do this by working from the last tableau if we adjust the objective-function row of that tableau for the change in the contribution coefficient of Y.

Since we are at a point where we are moving forward toward larger values of Y and since, as we move in this direction, both the average and the marginal contributions of Y decrease, I would suggest that we use as the next objective-function coefficient of Y a value that is just greater than the upper limit of the current objective-function coefficient range. Let us, then, use $1.30 as our next approximation of the per unit contribution of Y.

We are increasing the coefficient from $1.20 to $1.30, an increase of $0.10. We must make a corresponding adjustment in the shadow price of Y. Y has a shadow price of $+0.05$ when the starting point was -1.20; if the starting point had been -1.30, the shadow price of Y in the last tableau would be -0.05. We should make this adjustment in the objective-function row of the last tableau, and pivot that tableau once again. See Fig. 14–11.

Fourth Tableau, adjusted:

	X	Y	S_1	S_2	
S_1	0	1/2	1	−2	2 ◄
X	1	5/4	0	1	14
	0	−0.05	0	1	14 ◄

Note this adjustment

Fifth (and Final) Tableau:

	X	Y	S_1	S_2	
Y	0	1	2	−4	4
X	1	0	−5/2	6	9
	0	0	0.1	0.8	14.2

FIG. 14–11 *The tableaus*

Using $1.30 as the contribution of Y, we obtain a production plan which includes nine units of X and four units of Y. We can compute the total contribution as:

Contribution of X: (9 units) ($1 per unit)	= $ 9.00
Contribution of Y: $-0.12(4)^2 + 2.4(4)$	= 7.68
Total Contribution of X and Y:	$16.68

This is, indeed, an improvement over the last plan which would have resulted in a total contribution of $14.00. The only question is, does there exist a solution that is better still? We can answer this question by looking at the range of indifference for the objective-function-coefficient of Y. This range is

	Lower	*Current*	*Upper*
Y	$1.25	$1.30	$1.50

We are now planning to produce four units of Y. To increase the production we would have to justify the next unit. We could do this only if its marginal contribution were greater than \$1.50. The marginal contribution of the fourth unit is

$$f'(4) = -0.24(4) + 2.4 = 1.44$$

which falls within the objective-function-coefficient range of indifference. Because when the contribution function of Y is of this particular shape, the marginal contribution continues to decrease as the value of the variable increases, the marginal contribution of any increase in production—beyond four units—will be less than \$1.44. Since this is below the upper limit of the objective-function-coefficient range, we cannot justify increasing the production of Y. This solution is the optimal solution.

The area of feasible solutions for this model and the iso-profit line for the function

$$X + (-0.12Y^2 + 2.4Y) = P$$

are shown in Fig. 14–12.

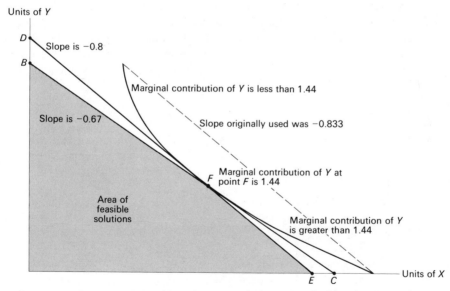

FIG. 14–12 The area of feasible solutions and the iso-profit line that is nonlinear $X + (-0.12Y^2 + 2.4Y) = P$

In some situations we might now have to repeat the process of ranging the objective-function coefficients of the variables, calculating the actual average contribution, seeing whether or not this fell within the range and if not, adjusting the objective-function row and pivoting the tableau again. But eventually both the coefficient used and the actual average contribution would fall within the range of indifference and the solution obtained would be optimal. For each suggested strategy, we would compute the actual value of the objective-function to ascertain that it was or was not better than the preceding solution.

Contribution is Increasing by a Increasing Amount

The process of finding the optimal solution when the contribution function of a variable is increasing at an increasing rate becomes more complicated. Note that for this type of function, the marginal contribution is increasing as the number of units produced increases. Hence, we are not able to assess the feasibility of movement in one direction or another simply by reference to the marginal contribution of the next unit. We would, instead, need to compute the net change in the value of the objective function as we moved from one corner point of the area of feasible solutions to another corner point.

When the Optimal Solution is not at a Corner Point

When the objective function is linear, an optimal solution to the linear programming model will always lie at a corner point of the area of feasible solutions. But, with a curvilinear objective function, this may not be the case at all. The optimal solution will always be that point along the boundary of the feasible region that last comes in contact with the iso-profit line as that line is pushed in the direction of optimization. If the objective function is curvilinear, this point may or may not be a corner point.

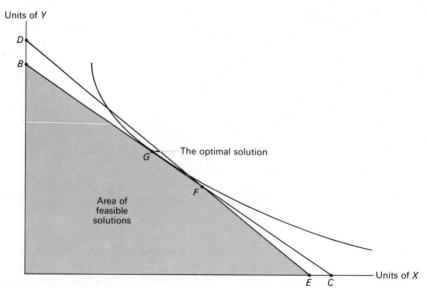

FIG. 14–13 The area of feasible solutions and a nonlinear objective function:
$$(0.7X) + (-0.12Y^2 + 2.4Y) = P$$

Let us return to the preceding illustration where the appropriate constraints are

Machine time $2X + 3Y \leqslant 30$

Raw material: $X + (5/4)Y \leqslant 14.$

The contribution function of Y is given by

$$f(Y) = -0.12Y^2 + 2.4Y \qquad \text{for} \qquad 0 \leqslant Y \leqslant 10.$$

Now let us assume that the contribution of X is \$0.70 per unit and that this is constant for any level of X. The objective function of the model is then

$$\text{Maximize: } (0.7X) + (-0.12Y^2 + 2.4Y) = P.$$

The model is pictured in Fig. 14–13. We can see immediately that the optimal solution is not going to be at a corner point but is, instead, at a point on the BF boundary line. But let us go back to the solution procedure we used previously.

Again let us approximate the contribution of Y by its average contribution at $Y = 10$, or by \$1.20. The objective function for the initial model is

$$\text{Maximize: } 0.7X + 1.2Y.$$

The resulting tableaus are shown in Fig. 14–14.

Initial Tableau:

	X	Y	S_1	S_2	
S_1	2	3	1	0	30 ←
S_2	1	5/4	0	1	14
	-0.7	-1.2	0	0	0

Second (and Final) Tableau:

	X	Y	S_1	S_2	
Y	2/3	1	1/3	0	10
S_2	1/6	0	$-5/12$	1	1.5
	0.1	0	0.4	0	12

FIG. 14–14   The tableaus

The model indicates that ten units of product Y and zero units of product X should constitute the production strategy. Refer to Fig. 14–13 and note that this solution is at corner point B.

The range of indifference for the objective-function coefficient of Y is:

	Lower	Current	Upper
Y	\$1.05	\$1.20	∞

If the contribution of Y is greater than \$1.05, this is the optimal solution. If the contribution is less than \$1.05, some other strategy will yield a higher value for the objective function.

Well, the marginal contribution of the tenth unit of Y was zero. (See Fig. 14–8(a).) For the ninth unit, the marginal contribution was only \$0.24. These contributions are far below the lower limit of the objective-function-coefficient range—which means that we have mislead the model by overstating the contribution of these last units. These last units of Y are not paying their way.

So, let us adjust the objective-function coefficient of Y and pivot the tableau again. We should set the coefficient of Y at a value just below the lower limit of the range—say at \$1.00—rather than at \$1.20. We compute

$$(-0.2)(2/3 \quad - \quad 1/3 \quad - \quad 10) = (-4/30 \quad - \quad -2/30 \quad - \quad -2).$$

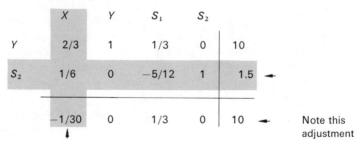

Second Tableau, Adjusted:

	X	Y	S_1	S_2	
Y	2/3	1	1/3	0	10
S_2	1/6	0	−5/12	1	1.5 ←
	−1/30	0	1/3	0	10 ←

Note this adjustment

Third (and Final) Tableau:

	X	Y	S_1	S_2	
Y	0	1	2	−4	4
X	1	0	−5/2	6	9
	0	0	1/4	0.2	10.3

FIG. 14–15 The tableaus

We combine this vector with the old objective-function row vector to obtain

$$(0.1 \quad 0 \quad 0.4 \quad 0 \quad 12) + (-4/30 \quad — \quad -2/30 \quad — \quad -2)$$
$$= (-1/30 \quad 0 \quad 1/3 \quad 0 \quad 10).$$

The next tableaus are shown in Fig. 14–15.

Now the solution strategy calls for 4 units of Y and 9 units of X and lies at corner point F on Fig. 14–13. The total profit contribution for this product mix is

Contribution of X: (9 units) ($0.70)	$ 6.30
Contribution of Y: $f(4) = -0.12(4)^2 + 2.4(4)$	7.68
Total Contribution of X and Y:	$13.98

Since we realize all too well that the $1 objective-function coefficient used for Y is still just an approximation, we are again vitally concerned with the range of indifference for this coefficient. The ranging shows

	Lower	Current	Upper
Y	$0.875	$1.00	$1.05

The marginal contribution at the current level of $Y = 4$ is

$$f'(4) = -0.24(4) + 2.4 = 1.44.$$

This marginal contribution is *greater* than the upper limit of the objective-function-coefficient range—indicating that production of Y should increase. If we increase the coefficient of Y and pivot the tableau again, the solution strategy would be that obtained earlier: $Y = 10$ and $X = 0$!

Look at Fig. 14–13 and note what is happening. We are moving back and forth along the boundary of the area of feasible solutions between point B and point F. This phenomenon occurs because the optimal solution falls at one point on that boundary line and not at either of the two corner points. The simplex technique examines corner points of the area of feasible solutions only. So as we change the objective-function coefficient of Y, the search would move back and forth from corner point B to corner point F back to corner point B and so on. The simplex technique does not evaluate strategies lying on the boundaries between corner points. But our objective-function-coefficient ranging gives us evidence that the optimal solution is on this boundary line rather than at a corner point. In Fig. 14–13 the iso-profit line has been drawn on the graph. Note that the last common point between this line and the feasible region is at point G, on the boundary between corner point B and corner point F.

The optimal solution (represented by point G in Fig. 14–13) occurs at the point where the iso-profit line is tangent to the limiting constraint line (which is the machine time constraint line). The point of tangency will occur where the slopes of the two lines are equal. We find the slope of the machine time constraint line (the *BC* line in Fig. 14–13) to be

$$2X + 3Y = 30$$
$$Y = 10 - (2/3)X$$
$$\text{slope} = -2/3.$$

The slope of the objective function will be given by the ratio of the marginal contribution of *X* to the marginal contribution of *Y*, or

$$\frac{\text{marginal contribution of } X}{\text{marginal contribution of } Y} = \frac{0.7}{-0.24Y + 2.4}.$$

We want to find the values of *X* and *Y* where these two slopes are equal. We compute

$$2/3 = 0.7/(-0.24Y + 2.4)$$
$$-0.24Y + 2.4 = 1.05.$$

Note that this equation states that the marginal contribution of *Y* should be $1.05 at the optimal strategy. This is the same $1.05 that kept recurring as a limit of the range of indifference for the objective-function coefficient of *Y*. So we could have begun our search simply by setting

$$-0.24Y + 2.4 = 1.05$$
$$Y = 5.625.$$

Because machine time is the limiting constraint, we need to substitute in this equation to find the value of *X* when $Y = 5.625$. We obtain

$$2X + 3(5.625) = 30$$
$$X = 6.5625.$$

Profit contribution for this production strategy will be

Contribution of X: (6.5625 units) (0.70)	$ 4.59
Contribution of Y: $f(5.625) = -0.12(5.625)^2 + 2.4(5.625)$	$ 9.69
Total contribution of X and Y	$14.28

Thus, we see that on occasion we are able to approximate a nonlinear objective function by a linear one. But we must be exceedingly careful in analyzing the result.

EXERCISES

1. The Beautiful Sinkframe Company makes three shapes of stainless steel sinkframes—rectangular, round, and oval. Ovals are purchased already bent to shape; the remaining material is purchased in straight lengths. The company has just improved their assembly line and doubled the potential output.

The finishing and packaging operations can process 1000 units per day. It takes two minutes to bend a rectangular frame and five minutes to bend a round frame. The four bending machines are operated 8 hours a day. Welding and grinding the weld takes one minute for the rectangular, two minutes for the round, and three minutes for the oval sinkframes. The four welding machines are operated 8 hours a day.

A building supply store has a contract to purchase all rectangular frames produced daily up to 300 at a price yielding the sinkframe company a contribution to profit of $1 per frame. Because of industry price increases, any additional rectangular frames can be sold at such a price as to contribute $1.40 to profits. The round and the oval frames will contribute $2.25 and $1, respectively.

The company would like to know the product mix that will maximize profit contribution.

2. Dexter Duncemore, industrial engineer, has recently been hired by Kooltool, Inc., a manufacturer of electrical hand tools. Dexter is anxious to quickly demonstrate his worth to the firm, as he sees excellent potential for advancement with this small, but rapidly expanding, company.

During his first week, Dexter discovered that Kooltool's two largest selling products, a portable electric saw and a portable electric drill, must share the same fabrication and packaging facilities. These processes have available a maximum of 3000 and 200 hours per week, respectively. One saw requires 2 fabrication hours and $\frac{1}{3}$ packaging hours while a drill requires 3 fabrication hours and $\frac{1}{5}$ packaging hours. No other factors limit production of these items, and Kooltool can sell its entire productive capacity of drills and saws.

Traditionally, Kooltool has split production equally between drills and saws. Dexter discovered this was the result of an uneasy agreement between the production and sales departments.

To his surprise, Dexter discovered that no definitive profit analysis had been made of these products, and he became certain that an analysis of such information could improve the firm's profit picture. Using revenue and costs directly attributable to the two products, he graphed the total profit contribution of drills and saws as follows:

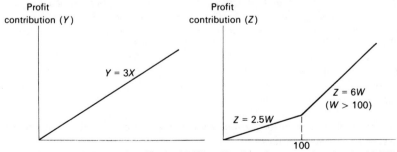

Use linear programming to help Dexter gain favor with the management of Kooltool.

3. Lawncare, Inc., manufactures two types of rotary lawn mowers. The Standard model is a push-type model while the Deluxe model is self-propelled.

These mowers are sold to dealers and department stores nationwide. It is believed that all production can be sold; however, Lawncare has firm orders for only 4000 Standard and 3000 Deluxe models per week. All unsold units must be stored at a charge of $0.25 per unit per week for each week after the production week. The current selling price of $50 for a Standard and $65 for a Deluxe model is believed to be valid only up to a weekly volume of 5000 Standard units and 4500 Deluxe units. Additional production will have to be sold at a reduced price of $46 for the Standard and $63 for the Deluxe model.

Lawncare has one plant in which it produces all its mowers. The plant may be operated two eight-hour shifts per day for a five-day week. The third shift is used for routine maintenance. Average wages for day-shift workers are $2.35 an hour. The union agreement requires night-shift workers to receive $0.12 per hour bonus. Productivity of day and nights shifts are equal.

At the present time 28,600 hours of day-shift labor and 26,800 hours of night-shift labor are available each week. Additional workers could be hired if needed but it will cost Lawncare $500 to train each such worker and it will be two weeks before the worker is fully trained and ready to begin production activity. Union agreements require that new workers be given at least four weeks of production work before they can be layed-off. A termination bonus of $200 must be given to all terminated employees. It is assumed that terminations are permanent and any re-hires must be retrained.

Process requirements per unit are as follows:

Department	Standard	Deluxe	Total machine or process time available per 40 hour shift
Engine	1.5 hours	1.9 hours	11,000 hours
Machine shop	0.8 hours	0.9 hours	6200 hours
Stamping	0.4 hours	0.2 hours	2800 hours
Paint shop	0.3 hours	0.2 hours	3000 hours
Assembly	0.7 hours	0.9 hours	6000 hours

Materials required for producing the mowers are steel, aluminium, paint and purchased parts. Material cost per unit are as follows:

Material	Standard model		Deluxe model	
	Cost per unit	Units required	Cost per unit	Units required
Steel	$0.42 lb	8.5 lb	$0.42 lb	9.4 lb
Aluminium	$0.68 lb	13.5 lb	$0.68 lb	20.9 lb
Paint	$4.17 gal	0.17 gal	$5.67 gal	0.24 gal
Purchased parts	$3.54		$3.48	

Materials are purchased from local suppliers at the lowest cost available in one-month production requirement quantities.

Lawncare, Inc., wants to know how many lawnmowers of each type to produce on each shift each week.

4. A company manufactures two products. The first product (A) uses one unit of raw material while the other product (B) uses two units of this material. The total supply of raw materials each week amounts to 16 units.

Product A and B each use two hours of labor time. Labor is limited to 20 man-hours per week.

The company wishes to determine the optimal product mix in order to maximize profit. The profit contribution of B amounts to $12 per unit. The profit contribution for A is given by the function

$$f(A) = -\frac{7X^2}{6} + \frac{118X}{6}$$

where $X_1 = $ the number of units of product A produced each week.

5. Given one product X_1 with a parabolic profit function going through the points:

$X_1 = 0,\quad$ Profit $= 0$
$X_1 = 4,\quad$ Profit $= 64$
$X_1 = 5,\quad$ Profit $= 75$

and another product X_2 with a profit of $1 per unit, and given three constraints:

$X_1 + X_2 \leqslant 10$
$2X_1 + X_2 \leqslant 12$
$4X_1 + X_2 \leqslant 20$

determine the optimal product mix.

Chapter 15

GOAL PROGRAMMING

A decision situation is seldom, if ever, characterized by a single objective. More often than not the decision maker has in mind many goals and subgoals, some of which may be complementary, many of which may be conflicting.

The linear programming model allows for only one goal to be quantified and used as its objective function. If the decision maker has multiple goals, he must single out one to serve as the objective. Of course, he may then, if he wishes, treat the goals not incorporated in the objective function as constraints for the model. The computational algorithm will select from the set of solutions that satisfy all the constraints—including the goals which are treated as constraints—the one (or ones) that maximize or minimize the objective function. This model structure, by requiring that the "optimal" solution fully satisfy all constraints, implies that all goals written into the model as constraints are of equal importance to the decision maker and that they have absolute priority over the goal serving as the objective function.

Goal programming is a special type of linear programming which is capable of handling decision situations which involve a single goal or multiple goals. In goal programming all of the decision maker's targets or goals may be incorporated into the objective function. Only the environmental conditions under which the decision maker must function are treated as constraints. The computational algorithm then selects from the set of solutions satisfying the true environmental constraints the one (or ones) which best fulfills the decision maker's specified goals.

ADVANTAGES OF THE GOAL PROGRAMMING MODEL

Frequently the multiple goals of a decision maker must be measured by different standards. Often one goal or set of goals can be achieved only at the expense of other goals or sets of goals. The goal programming model does not require a common yardstick. It, instead, allows for an ordinal ranking of goals so that low-priority goals are considered only after higher-priority goals have been satisfied to the fullest extent possible. The goal programming model is especially useful in situations where the multiple goals are conflicting and, hence, cannot all be fully achieved. If these goals were written into a linear programming model as constraints, the result would be no feasible solution, irrespective of the objective function used. The goal programming model has the flexibility to handle this type of problem situation.

Goal programming is also important to the decision maker who is a "satisficer" rather than an "optimizer." Since, when using the linear programming model, the decision maker seeks the highest possible value for the objective function, he is said to be following an optimizing behavior pattern. In using the goal programming model, where goals may be incorporated into the model at a value that is judged to be satisfactory but not necessarily the very best attainable, the decision maker is following a satisficing behavior pattern.

Goal programming, thus, is a version of linear programming adapted to finding a satisfactory solution in light of many objectives rather than the optimal solution in view of only a single objective.

THE GENERAL GOAL PROGRAMMING MODEL

The basic assumptions underlying the linear programming model apply as well to the goal programming model. The significant difference in structure is that the goal programming technique does not attempt to maximize or minimize the objective criterion directly as does the linear programming model. It, rather, seeks to minimize the deviations between the desired goals and the actual results according to the priorities assigned.

The general goal programming model is expressed as

$$\text{Minimize: } \sum_{i=1}^{m} (d_i^+ + d_i^-)$$

where d^+ represents degree of overachievement of a goal and d^- represents degree of underachievement of a goal, subject to

$$\left(\sum_{j=1}^{n} a_{ij} X_j \right) - d_i^+ + d_i^- = b_i$$

and

$$X_j, d_i^+, d_i^- \geq 0.$$

The deviational variable d^+ represents the overachievement of a goal while the variable d^- represents underachievement of the goal. We cannot have both over- and underachievement of a goal simultaneously. Hence, either one or both of these variables must have a zero value; that is,

$$d^+ \times d^- = 0.$$

Also, the nonnegativity requirement applies to these variables as to all other linear programming variables; that is,

$$d^+, d^- \geqslant 0.$$

Goal programming will move the values of these deviational variables as close to zero as possible within the environmental constraints and the goal structure outlined in the model.

Once the goal programming model is formulated, the computational procedure is almost identical to the procedure of the simplex method.

AN ILLUSTRATION—A SINGLE, SATISFICING GOAL

To illustrate the goal programming technique, let us refer again to the Furniture Manufacturing Company case. Recall that the problem was to determine the product mix (units of tables and units of benches to manufacture) that does not violate the constraints of limited assembly hours and limited finishing hours but will at the same time maximize profit contribution. The linear programming model was expressed as

Maximize: $20X_1 + 24X_2$ (profit contribution)

subject to

$$3X_1 + 6X_2 \leqslant 60 \quad \text{(assembly time)}$$
$$4X_1 + 2X_2 \leqslant 32 \quad \text{(finishing time)}$$

where X_1 is the number of tables to produce each day and X_2 is the number of benches to produce each day.

The optimal solution values were $X_1 = 4$ and $X_2 = 8$, yielding a total profit contribution of $272.

Assume that during the next planning period the firm will be undergoing major reorganizational changes. For this reason management believes that it would be imprudent to attempt to follow, during that period, the policy of maximizing profit contribution. It is believed, however, that a "satisfactory" level of profit contribution should be maintained. Management feels that a daily profit contribution of $250 would be satisfactory and would like to determine, given the constraints on production time, the product mix that would yield this rate of profit contribution.

To incorporate the $250 satisficing profit contribution into the model, we define the deviational variables

d^+ = overachievement of the satisficing profit (or amount by which realizable profit contribution exceeds the target profit contribution).

d^- = underachievement of the satisficing profit (or amount by which realizable profit contribution falls short of the target profit contribution).

This goal is written into the model as a constraint

$$20X_1 + 24X_2 - d^+ + d^- = 250 \quad \text{(target profit contribution).}$$

Note that although this is written as an equality, it is not the type of exactly-equal-to constraint used in the linear programming model. It is a target rather than an absolute requirement and deviations above or below the target may exist in the final solution.

Now working within the environmental constraints previously outlined, we formulate the goal programming model as

Minimize: $d^+ + d^-$

subject to

$$3X_1 + 6X_2 \leqslant 60 \qquad \text{(assembly time)}$$
$$4X_1 + 2X_2 \leqslant 32 \qquad \text{(finishing time)}$$
$$20X_1 + 24X_2 - d^+ + d^- = 250 \quad \text{(target profit contribution)}$$

and

$$X_1, X_2, d^+, d^- \geqslant 0.$$

If the target profit contribution of $250 is achieved exactly, both d^+ and d^- will equal zero. The fact that both d^+ and d^- appear in the objective function indicates that the decision maker is seeking exact achievement of the objective, that he wants the model to drive both deviational values as close to zero as possible. If overachievement of the goal were acceptable, d^+ would be eliminated from the objective function and the model would seek to minimize underachievement but would be indifferent as to overachievement. On the other hand, if underachievement were acceptable, d^- would be eliminated from the objective function and the model would seek to minimize overachievement but would be indifferent as to underachievement.

The fact that d^+ and d^- both appear in the objective function and both are assigned equal weights indicates that the decision maker would like to achieve the goal exactly but if exact achievement is not possible he has no preference between a positive deviation (overachievement) and a negative deviation (underachievement) from the target in attempting to come as close to the goal as possible.

The initial tableau for the goal programming model of the Furniture Manufacturing Company is shown in Fig. 15–1. In setting up the tableau, the inequalities are converted to equalities through the use of slack variables wherever required.

Initial Tableau:

	X_1	X_2	S_1	S_2	d^+	d^-	
S_1	3	6	1	0	0	0	60 ←
S_2	4	2	0	1	0	0	32
d^-	20	24	0	0	−1	1	250
	−20	−24	0	0	2	0	−250

Second Tableau:

	X_1	X_2	S_1	S_2	d^+	d^-	
X_2	1/2	1	1/6	0	0	0	10
S_2	3	0	−1/3	1	0	0	12
d^-	8	0	−4	0	−1	1	10 ←
	−8	0	4	0	2	0	−10

Third (and Final) Tableau:

	X_1	X_2	S_1	S_2	d^+	d^-	
X_2	0	1	5/12	0	1/16	−1/16	9.375
S_2	0	0	7/6	1	3/8	−3/8	8.25
X_1	1	0	−1/2	0	−1/8	1/8	1.25
	0	0	0	0	1	1	0

FIG. 15–1   The tableaus, goal programming model, Furniture Manufacturing Company case (a single satisficing goal)

These variables are given the usual linear programming interpretation. The deviation variable d^-, representing underachievement of the goal, labels the third row of the tableau and has an initial value of 250. That is, profit contribution at $X_1 = 0$ and $X_2 = 0$ is zero, which is 250 below the target.

c		X_1	X_2	S_1	S_2	d^+	d^-	
0	S_1	3	6	1	0	0	0	60
0	S_2	4	2	0	1	0	0	32
1	d^-	20	24	0	0	−1	1	250
c		0	0	0	0	1	1	
z		20	24	0	0	−1	1	250
$c-z$		−20	−24	0	0	2	0	−250

FIG. 15–2 Computation of the initial objective-function row

The values appearing in the objective-function row of the initial tableau require some explanation. They were computed as shown in Fig. 15–2. This procedure for computing the initial objective-function row values should be followed whenever a variable that is in the initial basis has a nonzero objective-function coefficient. The complete objective function of the model is

Minimize: $0X_1 + 0X_2 + 0S_1 + 0S_2 + 1d^+ + 1d^- = f.$

These coefficients are labeled c_j. The c coefficients for the basic variables (S_1, S_2, d^-) are used to form a vector $(0, 0, 1)$. This vector is multiplied times the a_{ij} coefficients to obtain a value we can denote z_j. The value for the jth column on the objective-function row is $c_j - z_j$. Consider the X_1 column. We know that to gain a unit of the variable heading the column we must give up what is listed in that column. To gain a unit of X_1 (to bring one unit of X_1 into solution), then, we must give up

Variable	Number of units		Objective-function coefficient		Result
S_1	3	×	0	=	0
S_2	4	×	0	=	0
d^-	20	×	1	=	20
					20

Realized profit contribution will be increased by $20 for each X_1 produced. The divergence between actual and targeted contribution—which is minus 250 at this point—will be increased by 20 for each X_1 produced.

The other numbers in the objective-function row of the initial tableau can be interpreted in a similar manner.

The tableaus are pivoted in the usual simplex way. The final tableau (see Fig. 15–1) indicates that the goal can be achieved exactly by producing 1.25 units of X_1 and 9.375 units of X_2. There will be 8.25 unused hours of finished time.

The d^+ column from the final tableau indicates that the value of $f = d^+ + d^-$ could be increased by one by making 1/8 units more of X_1 and 1/16 units fewer of X_2; that is,

$$(+1/8)(20) + (-1/16)(24) = 1.$$

The overage could be increased by 22 units in this manner. At that point, there would be zero unused units of finishing time.

The zero shadow price on the S_1 column denotes that the model would be indifferent to the exchanges outlined in that column. Hence, there exist other strategies that would yield exactly \$250 profit contribution. Refer to Fig. 15–3 and note that the final tableau is represented by point J on the area of feasible solutions.

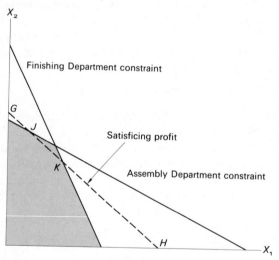

FIG. 15–3   The area of feasible solutions

The slope of the constraint line GH is identical to the slope of the objective function. Thus, points J, K, and all points on the line segment JK represent solutions that meet the objective criterion equally well. From the S_1 column of the final tableau, we see that the exchange of 5/12 units of X_2 for 1/2 units of X_1 would have zero effect on the profit contribution; that is,

$$(-5/12)(24) + (+1/2)(20) = 0.$$

This exchange could be made until corner point K on the area of feasible solutions was reached. Then further exchanges would be made at a different marginal rate of substitution and with a different effect on profit contribution.

And, thus, we see how goal programming can be used to find a satisficing strategy.

INCORPORATING A SECOND LEVEL OF GOAL

What happens if, instead of including only one goal in the objective function of the model, the decision maker wishes to include several goals? Moreover, what happens when the decision maker ranks these goals so that Goal #1 has absolute priority over Goal #2 and Goal #2 has absolute priority over Goal #3? The conventional linear programming technique fails when these complicating factors are introduced, but the goal programming method does not. It has the flexibility needed to deal with cases characterized by multiple goals and multiple levels of goals. And herein lies one of its greatest advantages. This feature of the goal programming model makes it particularly useful in those situations where the multiple goals are conflicting and hence cannot be fully achieved.

One possible formulation of this version of the model is to classify the goals into k ranks and assign a priority factor P_j ($j = 1, 2, ..., k$) to the deviational variables associated with the goals. The priority factors will have the relationship

$$P_j \gg nP_{j+1} \qquad (j = 1, 2, ..., k - 1)$$

The expression $P_j \gg nP_{j+1}$ implies that P_j is so much larger than P_{j+1} that no number n, however large it might be, can make nP_{j+1} equal to or greater than P_j.

Assume that the management of the Furniture Manufacturing Company wishes to disturb the production work force as little as possible during the coming reorganizational upheaval. It wishes, thus, within the framework of achieving the $250 satisficing profit contribution, to minimize idle production time. The goal programming model should be structured as:

Minimize: $P_1 d_3^+ + P_1 d_3^- + P_2 d_1^- + P_2 d_2^-$

given

$$3X_1 + 6X_2 - d_1^+ + d_1^- = 60 \qquad \text{(assembly time)}$$
$$4X_1 + 2X_2 - d_2^+ + d_2^- = 32 \qquad \text{(finishing time)}$$
$$20X_1 + 24X_2 - d_3^+ + d_3^- = 250 \quad \text{(target profit contribution)}$$
$$X_1, X_2, d_i^+, d_i^- \geqslant 0$$

where X_1 = number of tables to produce each day

X_2 = number of benches to produce each day

d_1^+ = overtime in assembly department each day (in hours)

$d_1^- =$ idle time in assembly department each day (in hours)

$d_2^+ =$ overtime in finishing department each day (in hours)

$d_2^- =$ idle time in assembly department each day (in hours)

$d_3^+ =$ overachievement of target profit contribution

$d_3^- =$ underachievement of target profit contribution.

Because both d_3^+ and d_3^- are included in the objective function the model will attempt to achieve exactly the $250 target profit contribution, minimizing deviations in either direction. With d_1^+ and d_2^+ omitted from the objective function, however, the model will be indifferent as to any overtime in either department and will strive only to minimize the idle time. Because the target profit contribution goal is assigned priority factor P_1 the model will attempt to achieve this goal to the fullest extent possible before it gives consideration to the secondary goal of minimizing idle production time.

The tableaus for the model are shown in Fig. 15–4.

	X_1	X_2	d_1^+	d_1^-	d_2^+	d_2^-	d_3^+	d_3^-	
d_1^-	3	6	−1	1	0	7	0	0	60 ←
d_2^-	4	2	0	0	−1	1	0	0	32
d_3^-	20	24	0	0	0	0	−1	1	250
P_2	−7	−8	1	0	1	0	0	0	−92
P_1	−20	−24	0	0	0	0	2	0	−250

	X_1	X_2	d_1^+	d_1^-	d_2^+	d_2^-	d_3^+	d_3^-	
X_2	1/2	1	−1/6	1/6	0	0	0	0	10
d_2^-	3	0	1/3	−1/3	−1	1	0	0	12
d_3^-	8	0	4	−4	6	0	−1	1	10 ←
P_2	−3	0	−1/3	4/3	1	0	0	0	−12
P_1	−8	0	−4	4	0	0	2	0	−10

	X_1	X_2	d_1^+	d_1^-	d_2^+	d_2^-	d_3^+	d_3^-	
X_2	0	1	$-5/12$	$5/12$	0	0	$1/16$	$-1/16$	9.375
d_2^-	0	0	$-7/6$	$7/6$	-1	1	$3/8$	$-3/8$	8.25 ←
X_1	1	0	$1/2$	$-1/2$	0	0	$-1/8$	$1/8$	1.25
P_2	0	0	$7/6$	$-1/6$	1	0	$-3/8$	$3/8$	-8.25
P_1	0	0	0	0	0	0	1	1	0

	X_1	X_2	d_1^+	d_1^-	d_2^+	d_2^-	d_3^+	d_3^-	
X_2	0	1	0	0	$5/14$	$-5/14$	$-1/14$	$1/14$	$6\frac{3}{7}$
d_2^-	0	0	-1	1	$-6/7$	$6/7$	$9/28$	$-9/28$	$7\frac{1}{14}$
X_1	1	0	0	0	$-3/7$	$3/7$	$1/28$	$-1/28$	$4\frac{11}{14}$
P_2	0	0	1	0	$6/7$	$1/7$	$-9/28$	$9/28$	$7\frac{1}{14}$
P_1	0	0	0	0	0	0	1	1	0

FIG. 15–4 The tableaus, goal programming Model II, Furniture Manufacturing Company case (multiple goals)

Note that the two levels of goals are set up in two different objective-function rows. The highest priority factor is on the bottom row; thus, the solution is directed from that row. All negative indicators should be cleared from this row before the negative indicators of a lower priority factor are considered. Negative indicators of a lower priority factor cannot be introduced into the program so long as there is an element other than zero in the same column of all higher priority factors.

The first and second tableaus were pivoted on negative indicators from the P_1 row. In the third tableau there were no negative indicators on the P_1 row so our attention was focused on the P_2 row. Only those columns which had a negative number on the P_2 row along with a zero on the P_1 row were eligible as pivot columns. Hence, in the fourth and final tableau, the $-9/28$ in the d_3^+ column could not be used as a pivot since to do so would cause a violation of the P_1 goal.

The final tableau indicates that $4\frac{11}{14}$ tables and $6\frac{3}{7}$ benches should be produced each day. The target profit contribution of $250 will be achieved exactly. The goal of minimizing idle time cannot be fully realized; there will be $7\frac{1}{14}$ unused hours of finishing time. But this is the minimum number of idle production hours possible given the exact achievement of the $250 profit contribution. If further decreases in idle time were made, the result would be overachievement of the profit goal.

Thus the goal programming model enables the decision maker to achieve incompatible goals as closely as possible within the given constraints and the goal priority structure.

ANOTHER ILLUSTRATION—ASSIGNING VARYING WEIGHTS TO SUBGOALS

Recall that in the original Furniture Manufacturing Company model the maximum profit contribution given 60 hours of assembly time and 32 hours of finishing time was $272. We have considered cases where managment would be satisfied, temporarily, with a production plan providing for a lesser profit contribution. Now let us think about a production plan that would yield a profit contribution greater than the $272.

Suppose that the management of the Furniture Manufacturing Company feels that a daily profit contribution of $300 must be realized during the next planning period and wonders how it can best achieve this goal. Of course, this means that some of the constraints previously adhered to will have to be broken. But assume that the 60 hours and the 32 hours represent production capabilities of the present workforce during regular hours only. Overtime would be possible in either or both departments so that deviations above, as well as below, the 60 and 32 hours are feasible. The overtime pay rate is $2 an hour in the Assembly Department and is $1 an hour in the Finishing Department.

The model would be formulated as follows:

$$\text{Minimize: } P_1 d_3^+ + P_1 d_3^- + 2P_2 d_1^+ + P_2 d_2^+$$

given

$$3X_1 + 6X_2 - d_1^+ + d_1^- = 60 \quad \text{(assembly time)}$$
$$4X_1 + 2X_2 - d_2^+ + d_2^- = 32 \quad \text{(finishing time)}$$
$$20X_1 + 24X_2 - d_3^+ + d_3^- = 300 \quad \text{(target profit contribution)}$$
$$X_1, X_2, d_i^+, d_i^- \geq 0.$$

The objective function indicates that management wants to zero-in on the $300 profit contribution; that is, it wants to achieve this target exactly, minimizing deviations in either direction. The model will be indifferent to idle time in either department but will concentrate on minimizing overtime. Also, the fact that overtime in the Assembly Department is twice as costly as overtime in the Finishing Department is incorporated into the objective function. Hence, on an hourly basis, the model will prefer overtime in the Finishing Department to overtime in the Assembly Department. Thus, it is not only possible to assign different priority factors to different levels of goals but it is also possible to assign different weights to the deviational variables within one level.

The tableaus for the model are shown in Fig. 15–5.

	X_1	X_2	d_1^+	d_1^-	d_2^+	d_2^-	d_3^+	d_3^-	
d_1^-	3	6	−1	1	0	0	0	0	60 ←
d_2^-	4	2	0	0	−1	1	0	0	32
d_3^-	20	24	0	0	0	0	−1	1	300
P_2	0	0	2	0	1	0	0	0	0
P_1	−20	−24	0	0	0	0	2	0	−300

	X_1	X_2	d_1^+	d_1^-	d_2^+	d_2^-	d_3^+	d_3^-	
X_2	1/2	1	−1/6	1/6	0	0	0	0	10
d_2^-	3	0	1/3	−1/3	−1	1	0	0	12 ←
d_3^-	8	0	4	−4	0	0	−1	1	60
P_2	0	0	2	0	1	0	0	0	0
P_1	−8	0	−4	4	0	0	2	0	−60

	X_1	X_2	d_1^+	d_1^-	d_2^+	d_2^-	d_3^+	d_3^-	
X_2	0	1	−2/9	2/9	1/6	−1/6	0	0	8
X_1	1	0	1/9	−1/9	−1/3	1/3	0	0	4
d_3^-	0	0	28/9	−28/9	8/3	−8/3	−1	1	28 ←
P_2	0	0	2	0	1	0	0	0	0
P_1	0	0	−28/9	28/9	−8/3	8/3	2	0	−28

	X_1	X_2	d_1^+	d_1^-	d_2^+	d_2^-	d_3^+	d_3^-	
X_2	0	1	0	0	5/21	−5/21	−1/14	1/14	10
X_1	1	0	0	0	−3/7	3/7	1/28	−1/28	3
d_1^+	0	0	1	−1	6/7	−6/7	−9/28	9/28	9 ←
P_2	0	0	0	2	−5/7 ↑	12/7	9/14	−9/14	−18
P_1	0	0	0	0	0	0	1	1	0

	X_1	X_2	d_1^+	d_1^-	d_2^+	d_2^-	d_3^+	d_3^-	
X_2	0	1	0	0	0	0	1/56	−1/56	7.5
X_1	1	0	1/2	−1/2	0	0	−1/8	1/8	6.0
d_2^+	0	0	7/6	−7/6	1	−1	−3/8	3/8	10.5
P_2	0	0	5/6	7/6	0	1	3/8	−3/8	10.5
P_1	0	0	0	0	0	0	1	1	0

FIG. 15–5 The tableaus, goal programming Model III, Furniture Manufacturing Company case (multiple, incompatible goals)

The best strategy would be to produce 6 units of X_1 and 7.5 units of X_2. The target of $300 profit contribution will be achieved exactly. There will be, however, a need for 10.5 hours of overtime in the Finishing Department. This is another case where both goals cannot be achieved simultaneously. Had we treated both the profit goal and the maximum working hours as constraints in a linear programming model, there would have been no feasible solution. The superiority of goal programming over linear programming in the situation where the multiple goals are incompatible is evident.

EXERCISES

1. A contractor who builds houses and small stores realizes that he wants to achieve several goals in his business and personal life which are not entirely compatible. Since he is only 30 years old he is more interested in his profit than his time off, yet he desires both.

For the coming year he has $80,000 that he can invest in new construction. Houses and stores require an investment of $20,000 each. Because of the time lag in building and selling these structures, the investment turnover is once annually.

He estimates that he can get workers for a total of 20,000 man-hours a year and that it takes 6000 man-hours to build each house and 2000 man-hours for each store.

His primary goal is to achieve a profit level of $8000. He earns $2000 from each house and $4000 from each store. His other important goal is to have 20 days of vacation each year. While building a house he can be away from the job for two days and while building a store he can be away from the job for six days.

What plans should the contractor make for next year?

2. The Magic Carpet Company produces two grades of carpet: Witchcraft and Widzardry. The production of Witchcraft is more automated that that of Widzardry and consequently requires less machine time. However, due to wastage on the automated line, Witchcraft carpet requires a greater amount of material. Production data for each 9-by-12 rug is as follows:

	Machine time	Units of material
Witchcraft	10 hours	16 units
Widzardry	30 hours	10 units

A 9-by-12 rug contributes $14 to overhead and profit if it is of the Witchcraft grade and $10 to overhead and profit if it is of the Widzardry grade.

On a daily basis, the company has available 1200 hours of machine time and 800 units of material.

The management feels that $750 daily contribution margin is a satisfactory rate of return and even though the Widzardry carpet has a smaller contribution margin, the company feels that it should maintain its present market position in the Widzardry line. This would require the production of 30 of the 9-by-12 Widzardry rugs each day.

The $750 target profit is considered the primary goal of the company and the level of Widzardry runs is considered to be the secondary goal. What production strategy should the firm follow?

3. "BLOONK!" the desk responded to the fast-descending fist of a perplexed, angry Ivan Petrokhov. This desk, confiscated during the Revolution, had survived the damp of the Ukrainian summer and the chill of the Siberian winter, so that now its warped, varnishless form was the central piece of furniture in the mean little office of the Peoples' Sock Factory of Niktagrad.

"You should be more respectful of the peoples' furniture, comrade," coolly reprimanded Yuri Grosnev, who shared the office with the plant manager. Yuri was Ivan's second-in-command; he was a bespectacled, dastardly little man, with an IQ which strained to achieve 85, but whose hardline party loyalty had earned him his present position.

Ivan's malevolent stare at Yuri was interrupted by the hum of machinery and the flying of lint as the office door swung open. The 60-watt Polish bulb revealed Josef Bulgarech, a Czechoslovak, formerly an exchange student to the United States, and now in Russia for retraining to the more advanced Socialist industrial methods. He carefully snubbed Yuri and addressed Ivan, "What causes this BLOONK?"

Ivan was now glaring at his ever-reddening hand. Seemingly ignoring Josef's question, he began to pour out his problem to Josef: "To be the manager of a peoples' plant is impossible! They give me more machinery than I can possibly use. But they give me quotas which are incompatible! Sometimes I wish I were a capitalist, by Stalin's mustache!"

A look of righteous indignation jumped onto the countenance of Yuri. He stood, flung back his chair, and noisily stomped from the office, muttering in a barely audible voice, "Is nothing sacred?"

Ivan leaned back in his chair, relieved; Josef, chuckling quietly, sat in the vacated seat. The latter spoke first: "Tell me the problem more specifically. Perhaps I can help."

Ivan picked up a tooth-gnawed pencil and wrote the pertinent numbers of the explanation: "The Peoples' Bureau of Commodities has set quotas for our two products: 12,000 pairs of workers' socks per day and 8000 pairs of quality socks per day. By itself, this is no problem. However, the Peoples' Bureau of Labor has set a quota of 100 workers employed full-time on our standard 10-hour day. It takes three minutes of labor to make a pair of workers' socks and four minutes for a pair of quality socks. To top it off, the Peoples' Bureau of Revenues requires a quota of 50,000 rubles of revenue-over-cost per day. We have a profit, as I like to call it, of two rubles for workers' socks and three rubles for each pair of quality socks. Now you can see that if we make 12,000 pairs of workers' socks and 8000 pairs of quality socks, we use 8000 minutes of labor per day too many and we make 2000 rubles per day too few. And its obvious that if we make the ruble or labor quota, our production quotas would not be met. It's enough to make Trotsky trot!"

"Why don't you just meet the most demanding quota and exceed the others?" asked Josef.

"To exceed quotas is a sure way to the firing squad!" exclaimed Ivan. "If I exceed my labor quota, for example, then next year they will send more workers and give me a higher quota. When my quotas get very high, a bad year will come when we are short of raw materials or some of our workers get the plague or prices for our socks are dropped; then I fail to reach most of my quotas and I am an enemy of the State."

Josef made a pensive frown. "I think I know a method which could help you find the product mix which will least endanger your position as manager. But first tell me which quota misses will hurt the most and the least."

Ivan thought a few minutes, all the while scratching his hairless dome. Finally he said, "It is equally bad to use one minute of labor too few, to make one pair of workers' socks too few or too many, or to make one pair of quality socks too many. It is probably twice as bad to make one too few pairs of quality socks or to miss the ruble quota by one ruble either way. And it is certainly twice as bad again to leave a worker unemployed for a minute."

What production plan should Ivan follow?

4. Ab. C. Defghi Company is planning a major expansion by use of a totally-owned subsidiary for the production of dyes to be used on vegetation. All the equity would be provided by the parent corporation and the long-term debt would be privately placed with the Scrooge Trust Company. The investment bank through which the debt was placed warned that Scrooge Trust Company had very conservative management and would have stringent requirements on the capital structure of the proposed subsidiary.

The financial vice-president of the parent has outlined the following guidelines for the fledgling firm. The new company would require at least $250,000 in both long-term debt and equity to begin. The company already has agreements with suppliers to provide goods on trade credit; this short-term debt could be varied between $10,000 and $20,000 by exercise or rejection of term discounts. The Scrooge Company would lend a maximum of $200,000 but they would require that 10% of the equity be used for short-term liquid assets and be sufficient to maintain a current ratio of two.

The parent is hoping to sell some of the equity to the public relatively soon. Their investment banker has advised that for this type of company, the capital structure most favored by investors is a debt to equity ratio of 1:1.

Defghi would like to know what plan it should follow?

5. Mr. Des Paire, production manager of the Fu-Tile Company, has just emerged from a production meeting and is obviously unhappy. His boss has just informed him that the Directors of Fu-Tile expect production to top 125,000 Hoops and 50,000 Loops for the next six weeks. The catch is that these figures are 25,000 Hoops and 10,000 Loops above normal production levels and the work force is not to be expanded for such a short period of time. Currently Mr. Paire has 100 employees who each work a normal 40-hour work week. Hoops take an average of two minutes of labor to make while Loops only require one minute of labor each. The only way Mr. Paire figures he can meet the production expectations is to work the men overtime. However, his overtime budget is limited to $4,000 a week. Each worker currently averages $4 an hour so overtime would be at a rate of $6 an hour. One additional problem facing Mr. Paire is that the total number of rejects for Hoops and Loops cannot be allowed to increase! Experience has shown that 5% of all Hoops and 6% of all Loops were rejected because of quality control standards.

After much mental torment, Mr. Paire decides that something must give. He then decides that it would be equally undesirable to have less than 800 rejects, to produce over 125,000 Hoops, to make over 50,000 Loops, or to use less than 666.6 hours of overtime. He further decides that it would be twice as undesirable to use over 666.6 hours of overtime or to have over 800 rejects. And he concludes that it would be three times as undesirable to make less than 125,000 Hoop   or less than 50,000 Loops.

What should Des Paire do?

6. The Stone Mountain Stadium Authority is planning to build a stadium for the Stone Mountain Pebbles baseball team and the Stone Mountain Crushers football team. The Authority desires to build the stadium, Rock Park, in such a way that both baseball and football fans will receive maximum viewing of the games. Because the baseball fans like field-level seating and football fans prefer above-the-field seating, the problem of proper seating combinations is of major importance.   The Authority is also interested in maximizing revenues from the stadium events.

The Authority has decided to build a stadium that will seat 58,000 fans for a baseball game and 62,000 fans for a football game. Because the playing field is smaller for a football game, the stadium will have 4000 portable seats on the field level for use at these games. In order to give the fans maximum viewing the stadium will be built with three seating levels. The Authority is interested in the number of seats to be placed in each level that will satisfy the most fans and at the same time result in the largest amount of revenue.

The contractor has furnished the following seating constraints for each level:

Lower level—24,000 to 28,000 seats for baseball and 24,000 to 32,000 for football;
Middle level— 8000 to 14,000 for both sports;
Upper level—0 to 30,000 for both sports.

These building constraints must be maintained for a stadium of this size.

After consulting with other stadium authorities the Stone Mountain Authority has decided to establish the following seating prices at least for the first few years.

Seating level	Baseball game	Football game
Lower	$5	$5
Middle	$3.50	$7
Upper	$2.50	$6

(The reason that the Middle-level football tickets can be priced higher than the others is that the Middle level is completely sheltered.)

The Authority is expecting the attendance to average one million fans for baseball and one-half million fans for football per year. From the experience of other stadiums the Authority found that fans prefer to sit in the different levels in the following percentages:

Seating level	Baseball fans	Football fans
Lower	50%	35%
Middle	20%	25%
Upper	30%	40%

From examining stadiums of similar size, the Authority has established the following seating constraints which follow the average attendance pattern of the other stadiums.

Seating level	Baseball	Football
Lower	at least 25,000	—
Middle	—	at least 10,000
Upper	less than 26,000	at least 20,000

How many seats should the Authority specify for each of the three levels?

Chapter 16

INTEGER PROGRAMMING

One of the basic assumptions of the linear programming model is that all variables are continuous; they are allowed to take on fractional as well as integer values. In many instances fractional values for the solution variables are completely satisfactory; in many other decision situations only integer values for the solution variables will be appropriate. For example, a mill might well be able to follow a production strategy that called for $6\frac{1}{2}$ tons of Feed Mix #1 and $9\frac{2}{3}$ tons of Feed Mix #3 but would not be able to implement an investment strategy specifying purchase of $4\frac{1}{4}$ heavy-duty and 5.913 light-haul trucks.

So, because the conventional linear programming model promises only non-negative answers while a problem may require nonnegative integer answers, we must often revert to another solution technique. The algorithm used for obtaining integer solutions to linear-programming type problems is *integer programming*.

THE GENERAL INTEGER PROGRAMMING MODEL

The general integer programming model can be stated as:

Maximize: $Z = \sum_{j=1}^{n} c_i X_j$

subject to:

$$\sum_{j=1}^{n} a_{ij} X_j \leqslant b_i \quad \text{for all} \quad i = 1, 2, \ldots, m$$

and

$$X_j = 0, 1, 2, \ldots, \quad \text{integer} \quad (j = 1, 2, \ldots, n).$$

The only difference between this formulation and that for the general linear programming model lies in the nonnegativity requirement

$$X_j \geqslant 0$$

which has been altered to require that

$$X_j = 0, 1, 2, \ldots, \text{integer}$$

(that all X_j be integers that are greater than or equal to zero).

Although a great variety of algorithms for the solution of integer programming problems have been proposed, truly efficient solution procedures are still scarce. Much research is being conducted in this area.

AN ILLUSTRATIVE
INTEGER PROGRAMMING PROBLEM

As a simple example of the technique, let us find the integer values which

Maximize: $3X + 4Y = P$

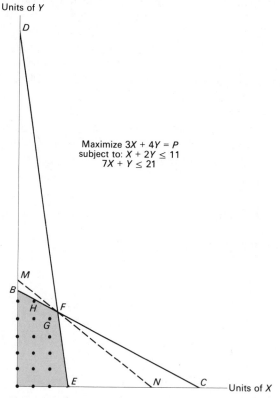

FIG. 16–1 *The area of feasible linear programming solutions and the feasible integer solutions*

subject to the constraints

$X + 2Y \leqslant 11$

$7X + Y \leqslant 21.$

These constraints and the objective function have been plotted in Fig. 16–1. The area of feasible solutions (disregarding the integrality requirement) is shaded; the feasible integer solutions are represented by the heavy dots in this area.

The Linear Programming Optimal Solution

Even when integer solution values are required, we ordinarily begin with the optimal solution determined by the regular linear programming procedure. If this solution, by chance, is an integer solution, well and good; the integer problem is solved. If this is not the case (and usually it is not), additional computational steps that adjust this solution can be taken.

So we add the usual slack variables and by the simplex method find the optimal linear programming solution. The initial and the final tableaus for the current illustration are shown in Fig. 16–2.

Initial Tableau:

	X	Y	S_1	S_2	
S_1	1	2	1	0	11
S_2	7	1	0	1	21
	−3	−4	0	0	0

Final Tableau:

	X	Y	S_1	S_2	
Y	0	1	7/13	−1/13	$4\frac{4}{13}$
X	1	0	−1/13	2/13	$2\frac{5}{13}$
	0	0	25/13	2/13	$24\frac{5}{13}$

FIG. 16–2 *Initial and final simplex tableaus*

In the optimal linear programming solution, the activity variables assume the values

$X = 2\frac{5}{13} \quad$ and $\quad Y = 4\frac{4}{13}$

for a total value of the objective function of $P = 24\frac{5}{13}$. Since the activity variables do not have integer values, this solution strategy is not feasible in the integer programming problem.

We are tempted to assume that the optimal integer solution can be obtained simply by rounding the noninteger solution. We can see from Fig. 16–1 that the rounded values

$$X = 2 \quad \text{and} \quad Y = 4$$

constitute a feasible solution (point G on the graph) and yield an objective-function value of

$$P = (3)(2) + (4)(4) = 22.$$

As a matter of fact, however, the optimal integer solution may be quite different from the optimal noninteger solution obtained through the simplex procedure. A "rounded" version of this solution may provide an acceptable strategy but it will not necessarily be the optimal integer solution.

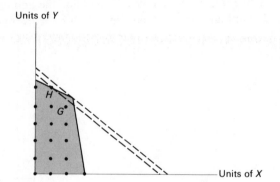

FIG. 16–3   The optimal integer solution

Refer to Fig. 16–3 where the objective function has been shifted to the left, parallel to itself, until it reaches the first feasible integer solution. This solution is at point H, where $X = 1$ and $Y = 5$, and not at point G, where $X = 3$ and $Y = 4$. We can verify that at point H the value of the objective function becomes

$$P = (3)(1) + (4)(5) = 23$$

which is an improvement over the $P = 22$ value at point G.

It should be apparent that the optimal integer solution can never provide a value of the objective function that is higher than the value of the noninteger solution when the case is a maximizing one or lower than the value of the non-integer solution when the case is a minimizing one.

What we require now is a method for moving from the optimal noninteger solution to the optimal integer solution.

THE CUTTING PLANE

The next step in the procedure is to construct a new constraint that will "cut" the optimal noninteger solution away from the region of feasible solutions so that it will no longer be a candidate. We do not want this constraint to cut away any of the feasible integer solutions, however.

But before we can proceed, we need to explore briefly the concept of congruence.

Congruence

If the difference between two numbers is an integer, those two numbers are said to be *congruent*. Symbolically, we state that X is congruent to Y by the notation

$X \equiv Y$.

By definition, $X \equiv Y$ if and only if $X - Y =$ an integer. It follows that

$30/9 \equiv 21/9 \equiv 12/9$

since

$30/9 - 21/9 = 9/9 = 1$;
$30/9 - 12/9 = 18/9 = 2$;

and

$21/9 - 12/9 = 9/9 = 1.$

Now it is also true that

$-4/9 \equiv 5/9$

since

$5/9 - (-4/9) = 1.$

The *fractional* part of a number, X, can be considered to be the smallest nonnegative number that is congruent to X. If $X = 10/9$, its fractional part is $1/9$; it follows that

$10/9 \equiv 1/9$

since

$10/9 - 1/9 = 1.$

Or, if $X = -2/3$, its fractional part is $1/3$; that is.

$-2/3 \equiv 1/3$

since

$1/3 - (-2/3) = 1.$

The cutting plane used in the search for the optimal integer solution is formed by using the smallest nonnegative numbers that are congruent to the coefficients of the equation yielding the noninteger solution.

FORMULATING THE
NEW SET OF CONSTRAINTS

Since the original set of constraints resulted in a noninteger solution, we must establish a new set of constraints. We begin by locating in the final tableau the variable with the largest fractional part. From Fig. 16–2 we see that this variable is X, with a fractional part of 5/13. We write the equation of this row from the final tableau:

$$1X + 0Y - (1/13)S_1 + (2/13)S_2 = 2\tfrac{5}{13}. \tag{1}$$

Next we separate each coefficient in this equation and the right-hand-side constant into two parts: (1) the integer part and (2) the nonnegative fractional part. We obtain

$$1X + (-1 + 12/13)S_1 + (0 + 2/13)S_2 = (2 + 5/13). \tag{2}$$

We rearrange the equation so that the fractional parts are grouped together and the integer parts are grouped together, as

$$X = \text{(fractional part)} + \text{(integer part)}$$
$$X = (5/13 - 12/13S_1 - 2/13S_2) + (2 + 1S_1 - 0S_2). \tag{3}$$

Note that for any integer solution, the terms on the far right will be integers just as they presently appear. Hence, we need to concentrate our efforts on the fractional terms because if X is to be an integer, the sum of these terms

$$5/13 - (12/13)S_1 - (2/13)S_2 \tag{4}$$

must also be an integer.

The sum of the terms in (4) could be *positive* for integer values of S_1 and S_2 only as a fraction. For example, let $S_1 = 0$ and $S_2 = 0$; then

$$5/13 - (12/13)(0) - (2/13)(0) = 5/13.$$

Or let $S_1 = 0$ and $S_2 = 1$; then

$$5/13 - (12/13)(0) - (2/13)(1) = 3/13.$$

If the sum is a fraction, X will not be an integer—and we are insisting that X be an integer. The sum, thus, must be less than or equal to zero; that is

$$5/13 - (12/13)S_1 - (2/13)S_2 \leqslant 0. \tag{5}$$

As a matter of fact, whenever we separate the coefficients and the right-hand-side constant of an equation into integer and fractional parts, we will obtain a positive fraction followed by a series of minus terms with fractional coefficients which will be restrained to be less than or equal to zero.

The "cutting plane" is thus obtained.

The New Constraint

We add to the new constraint

$$5/13 - (12/13)S_1 - (2/13)S_2 \leqslant 0$$

a slack variable and obtain the equation

$$-(12/13)S_1 - (2/13)S_2 + S_3 = -5/13. \tag{6}$$

This new constraint becomes a vital part of the model. Any solution to the original set of constraints must now satisfy this additional constraint as well.

Before continuing with the manipulations of the tableaus, however, let us depict the new constraint graphically. If the new constraint is to be graphed with the two original constraints, it must be transformed so that it is expressed in terms of X and Y. This transformation can be accomplished by setting $S_3 = 0$ and substituting from the original equations:

$$X + 2Y + S_1 = 11$$
$$S_1 = 11 - X - 2Y$$

and

$$7X + Y + S_2 = 21$$
$$S_2 = 21 - 7X - Y.$$

Thus,

$$-(12/13)S_1 - (2/13)S_2 + S_3 = -5/13$$

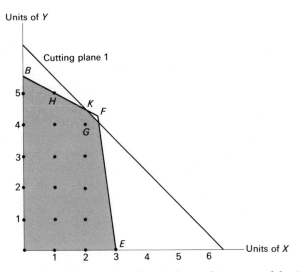

FIG. 16–4 *Cutting plane 1 and the resulting area of feasible solutions*

is equivalent to

$$-(12/13)(11 - X - 2Y) - (2/13)(21 - 7X - Y) + 0 = -5/13$$
$$X + Y = 6.5$$

We see in Fig. 16–4 that the effect of this new constraint is to cut away that small triangular part of the previous area of feasible solutions that contained the optimal noninteger solution. Not any of the feasible integer solutions were eliminated.

First Adjusted Tableau:

	X	Y	S_1	S_2	S_3	
Y	0	1	7/13	−1/13	0	56/13
X	1	0	−1/13	2/13	0	31/13
S_3	0	0	−12/13	−2/13	1	−5/13 ←
	0	0	25/13	2/13	0	317/13

Second "Optimal" Solution:

	X	Y	S_1	S_2	S_3	
Y	0	1	1	0	−1/2	$117/26 = 4\frac{1}{2}$
X	1	0	−1	0	1	2
S_2	0	0	6	1	−13/2	5/2
	0	0	1	0	1	312/13

FIG. 16–5 The tableaus, continued

We continue with the manipulation of the tableaus by appending Eqn (6) to the other equations in the last tableau. The result is shown in Fig. 16–5. We then pivot this tableau again. The S_3 row must be selected as the pivot row because of the minus b-vector value. The ratios used for determining the pivot column are

S_1 column: $25/13 \div -12/13 = -25/12$
S_2 column: $2/13 \div -2/13 = -1$.

The largest ratio is -1; S_3 is the pivot column.

The second solution (shown in Fig. 16–5) results from this iteration. The solution values of the activity variables are

$$X = 2 \quad \text{and} \quad Y = 4\tfrac{1}{2}.$$

(The solution occurs at point K on Fig. 16–4.) However, this is still not an integer solution so the search must continue.

THE SECOND CUTTING PLANE

We repeat the procedure of constructing a cutting plane, appending the new constraint to the last tableau, and pivoting to find a new optimal solution. So, again, we select from the last tableau the variable with the largest fractional part and write its equation:

$$0X + 1Y + 1S_1 + 0S_2 - \tfrac{1}{2}S_3 = 4\tfrac{1}{2}. \tag{7}$$

We separate each coefficient and the right-hand-side constant into integer and fractional parts as

$$Y + S_1 + (-1 + 1/2)S_3 = (4 + 1/2) \tag{8}$$

and group these terms so that the fractional parts are together and the integer parts are together, as

$$Y = (\tfrac{1}{2} - \tfrac{1}{2}S_3) + (4 - S_1 + S_3). \tag{9}$$

Again, we may infer

$$1/2 - (1/2)S_3 \leqslant 0 \tag{10}$$

and this becomes the new cutting plane.

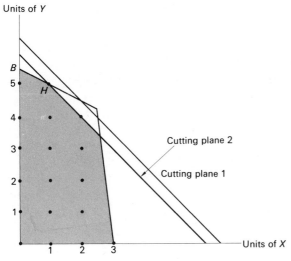

FIG. 16–6 Cutting plane 2 and the resulting area of feasible solutions

So that this constraint can be graphed on the same chart with the other constraints, it, too, must be expressed in terms of X and Y. We make the transformation:

$$S_3 = -5/13 + (12/13)S_1 + (2/13)S_2$$
$$S_3 = -5/13 + (12/13)(11 - X - 2Y) + (2/13)(21 - 7X - Y)$$
$$S_3 = 13 - 2X - 2Y. \tag{11}$$

A new slack variable S_4 is added to the inequality, resulting in the equation

$$1/2 - (1/2)S_3 + S_4 = 0. \tag{12}$$

Now S_4 is set equal to zero and the substitution is made

$$1/2 - (1/2)(12 - 2X - 2Y) = 0$$
$$X + Y = 6. \tag{13}$$

This constraint is shown along with the others in Fig. 16–6.

Second Adjusted Tableau:

	X	Y	S_1	S_2	S_3	S_4	
Y	0	1	1	0	−1/2	0	9/2
X	1	0	−1	0	1	0	2
S_2	0	0	6	1	−13/2	0	5/2
S_4	0	0	0	0	−1/2	1	−1/2 ←
	0	0	1	0	1	0	312/13

Third "Optimal" Solution—The Optimal Integer Solution:

	X	Y	S_1	S_2	S_3	S_4	
Y	0	1	1	0	0	−1	5
X	1	0	−1	0	0	2	1
S_2	0	0	6	1	0	−13	9
S_3	0	0	0	0	1	−2	1
	0	0	1	0	0	2	23

FIG. 16–7 The tableaus, continued

This constraint, too, cuts away that small part of the previous feasible region containing the last optimal noninteger solution.

The equation is included with those from the last tableau, as shown in Fig. 16–7, and the simplex manipulations continue. The optimal solution resulting from this pivoting does, indeed, yield integer values for the activity variables; that is,

$$X = 1 \quad \text{and} \quad Y = 5.$$

The solution is at point H on Fig. 16–6. The value of the objective fuction is

$$P = (3)(1) + (4)(5) = 23$$

and this is the optimal integer solution.

If an integer solution had not occurred on the last pivoting, we would generate another cutting plane, and so forth. The process would continue until an integer solution is reached.

A FEW OBSERVATIONS ON THE INTEGER PROGRAMMING ALGORITHM

Probably the first observation is that the algorithm is rather cumbersome and inefficient. This very simple illustrative problem required a relatively large number of tableaus. Because of the additional computations required, the optimal integer solution is generally more costly to obtain than is the optimal noninteger solution. For this reason we often simply round-off the noninteger solution values and compare the resulting objective-function value to that for the optimal noninteger solution. If the difference is small, the cost of the extra calculations required in the integer programming outweighs the potential gains. The converse may also be true.

Integer programming is a most useful tool, albeit somewhat cumbersome.

EXERCISES

1. Lloyd Productions Formidable Mechanisms, Inc., better known as LP FOR ME, is interested in producing battery-powered cars for children simulating the British styles of the MG and Rolls-Royce.

The labor requirement for one MG is 30 hours and for one Rolls-Royce is 20 hours.

The body of the MG requires 25 pounds of fiberglass, and the body of the Rolls-Royce requires 75 pounds.

Other miscellaneous parts required are of negligible cost and are plentiful in supply.

Labor charges are $3 an hour and 3000 hours are available during the year of production.

Fiberglass can be purchased for $1 per pound and 5000 pounds of fiberglass are available during the year of production.

The selling price of the MG on the American market is $400. The selling price of the Rolls-Royce on the American market is $415. All cars produced can be sold at these prices.

Use integer programming to find the number of each type of car that should be produced in the production year to maximize profit.

2. An airline has three different types of aircraft available to fly on a given route each day. There are restrictions of crew availability, expected demand, and numbers of flights per day. These restrictions are:

Maximum crew members available	75
Maximum passengers expected per day	1500
Maximum flights allowed per day	16

The requirements, by aircraft type, are as follows:

	Type A	Type B	Type C
Crew	4	20	5
Capacity (passengers)	100	300	188
Profit contribution per flight	$500	$1600	$950

Use integer programming to determine the optimum number of each type of aircraft to use on the route each day.

3. Hashimoto Motorcycle Corporation, whose home office is located in Tokyo, is a manufacturer and distributor of quality motorcycles. Hashimoto has been active on the international market for the last nine years and was the first Japanese exporter of motorcycles to the United States.

Recently, Hashimoto has been facing increased competition in the United States market from its fellow countrymen in the form of less expensive, less durable cycles. As a consequence, the President of Hashimoto has decided to call in a marketing consulting firm to help plan their marketing strategy. The consulting firm was immediately asked for advice on the advertising program for the next year.

The consultants, in examining previous advertising expenditures, found that all advertising dollars were spent on teenage TV programs and publications. New television advertising dollars will be spent on shows which appeal to young males under 35 years of age, such as *Then Came Sponson*. (The leading character in the series rides a Hashimoto 1200 motorcycle from town to town in his adventures.)

Another facet of the problem is the allocation of funds among magazines. Since there is no direct quantitive relationship between advertising and sales or profits, some other measure has to be found. It is known that advertising creates sales and that advertising to other than the target is wasted. To maximize sales through advertising, the generally accepted method is to maximize exposure units in the target market. The number of times an ad is seen (even by the same person) can be defined as the number of exposure units an ad generates.

Many magazines were researched to determine circulation statistics desired for the Hashimoto target market. Two magazines were selected on the basis of number of issues circulated, average number of times each issue is read, percentage of male readers, and percentage of readers between 18 and 34 years of age. These magazines, *Playmate* and

Illustrated Sport, are nationally circulated. *Playmate* magazine has a division in Tokyo publishing a sister magazine, *Praymate*. Circulation statistics gathered are as follows:

Playmate: Circulation: 5,253,400 monthly; Average exposures per issue: 4.7; 90% male readers; Age distribution percentages for males:

Age 1 — 17 2%
      18 — 24 20%
      25 — 34 25%
      35 — 50 30%
      over 50 23%

Illustrated Sport: Circulation: 10,860,500 monthly; Average exposures per issue: 2.1; 95% male readers; Age distribution percentages for males:

Age 1 — 17 18%
      18 — 24 35%
      24 — 34 25%
      35 — 50 12%
      over 50 10%

To calculate the target market exposure units for each magazine, multiply (the circulation) × (percentage of male readers) × (percentage of readers between 18 and 34 years) × (average number of times each issue is read).

The funds allocated for magazine advertising during this campaign is $85,000. A full-page advertisement in *Playmate* costs $20,000 and a full-page in *Illustrated Sport* costs $15,000. Ads are not sold in units other than a full page.

Because advertisements for the second quarter of the year (the peak sales period) must be ready by March, only four months of ad-preparation time is available for Hashimoto's advertising department and only three members are free to work on magazine ads (12 man-months of effort). It is estimated by the consultants that four man-months of advertising talent will be required for each *Illustrated Sport* ad because travel is required and language presents difficulties. *Praymate* magazine also has a Japanese staff and can assist Hashimoto personnel without travel and language difficulties. It is, therefore, estimated that only two man-months of effort is required per ad in *Playmate*. Because of time, facilities for art work, and training, and so forth, it has been decided to limit the total number of ads to not more than seven.

How many ads should Hashimoto place in each of the publications?

Chapter 17

TWO SPECIAL-PURPOSE ALGORITHMS: THE TRANSPORTATION METHOD AND THE ASSIGNMENT METHOD

Special computational techniques have been developed for certain types of linear programs. One of the most useful of these special-purpose algorithms is the *transportation method*.

The transportation method was first formulated as a means of finding the minimum-cost plan for shipping a homogeneous product from a number of supply points (sources) to a number of points of demand (destinations). But the use of this method is not restricted to "shipping" problems alone. It can be used to solve that category of linear programming problems in which (1) the sum of the resources is equal to the sum of the requirements, both of these being stated in only one kind of units, and (2) the exchange coefficients of the problem are all either zero or one in value.

The *assignment method* is a special case of the more general transportation method and is applicable to that class of problems in which *n* tasks must be assigned to *n* facilities, any of which could handle any of the tasks but all of which have different performance characteristics.

These techniques are presented here, not because they solve problems the simplex method cannot solve, but because they offer significant computational efficiency over the simplex method for types of problems that are frequently encountered.

THE TRANSPORTATION METHOD

The transportation method is most often associated with those problem situations where a product is to be transferred from a number of sources to a number of destinations. It must be a homogeneous product that could go from any of the sources to any of the destinations. For a specified time period each source has a given capacity for producing this product and each destination has a given requirement for the product. Costs of transporting a unit of the product from each source to each destination are known. The objective is to find that distribution program which will minimize total transportation costs.

The transportation method, like the simplex technique, is an iterative procedure. First, an initial solution is formulated. Then this solution is evaluated to determine whether or not any improvement could be made in it. The transportation method provides a logical step-by-step procedure for developing improved solutions until the least-cost solution has been found.

The process is most easily explained by reference to a simple problem. Consider a manufacturing firm that operates three factories at various geographical locations. These factories manufacture a single product which is shipped to three different distribution centers, these, too, being located in different geographical regions. The factories and their capacities along with the distribution centers and their requirements for the product are shown in Fig. 17–1. (Shipping ordinarily takes place only in the direction of the arrows; however, this restriction may at times be relaxed to allow transshipments between destinations.)

Capacity	Source		Destination	Requirement
150 units	Factory #1		Center A	70 units
110 units	Factory #2		Center B	100 units
120 units	Factory #3		Center C	160 units
380 units available				330 units required

FIG. 17–1 Sources and destinations: Capacities and requirements

Given the quantities of product required at each of the destinations and the quantities available from each of the sources, the firm's problem is that of scheduling shipments from factories to distribution centers in such a way as to achieve the minimum total transportation cast. cost

From (Source)	To (Destination)		
	A	B	C
1	2.50	2.80	4.50
2	3.50	2.10	3.50
3	2.80	2.40	3.80

FIG. 17–2 Cost of shipping one unit of product

The cost of shipping one unit of the product from each of the factories to each of the distribution centers is given in the cost matrix in Fig. 17–2.

As in all linear programming problems, the variables here must be linearly related. Thus, delivery costs must vary directly with the quantities shipped; that is, the per unit cost when 10 units are shipped must be identical to the per unit cost when 100 units are shipped.

Notice these additional similarities between the transportation problem and the general linear programming problem. There is an objective—to minimize total transportation cost. There are alternative ways of achieving this objective—the different source–destination combinations. There are constraints on the attainment of the objective—imposed by the plant capacities and by the destination requirements.

With this information on resources, requirements and costs, we can begin our search for the optimal shipping plan. This step-by-step procedure should be followed.

Step 1. Set up the transportation tableau

The *transportation tableau* provides a framework for presenting in a concise manner the relevant data of the problem and, thus, facilitates the search for the optimal solution. In the tableau displayed in Fig. 17–3, each source is represented by a row, each destination by a column. The capacity of each source is shown in the rightmost column; the requirement at each destination is shown in the bottom row.

Destination

Factory	A	B	C	S	Factory capacity
1	2.50 X_{1A}	2.80 X_{1B}	4.50 X_{1C}	0 X_{1S}	150
2	3.50 X_{2A}	2.10 X_{2B}	3.50 X_{2C}	0 X_{2S}	110
3	2.80 X_{3A}	2.40 X_{3B}	3.80 X_{3C}	0 X_{3S}	120
Destination requirements	70	100	160	50	380

FIG. 17–3 *The transportation tableau*

These are the constraints of the model. The capacity and requirement constraints are also referred to as the *rim requirements*. The number of rim requirements is always equal to the number of rows plus the number of columns in the tableau. For this tableau the total number of rim requirements is seven.

Note that in addition to the three distribution center destinations, another "destination" is shown in the tableau. This is a "slack" destination. In order for the transportation method to be used, the total number of units required must exactly equal the total number of units available. From Fig. 17–3 we see that total requirements at the destinations are only 330 units where total plant capacity is 380 units. This is called an "unbalanced" condition—the requirements and capacities are not equal. In this case the capacities exceed the requirements so there must be created a "dummy" destination to absorb the slack capacities. In those problems where the requirements exceed the capacities, a dummy source is generated to "supply" the surplus requirement.

The slack destination S of the current problem is used to equate requirements and resources and is thus equal to 50 units. The final solution will contain 50 units of unused plant capacity; that is, there will be a total of 50 units available from the factories that will not be shipped to any of the distribution centers.

The cells in the body of the tableau represent each of the alternative source-to-destination assignments. The quantities to be shipped from each factory to each distribution center, the decision variables of the problem, are found in these cells and are denoted X_{1A}, X_{1B}, etc.

The per unit shipping cost for each source-to-destination appears in the upper right-hand corner of that particular cell. Obviously the cost when a unit is not shipped is zero; hence, the costs in the dummy destination are all zero. These costs are the coefficients for the objective function.

Step 2. Develop an initial solution

After the problem situation has been defined, the next step is to determine an initial solution. The only requirement for the initial solution is that it must be feasible; that is, it must satisfy all of the rim requirements. The initial solution may be determined in a variety of ways. It can be developed by inspection or by the use of the present transportation program if one exists. Or, there has been devised a logical systematic procedure for setting up the initial solution that is commonly known as the *Northwest Corner Rule*.

The Northwest Corner Rule may be stated as follows:

Beginning at the upper left-hand corner (the "northwest" corner) of the tableau, assign quantities to the cells in that row until the destination requirements or source capacities are fully utilized. Then move to the next row or column and assign quantities until the requirements are met. Always, the rim requirements of any column should be fully met before moving to the next column to the right; the quantities available at each row should be exhausted before moving down to the next row. Continue in this manner through the entire tableau. When finished, check once again to see that no rim requirements are violated.

In our problem we begin in cell $1A$ by assigning 70 units from Factory 1 to Destination A (see Fig. 17–4). This fulfills the requirement of Destination A and still leaves 80 units of Factory 1 capacity unused. We move to the next column and notice that the requirement at Destination *B* exceeds the 80 remaining units at Factory 1. So these units are all applied to Destination *B*. But the requirement of Destination *B* is 100 units, so we move to the next row, representing Factory 2, for the additional 20 units needed by *B*. The requirement at Destination *B* are thus satisfied, and the remaining capacity of Factory 2 (90 units) is assigned to Destination *C*. We continue in this manner through the matrix until all units are assigned and all requirements fulfilled.

	A	*B*	*C*	*S*	
1	2.50 (70)	2.80 (80)	4.50	0	150
2	3.50	2.10 (20)	3.50 (90)	0	110
3	2.80	2.40	3.80 (70)	0 (50)	120
	70	100	160	50	380

FIG. 17–4 Initial solution using northwest corner rule

Before attempting to evaluate this solution, let us note a few things of importance about it. First, although it is a rather arbitrary solution, it is feasible; all rim requirements are met. Next, notice that there are empty cells. The cells containing no shipment quantities, such as cells 2*A* and 3*A*, are called *unused squares*; no units are being transferred from the source to the destination represented by that square. For any solution, the number of used squares must equal the total number of rim requirements minus one; that is

$$\text{Used squares} = \text{Number of rim requirements} - 1.$$

For this example,

$$6 = 7 - 1.$$

When any solution does not conform to the above rule, a condition referred to as *degeneracy* exists. The procedure for handling a degenerate solution will be discussed later. The important point to make here is that each solution should be tested for degeneracy.

Cells that are used, that do contain quantities to be shipped, are sometimes referred to as "stone squares."

Now, we are, of course, concerned with the cost of this shipping program. The cost of the initial solution has been computed in Fig. 17–5 to be \$1022.

From source	To destination	Number of units shipped	Shipping cost per unit	Total cost
1	*A*	70	2.50	$175.00
1	*B*	80	2.80	224.00
2	*B*	20	2.10	42.00
2	*C*	90	3.50	315.00
3	*C*	70	3.80	266.00
3	*S*	50	∅	∅
				$1022.00

FIG. 17–5 Total cost of initial solution

Step 3. Test the solution for possible improvement

The next step we take is that of determining whether or not the solution we have formulated is the best solution. We want to determine if there is any other shipping plan that when put into operation would result in a lower total shipping cost. Hence, the alternative shipping strategies must be examined. The alternative courses of action are represented by the cells in the tableau that are not presently being used, the unused squares. We must analyze each unused square in the tableau to determine the effect on total cost of bringing that source-to-destination into solution.

One plan for evaluating the unused squares is called the "stepping-stone" method. Let's see how it works by evaluating cell 2*A* (see Fig. 17–6). Adding one

Source	Destination *A*	Destination *B*	Destination *C*	Destination *S*	Source capacities
1	2.50 (70) −1	2.80 (80) +1	4.50	0	150
2	3.50 (0) +1	2.10 (20) −1	3.50 (90)	0	110
3	2.80	2.40	3.80 (70)	0 (50)	120
Destination requirements	70	100	160	50	380

FIG. 17–6 Evaluation of unused square 2A

unit to cell $2A$ will increase cost by $3.50. Such an addition will also cause the rim requirement for Destination A to be exceeded; therefore, one unit must be subtracted from cell $1A$. This last move will cause costs to decrease by $2.50. Now, however, factory capacities are not being satisfied, so to correct the problem we must add one unit to cell $1B$ (increasing cost by $2.80) and subtract one unit from cell $2B$ (decreasing cost by $2.10). The net effect on total cost of such a move would be

$$+ \$3.50 - \$2.50 + \$2.80 - \$2.10 = +\$1.70.$$

(The $1.70 is called the "improvement index" for cell $2A$.) The fact that cell $2A$ evaluated as $+\$1.70$ indicates that, at this point in the solution, shipping one unit of product from Factory 2 to Destination A would add $1.70 to the total. Because this results in an increase in cost, we would not make this change in the shipping plan. We cannot know, however, whether the present solution is optimal or not until all unused cells have been evaluated. Nonetheless, it should be apparent that any unused cell which evaluates at a positive change in total cost will not be considered for inclusion in a new solution. If the evaluation of an unused square indicates that the change in total cost would be negative (a decrease) that cell will be considered for inclusion in a new solution. The exact cell that will be brought into the next solution is determined by the magnitude of the evaluation; it is the unused cell with the most negative improvement index that will be introduced into the next solution. So we must proceed through the tableau evaluating each unused cell. But before we continue, let us view more carefully the route followed in evaluating an unused cell.

A route such as the one followed in evaluating cell $2A$ can be called a "closed-path." A closed-path evaluation, then, is an evaluation that starts in an unused square and, by a series of vertical and horizontal moves, passes through used squares until it returns to the original starting point. Although the path may skip over unused squares, corners of the closed path may occur only at used squares or the unused square being evaluated.

The most direct path must be followed through the tableau. Only one closed-path exists for each unused square in a given solution.

The procedure for evaluating each unused square is this:

1. Select the unused square to be evaluated and trace its closed-path through the tableau.

2. Beginning with a plus ($+$) sign in the unused square being evaluated, assign on an alternating basis ($+$) and minus ($-$) signs at each corner of the closed path. These positive and negative signs represent the addition or subtraction of one unit to that square.

3. Determine the net effect on total cost by adding the unit cost in each square with a positive sign and subtracting the unit cost of each square with a negative sign. This sum is the *improvement index* for that unused square.

All unused squares are evaluated in this manner. If all the improvement indexes are greater than or equal to zero, the solution is an optimal solution. Conversely, if any improvement index is negative, an improved solution, one with a smaller total cost, is possible.

This method of evaluating alternative solutions is often referred to as the *stepping-stone method.*

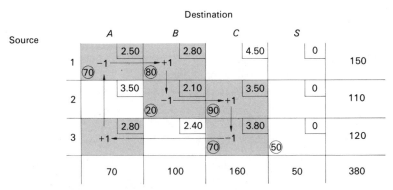

FIG. 17-7   *Evaluation of unused square 3A*

Let us follow the evaluation of one more unused cell to further demonstrate the stepping-stone procedure. Let us compute the improvement index for cell 3A. The closed-path for this cell is shown in Fig. 17-7. Note that if we add one unit to 3A we add $2.80 to the total cost. But again we must consider the rim requirements. Therefore, we shall subtract a unit from 1A (decreasing cost by $2.50), add a unit to 1B (increasing cost by $2.80), subtract a unit from 2B (decreasing cost by $2.10), add a unit to 2C (increasing cost by $3.50), and subtract a unit from 3C (decreasing cost by $3.80). The net effect on total cost of using 3A by the route $3A \rightarrow 1A \rightarrow 1B \rightarrow 2B \rightarrow 2C \rightarrow 3C \rightarrow 3A$ is

$$+2.80 - 2.50 + 2.80 - 2.10 + 3.50 - 3.80 = =0.70.$$

Destination

Source		A	B	C	S	
1		2.50	2.80	4.50	0	150
		⑦⓪	⑧⓪			
2		3.50	2.10	3.50	0	110
		②⓪		⑨⓪		
3		2.80	2.40	3.80	0	120
				⑦⓪	⑤⓪	
		70	100	160	50	380

FIG. 17-8   *Evaluation of unused square 3B*

In other words, at this stage of the solution, the adjustments described above will increase total cost by \$0.70 per unit shipped from Factory 3 to Destination A. The evaluation of the remaining unused cells would be as follows. The closed-path for unused square $3B$ is shown in Fig. 17–8. The improvement index is

$$+2.40 - 2.10 + 3.50 - 3.80 = \emptyset.$$

The closed-path for each of the remaining unused cells are shown in Figs. 17–9, 17–10, and 17–11.

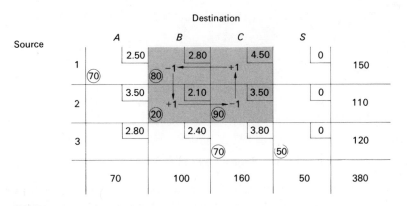

FIG. 17–9   Evaluation of unused square 1C

Improvement index:

$$+4.50 - 2.80 + 2.10 - 3.50 = +0.30.$$

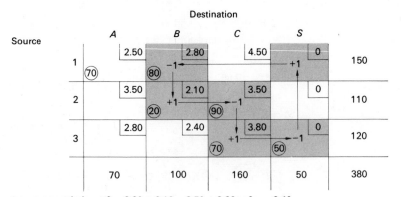

Improvement index: $+0 - 2.80 + 2.10 - 3.50 + 3.80 - 0 = -0.40$

FIG. 17–10   Evaluation of unused square 1S

Improvement index:

$$+0 - 2.80 + 2.10 - 3.50 + 3.80 - 0 = -0.40.$$

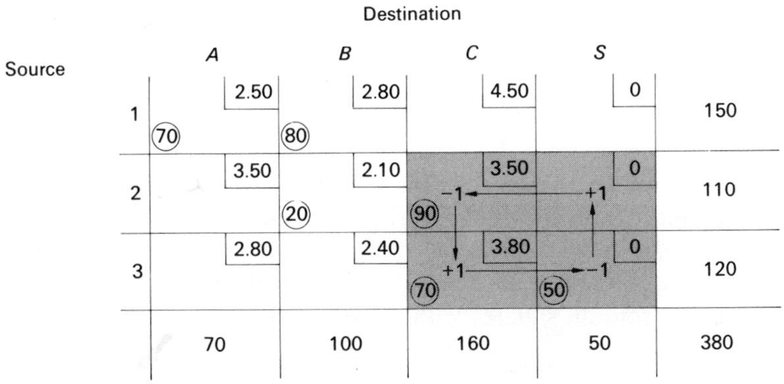

Improvement index: +0 − 3.50 + 3.80 − 0 = +0.30

FIG. 17–11 Evaluation of unused square 2S

Improvement index:

$$+0 - 3.50 + 3.80 - 0 = +0.30.$$

We have found that the improvement indexes for the unused squares are as follows:

Unused square	*Improvement index*
2*A*	+1.70
3*A*	+0.70
3*B*	∅
1*C*	+0.30
1*S*	−0.40 ← most negative number
2*S*	+0.30.

Each negative improvement index represents the amount by which total shipping costs could be reduced by transferring one unit of product via that source-to-destination combination, making the concurrent changes shown on that cell's closed-path.

Step 4. Develop a new solution

If it is desirable to make a one-unit change in the shipping strategy, it will be advantageous to include as many units as possible in the change. Let us reconstruct the closed-path for unused cell 1*S* and pay particular attention to the quantities in the unused squares along this path.

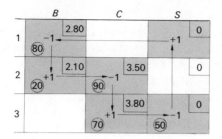

The maximum quantity that we can ship from Factory 1 to Destination S is given by the smallest quantity in a used square assigned a minus sign on the closed-path for this source-destination cell. It is 50 units, as shown in cell $3S$. The new solution is obtained by adding 50 units to all squares on the closed path with plus signs and subtracting 50 units from all squares with minus signs (see Fig. 17–12).

Destination

Source	A		B		C		S		
1	2.50 (70)		2.80 (30)		4.50	(50)	0		150
2	3.50		2.10 (70)		3.50 (40)		0		110
3	2.80		2.40	(120)	3.80		0		120
	70		100		160		50		380

FIG. 17-12 Second solution

The total cost of this solution is given in Fig. 17–13 as $1002.00.

From Source	To Destination	Number of units shipped	Shipping cost per unit	Total cost
1	A	70	2.50	175.00
1	B	30	2.80	84.00
2	B	70	2.10	147.00
2	C	40	3.50	140.00
3	C	120	3.80	456.00
1	S	50	∅	∅
				$1002.00

FIG. 17–13 Total cost of second solution

This represents a cost reduction of

50 units × 0.40 = $20.00.

Now we must go once again to step 3 in the sequence to evaluate the unused cells in the second tableau in order to determine whether further improvement in the shipping program is possible. We compute these improvement indexes.

Square $2A: 2A \rightarrow 1A \rightarrow 1B \rightarrow 2B \rightarrow 2A$

$\qquad +3.50 - 2.50 + 2.80 - 2.10 = +1.70$

Square $3A: 3A \rightarrow 1A \rightarrow 1B \rightarrow 2B \rightarrow 2C \rightarrow 3C \rightarrow 3A$

$\qquad +2.80 - 2.50 + 2.80 - 2.10 + 3.50 - 3.80 = +0.70$

Square $3B: 3B \rightarrow 2B \rightarrow 2C \rightarrow 3C \rightarrow 3B$

$\qquad +2.40 - 2.10 + 3.50 - 3.80 = \emptyset$

Square $1C: 1C \rightarrow 1B \rightarrow 2B \rightarrow 2C \rightarrow 1C$

$\qquad +4.50 - 2.80 + 2.10 - 3.50 = +0.30$

Square $2S: 2S \rightarrow 1S \rightarrow 1B \rightarrow 2B \rightarrow 2S$

$\qquad +0 - 0 + 2.80 - 2.10 = +0.70$

Square $3S: 3S \rightarrow 1S \rightarrow 1B \rightarrow 2B \rightarrow 2C \rightarrow 3C \rightarrow 3S$

$\qquad +0 - 0 + 2.80 - 2.10 + 3.50 - 3.80 = +0.40.$

Because all of these indexes are positive, there is no better solution; this is the least-cost shipping program.

Alternative Optimal Solutions

The improvement index for square $3B$ is zero, signifying that there exists an alternative optimal solution. If this closed-path were brought into the solution, the shipping program would change but the total transportation cost would be be the same. The alternate optimal solution is obtained by transferring 70 units over the closed-path for unused square $3B$. This solution is shown in Fig. 17–14.

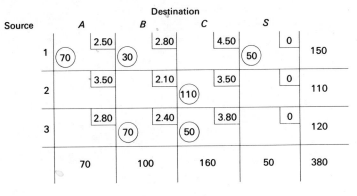

FIG. 17–14A   *Alternative optimal solution destination*

From Source	To Destination	Number of units shipped	Shipping cost per unit	Total cost
1	A	70	2.50	175.00
1	B	30	2.80	84.00
3	B	70	2.40	168.00
2	C	110	3.50	385.00
3	C	50	3.80	190.00
1	S	50	∅	∅
				$1002.00

FIG. 17–14B   Total cost of alternative optimum solution

The MODI Method of Evaluating a Solution

The modified-distribution (MODI) method is a more efficient procedure than the stepping-stone method for computing the improvement indexes for the unused squares.

By the MODI method the improvement indexes can be calculated without tracing each closed-path through the tableau. Instead, a value is computed for each row and column in the tableau by the simple equation

$$R_i + K_j = C_{ij}$$

where R_i is the value assigned to row i; K_j is the value assigned to column j; and C_{ij} is the unit transportation cost shown in the upper right-hand corner of square ij. This equation is applied only to the used squares of a given solution.

Source		A	B	C	S	
$R_1 = 0$	1	2.50 (70)	2.80 (80)	4.50	0	150
$R_2 = -0.70$	2	3.50	2.10 (20)	3.50 (90)	0	110
$R_3 = -0.40$	3	2.80	2.40 (70)	3.80 (50)	0	120
		70	100	160	50	380
		$K_A = 2.50$	$K_B = 2.80$	$K_C = 4.20$	$K_S = 0.40$	

FIG. 17–15   The initial solution

We have set forth in Fig. 17–15 the initial solution to the current illustrative problem obtained by the Northwest Corner Rule. Only a slight change is made in the tableau; a R_i column and a K_j row have been built into the tableau. In order to begin computing the indexes, a starting point is selected and that R_i value set equal to zero. Conventionally, we begin by letting $R_1 = 0$. Such an arbitrary move is entirely legitimate since we are interested in the relative, rather than the absolute values of the indexes computed. We proceed as follows:

Since $R_1 = 0$

$$R_i + K_j = C_{ij}$$
$$0 + K_A = 2.50$$
$$K_A = 2.50.$$

Since $R_1 = 0$

$$0 + K_B = 2.80$$
$$K_B = 2.80.$$

Since $K_B = 2.80$

$$R_2 + 2.80 = 2.10$$
$$R_2 = 2.10 - 2.80 = -0.70.$$

Since $R_2 = -0.70$

$$-0.70 + K_C = 3.50$$
$$K_C = 3.50 + 0.70 = 4.20.$$

Since $K_C = 4.20$

$$R_3 + 4.20 = 3.80$$
$$R_3 = 3.80 - 4.20 = -0.40.$$

Since $R_3 = -0.40$

$$-0.40 + K_S = \emptyset$$
$$K_S = 0.40.$$

The R and K values in a given problem may be positive, zero, or negative. These values for the current case are shown in Fig. 17–15.

The next step of the MODI method is to evaluate each unused square of the present solution; that is, the improvement indexes must be computed. The improvement index for an unused square is found by calculating

$$C_{ij} - R_i - K_j = \text{Improvement index for cell } ij.$$

For example, for cell $3A$, the index is found to be

$$2.80 - (-0.40) - (2.50) = +1.70$$

as before. If there are no negative indexes, the current solution represents the least-cost shipping plan. If the index of any unused cell is negative, further improvement in the shipping program is possible. To bring an unused cell into solution, we proceed as before by tracing its closed-path so that we may determine the adjustments to be made in the strategy.

THE PROBLEM DEGENERACY

We have previously stated that the number of used squares in any solution must be equal to the number of rim requirements minus one. If this rule is not met, the solution is said to be *degenerate*. However, a degenerate solution is only a small stumbling block. We can resolve this problem of degeneracy by making use of an artificial quantity that we shall denote by the Greek letter "delta" (Δ). If Δ is placed in the lower left-hand corner of a cell, that cell is considered to be occupied by a very small quantity, a quantity so small that it affects neither the source restrictions, nor the destination requirement, nor the total total, even if it should appear in the final solution. It is used solely in evaluating the unused cells.

THE ASSIGNMENT METHOD

Another special-purpose algorithm used in linear programming is the *assignment method*. The assignment problem is actually a special case of the more general transportation problem. Like the transportation method, the assignment method is computationally more efficient than the simplex method for a special type of linear programming problem.

The assignment method is used when there are m tasks and n facilities for accomplishing those tasks. While any task–facility combination is feasible, the different combinations have varying degrees of effectiveness. The assignment algorithm will match the tasks and facilities so as to optimize the given measure of effectiveness.

Let us illustrate this procedure by means of a simple problem. A company that customizes automobiles has three jobs scheduled to be brought into its plant on Monday morning. There are four possible work-centers at which the vehicles could be processed. Each of the work-centers is equipped with different tools and machinery and skilled technicians with various types of expertise in customizing work. Given the characteristics of the three work-orders and the properties of the four work-centers, the shop manager has been able to obtain these estimates of the number of hours that would be required to complete each of the customizing jobs at each of the four stations. These estimates are displayed in Fig. 17–16.

		Job-order	
Work station	1	2	3
A	16	30	40
B	24	25	32
C	30	28	48

FIG. 17–16   *Time estimates (in hours) for completing customizing jobs*

The shop manager wishes to assign the three jobs to the four stations in such a way as to minimize the total time required for completing the work.

Before we begin to solve the problem by the assignment method, there are a few things we should note about the preceding table. In an assignment tableau, the number of rows (facilities) must equal the number of columns (tasks). (If this is not the case, we make use of a slack variable; we introduce a dummy task or dummy facility.) Another characteristic of the assignment method is that in the optimal solution there will be only one assignment in a given row or column of the assignment table.

Much of the rationale underlying the assignment method is embedded in the concept of opportunity cost. We realize that the "cost" of any kind of action includes the opportunities that we forego when we decide to take that particular action. Consider work Station *A*, for example. If we assign Job-order #3 to Station *A*, the time required to complete the job will be 40 hours. Since work Station *B* could also process Job-order #3 and would require only 32 hours, we see that the assignment of Job #3 to Station *A* is not the best decision if we are interested in minimizing processing time. The assignment carries with it an opportunity cost of $40 - 32 = 8$ hours; we sacrificed an extra 8 hours of processing time by making the assignment of Job #3 to Station *A* rather than Station *B*.

The assignment method searches for the best possible assignment—the assignment that will minimize the opportunity cost.

After the performance matrix is set up, there are basically three steps in the assignment procedure.

Step 1. Determine the total opportunity-cost matrix

Subtract the lowest entry in each column of the original performance matrix from every entry in that column. The resulting table is the task opportunity-cost matrix (see Fig. 17–17). The best assignment for any task would be the least-time assignment; this is represented by the smallest number in that task's column. This best assignment carries with it a zero opportunity-cost. Any other assignment for that task has an opportunity-cost (in terms of hours of processing time) that is the difference between the time required by that assignment and the least-time assignment.

The numbers in the task opportunity-cost table, then, are processing hours sacrificed if the best assignment is not made.

| | Job-order | | |
Work station	1	2	3
A	0	5	8
B	8	0	0
C	14	3	16

FIG. 17–17   *Task opportunity-cost matrix*

Now the objective is to compile not just a task opportunity-cost matrix but, instead, a total opportunity-cost matrix. That is, we want to consider facility opportunity-cost along with task opportunity-cost. Thus, we locate the smallest entry in each row of the task opportunity-cost matrix and subtract that value from each entry in that row. The resulting matrix is a total opportunity-cost matrix; it considers both task and facility opportunity-costs. (See Fig. 17–18).

| | Job-order | | |
Work station	1	2	3
A	0	5	8
B	8	0	0
B	11	0	13

FIG. 17–18   *Total opportunity-cost matrix*

Step 2. Determine whether an Optimal Assignment can be made

The objective of assigning tasks to facilities so as to minimize total processing time can be achieved only if we assign jobs to work stations in such a way as to obtain a total opportunity-cost of zero. Referring to Fig. 17–18, we see that if Job-order #1 is assigned to work Station A, Job-order #3 to work Station B, and Job-order #2 to work Station C the total opportunity-cost is zero. This is the optimal assignment, the assignment that will minimize total processing time. This will be

16 + 32 + 28 = 76 hours.

There is a rather simplistic, but convenient, way of determining whether an optimal assignment can be made. Straight lines are drawn (either vertically or horizontally) through the total opportunity-cost matrix so as to cover all zero squares, but by using only the minimum number of lines (see Fig. 17–19). If the number of lines required to cover all the zeros is equal to the number of columns in the table, an optimal assignment can be made and solution to the problem has been attained. However, if the number of lines is less than the number of columns, an optimal assignment cannot yet be made and we must develop a new total opportunity-cost matrix.

	Job-order		
Work station	1	2	3
A	0	5	8
B	8	0	0
C	11	0	13

FIG. 17–19   Determining whether an optimal assignment can be made

Step 3. Revise the total opportunity-cost matrix

If an optimal assignment could not be made from the preceding total opportunity-cost matrix, a new matrix must be developed. Consider the matrix in Fig. 17–20; an optimal assignment is not feasible from this table. The procedure for modifying

	Task			
Facility	1	2	3	4
A	0	5	12	0
B	3	2	7	8
C	4	0	13	6
D	8	0	0	12

FIG. 17–20   Hypothetical total opportunity-cost matrix

the opportunity-cost matrix is as follows: (1) select the smallest number in the matrix not covered by one of the straight lines, (2) subtract this number from all numbers not covered by a straight line, and (3) add this same smallest number to the numbers at the intersection of any two lines. The revised total opportunity-cost matrix is shown in Fig. 17–21.

Facility	Task			
	1	2	3	4
A	0̶	8̶	1̶2̶	0̶
B	0̶	2̶	4̶	5̶
C	1̶	0̶	1̶0̶	3̶
D	8̶	3̶	0̶	1̶2̶

FIG. 17–21   Revised total opportunity-cost matrix

Now Task 4 is assigned to Facility *A*, Task 1 to Facility *B*, Task 2 to Facility *C* and Task 3 to Facility *D*.

However, had an optimal assignment still not been possible, the above matrix would have been revised again by the same rules. In fact, this procedure is repeated until an optimal assignments is possible.

EXERCISES

1. Given the following cost matrix, use the transportation method to find the least cost shipping plan.

Shipping from sources	Shipping to destinations				Units available
	1	2	3	4	
A	0.50	0.30	0.32	0.47	300
B	0.30	0.33	0.37	0.32	200
C	0.35	0.45	0.38	0.50	100
D	0.45	0.37	0.33	0.42	100
E	0.38	0.42	0.34	0.40	100
Units required	100	250	300	150	

2. The Phillip Manufacturing Company makes office equipment, primarily file cabinets. At the present time they are changing one of their oldest policies. This policy is to have the dealer pay the transportation cost for distribution of their products. In the future, Phillip will pay all transportation costs.

They have decided to use one of their newest product lines to test the new policy. The product is the latest kind of file cabinet on the market. It is five feet tall, four feet wide, and one foot deep. It opens in the front but then the files must be viewed on the side and the person using these can see all of the files in the drawer at one time. The cabinet is fire proof and weighs one hundred pounds.

The company has plants in Fitzgerald, Dublin, Brunswick, Americus, and Albany. The capacities of these plants for this one item are as follows, on a weekly basis:

Fitzgerald	140 units	Americus	140 units
Dublin	100 units	Albany	160 units
Brunswick	160 units		

These plants serve the following major cities: Augusta, Athens, Columbus, Macon, Rome, Savannah, and Valdosta. The dealers in each of the cities involved have indicated to Phillip that they can sell certain quantities of these files each week. These quantities are as follows:

Augusta	110 units	Rome	60 units
Athens	70 units	Savannah	90 units
Columbus	125 units	Valdosta	75 units
Macon	170 units		

The problem exists as to how to get the product from the plant to the dealer at the minimum cost.

Phillip has conducted exhaustive research into rates of various carriers such as trucks and trains and found that overall the cheapest way to send these cabinets was by an express company which had agreed to charge a set rate for each cabinet for a particular mileage. These rates turned out to be as shown below.

				Shipped to			
Shipped from	*Augusta*	*Athens*	*Columbus*	*Macon*	*Rome*	*Savannah*	*Valdosta*
Fitzgerald	$3.00	$3.00	$2.60	$2.15	$3.50	$2.80	$1.80
Dublin	2.30	2.50	2.60	1.55	3.20	2.55	2.60
Brunswick	3.05	3.50	3.50	3.05	4.20	2.15	2.55
Americus	3.05	2.90	1.80	1.80	3.05	3.20	2.50
Albany	3.20	3.10	2.15	2.45	3.35	3.20	2.15

Determine the optimal shipping plan.

3. The National Air Transport Company is faced with the problem of procuring at the least possible cost fuel for its fleets of planes. These planes are operated out of four different bases. Every six months NATC accepts bids from petroleum companies and awards contracts so that the delivered cost of the fuel will be the lowest possible. During the next six months, it is expected that the requirements at the different bases will be:

Depot #1	1000 gallons daily
Depot #2	1500 gallons daily
Depot #3	2000 gallons daily

Four companies have submitted bids to furnish a specified maximum quantity of fuel. Each company could supply a lesser quantity but none could supply more than the maximum stated below.

Supplier *A*	800 gallons daily, maximum
Supplier *B*	1200 gallons daily, maximum
Supplier *C*	1100 gallons daily, maximum
Supplier *D*	3000 gallons daily, maximum

The delivered, per gallon, price (in cents) from each of the suppliers to each of the depots is as set forth in the tableau below:

	Depot #1	Depot #2	Depot #3
Supplier A	52	30	45
Supplier B	48	32	50
Supplier C	60	40	55
Supplier D	52	41	60

What quantities of fuel should be obtained from each of the suppliers for each of the depots?

4. A manufacturer of prefabricated buildings has decided to subcontract three component parts for the buildings. Several different firms are interested in these subcontracts but none can handle more than one such subcontract because of capacity restrictions. Quality of the work performed is not expected to vary from one firm to the next on any of the jobs. The firms have submitted these bids for the different jobs.

		Bidder		
Job	#1	#2	#3	#4
A	180	215	198	202
B	200	190	225	175
C	325	315	309	300
D	380	398	440	442

Use the assignment technique to determine which job should be let to which subcontractor.

5. A construction company has to move four large cranes from old construction sites to new construction sites. The distance (in miles) between the old locations and the new are given in the following matrix:

Old construction sites	New construction sites			
	N_1	N_2	N_3	N_4
O_1	25	30	17	43
O_2	20	23	45	30
O_3	42	32	18	26
O_4	17	21	40	50

Any of the cranes work equally well on any of the new sites.

Determine a plan for moving the cranes that will minimize the total distance involved in the move.

Chapter 18

SITUATIONAL PROBLEMS

THE BENSON PRINTING COMPANY CASE

Benson Printing Company is a commercial job printer. It is an old established firm, one of the largest of its kind in the South. It prints a wide variety of magazines and books on a contract basis. The company is presently owned and operated by the Benson brothers, Ted and Bill, who acquired control ten years ago following the retirement of their father. The younger Bensons are very ambitious and industrious. Under their leadership and in response to expanding sales volume, new, enlarged, and modern facilities have been built. Even this new plant is now operating near capacity.

This phenomenal growth of the business must be attributed, in part, to a current trend for national publishers to print and distribute on a regional basis. For example, the Bensons have recently contracted to print the Southeastern edition of a leading national news daily. They have, also, just been contacted by a book publisher with a contract offer. This book publisher, Zeus Books, Inc., publishes an assorted line of entertainment fiction. The line includes westerns, science-fiction, juveniles, romances, and detective novels. The authors are by no means the best in their fields. The books are largely unoriginal and stereotyped and follow formats which the publishers know will sell. The books are clothbound and sell for $3.00 a copy. They are of uniform length; therefore, the printing time and raw materials required for each book are constants. Although no individual novel is a "best seller," overall demand for these books is great. In fact, the publisher has been unable to meet the demand. As a result, Zeus, after careful market research, has decided to increase output. Their present printers are unable to supply significantly greater quantities. Thus, upon the recommendation of another publisher, Zeus decided to approach Benson Printing about a printing contract.

Zeus offered Benson a five-year contract under which Benson would print a maximum of 100,000 copies a week of various books for a price of one dollar each. This seemed to be a very attractive offer to the Bensons, so they immediately consulted their finance officer and plant manager to see if it would be feasible to accept.

The plant manager reported that new presses would definitely be needed because the present ones were not suited for this type of job and, in any case, were now being operated at virtual capacity. He noted, however, that plant space was again becoming a problem and that only 1488 square feet are not now in use. The plant manager was instructed to contact the appropriate manufacturers for information on available machines.

On the following day the plant manager informed the Benson brothers that contacts with manufacturers had revealed three different possibilities concerning machines. Machine X had a cost of $150,000, required 48 square feet of floor space and two workers, and would produce 480 copies each day. Machine Y cost $180,000, required 55 square feet of floor space and three workers, and would produce 600 copies each day. Machine Z had a cost of $220,000, required 66 square feet of space and four workers, and would produce 760 copies each day. All production figures were based on the assumption of an eight-hour day and were derived from specifications quoted by the various manufacturers.

Additional decision information was provided by the plant manager. From the current employment situation, he estimated that no more than 72 new workers could be obtained at the present pay scale of $2.00 per hour. This restriction resulted in part from the level of skill required to handle the job. Materials cost was estimated at 23 cents per copy. This included an allowance for waste, based upon past experience. When the machines were operated eight hours per day, he estimated that average daily maintenance cost would be incurred at a rate of $6, $8, and $10 for machines X, Y, and Z, respectively. In making these estimates, the plant manager relied on his knowledge of comparable equipment.

The finance officer, after studying the firm's current position and his forecasts for the future, reported that the company would be able to obtain up to $5,000,000 for investing in this venture. The funds could be obtained through a term loan from the company's commercial bank.

The finance officer was assigned the task of evaluating the alternatives and suggesting a plan of action. In studying the situation, he noted the linear aspect of revenue due to the contract terms. The cost factors were not as clear-cut, but he felt that here, too, it was safe to assume linearity since the proposed changes in output would not alter the cost relationships significantly. He noted, as well, the existence of resource constraints and of a contractual constraint on output. Because of these factors, he felt that the linear programming would be applicable to the situation. This is how he set up his model.

The controllable variables are:

X_1 = the number of machine X's to purchase,
X_2 = the number of machine Y's to purchase,
X_3 = the number of machine Z's to purchase.

The objective function is determined by

	X_1	X_2	X_3
Total daily revenue	480	600	760
Daily labor cost	−32†	−48	−64
Raw materials cost	−110‡	−138	−175
Maintenance cost	−6	−8	−10
Profit contribution	332	406	511

†2 men × 8 hours per day × $2 per hour.
‡$0.23 material cost per copy × 480 copies.

Maximize: $332X_1 + 406X_2 + 511X_3$.

The constraints are expressed

Capital: ($1000's)	$150X_1 + 180X_2 + 220X_3 \leqslant 5000$
Space: (square feet)	$48X_1 + 55X_2 + 66X_3 \leqslant 1488$
Labor: (number new workers at $2.00 per hour)	$2X_1 + 3X_2 + 4X_3 \leqslant 72$
Output: (copies per day)	$480X_1 + 600X_2 + 760X_3 \leqslant 20{,}000$

The capital constraint is in thousands of dollars. The output constraint was developed from the contract offered. The publisher will buy 100,000 copies per week but no more. The constraint is based on the assumption that they will accept less than 100,000 copies per week and is stated in terms of maximum output per day based on the present five-day work week.

The initial and the final solution tableaus are shown in Fig. 18–1.

Initial Tableau:

	X_1	X_2	X_3	S_1	S_2	S_3	S_4	
S_1	150	180	220	1	0	0	0	5,000
S_2	48	55	66	0	1	0	0	1,488
S_3	2	3	4	0	0	1	0	72
S_4	480	600	760	0	0	0	1	20,000
	−322	−406	−511	0	0	0	0	0

Final Tableau:

	X_1	X_2	X_3	S_1	S_2	S_3	S_4	
S_1	0	1/3	0	1	−8/3	−11	0	240
X_1	1	11/30	0	0	1/15	−1.1	0	20
X_3	0	17/30	1	0	−1/30	0.8	0	8
S_4	0	−20/3	0	0	−20/3	−80	1	4,320
	0	5.3	0	0	5.1	43.6	0	10,728

FIG. 18–1 The tableaus, Benson Printing Company Case

The finance officer read these results from the final tableau:

Purchase 20 units of machine X.

Purchase none of machine Y.

Purchase 8 units of machine Z.

Use all 72 available workers.

Use all 1488 square feet of available space.

Use all except $240,000 of capital, which means use
$5,000,000 − 240,000 = $4,760,000.

Output is 4320 units below the daily maximum or is
20,000 − 4320 = 15,680 units per day.

Profit contribution realized is:

$10,728 per day or

$53,640 per week (based on a 5-day week) or

$2,789,280 per year (based on a 52-week year).

A vital question which must be considered is whether or not this venture is going to be profitable enough to warrant its undertaking. If the suggested strategy is followed, $4,760,000 will be invested in the project. A profit contribution of $2,789,000 per year will be realized. The financing cost, assuming a ten-year term loan with an effective rate of 12%, will average around $285,600 per year. This will reduce the profit contribution to about $2,500,000. For tax purposes, depreciation will be deducted on a straight-line basis for twenty years or at a rate of $238,000 a year. Profit after depreciation will be approximately $2,262,000. With an effective tax rate of 50%, profit after depreciation and taxes will be only $1,131,000. Net cash flow will average $1,131,000 + $238,000 = $1,369,000 a year.

Using the payback criterion, the firm would recover its initial investment in approximately 3.5 years. This is very good since the contract would run for five years. As a general rule, management prefers short payback periods because of the greater present value of these more certain returns.

As a further criterion for evaluation of the venture, the expected average rate of return for the next five years would be about 27%. This is computed by dividing average profit ($1,131,000) by average investment ($4,165,000) where average investment is initial investment ($4,760,000) plus depreciated value at the end of five years ($3,570,000) divided by two. Looking beyond the next five years, management anticipates the renewal of the present contract; and even if the contract is not renewed, sees no difficulty in finding an alternative use for the machines. The expected average rate of return of 27% compares very favorably with the firm's present earnings rate on total operating assets of 18%.

The finance officer also considered the discounted present value method might be another appropriate criterion to study. The firm's weighted average cost of capital is 8%. Discounting the annual cash flow for only the next five years gives a value for the project of $5,510,000 which is 15% greater than the initial investment. Since the useful life of the equipment is expected to exceed five years, this, as well as the other decision criteria, suggests that it would definitely be profitable to accept the contract.

The officer felt that he should also evaluate the optimal strategy outlined by the linear programming model in light of its solidarity and of the possibilities for improvement. He looked first at the fully exhausted resources to see what potential gains could be realized by changing them. The entire amount of available floor space was used. If this resource could be increased, daily profit would be increased by $5.10 for every unit increase in the floor space available. The change would be accomplished by using 8/3 of a unit of the capital, reducing the number of machine Z's by 1/30 units and increasing the number of machine X's by 1/15 units; this would allow an increase in production of 20/3 units. Decreases in the floor space available for use would have the opposite effect. These relationships hold true over the range from 1188 to 1578 square feet of space. The amount of space now used is only 90 units from the upper range limit. If the resource could be increased by 90 units, profit would increase by $459 per day or $119,340 a year. This would dictate the purchase of six more units of machine X and three fewer units of machine Z. The exchange rates listed in the final tableau would not hold true past 1578 square feet of space because another constraint would become limiting. The allocated capital would be exhausted. However, the analysis indicates that consideration should be given to obtaining extra space if it can be diverted from a significantly less profitable usage.

The labor supply has also been exhausted. Unit increases in this resource stand to contribute additional profit of $43.60 per day or $11,336 per year. The effective range for the substitution rates shown in the final tableau is 62 through 90 workers. Thus, eighteen additional workers could be hired before another constraint becomes limiting. The additional 18 workers would raise annual profit contribution by $204,048 and should be worth consideration if the cost of such a change is not too great or if qualified workers could be found. It should be remembered that a change in the number of workers might necessitate an increase in wages that would effect the model by reducing the objective-function coefficients for each of the variables. If substantial across-the-board wage increases were required, attempts to increase the supply of this resource might prove to be unwise. Nonetheless, this alternative should be investigated.

Under the present solution, no units of machine Y would be purchased. If, for any reason, the company desired to include them, this move would result in the loss of $5.30 per day or $1378.00 per year for each machine Y added. Probably the only reason why this change might be considered would be that the manufacturer of this machine was regarded more highly than the manufacturers of the other two machines.

Another question is raised by the unused portion of the output constraint. The publisher would accept 4320 more units daily than is being produced, or 21,600 more per week. Profit could be increased by scheduling an extra day of work, perhaps. In an extra 8-hour day, 15,680 more books could be produced each week, resulting in an increase in profit of about $10,728 per week or $557,856 per year. The profit figure would surely be somewhat less than this because the overtime pay for the extra time worked would reduce the profit coefficients. In addition, extension of the working hours might require adjustment of the average maintenance costs for the machines. In any case, this is another alternative which should be studied.

The ranges for the objective-function coefficients over which this solution will remain optimal are as follows:

	Low	Current	High
X_1	317.5	332	371.6
X_3	501.6	511	644
X_2	$-\infty$	406	411.3

If the actual contribution coefficient estimates were fairly close to the range extremes it would not take much of an error in the estimate to change the optimum solution, and it becomes most important to consider the likelihood that the coefficients are in error. Total revenue per unit is, of course, set by the contract with Zeus. The certainty of the selling price does reduce the possibility of significant error but does not completely rule it out. The production rates and costs are considered to be reasonably accurate estimates. Past experience and knowledge should be brought into play here to determine the potentiality and the possible magnitude or errors in these estimates. Careful analysis in the area of contribution coefficients is always desirable before a final decision is made.

THE CHOCTAW CHEMICAL COMPANY CASE

Choctaw Chemical Company is headquartered on the outskirts of a growing midwestern city which has a population of 150,000. The company serves an area within a 200-mile radius of the central warehouse.

Choctaw now employs 34 people. Yearly sales are around $1,000,000. The company has been in existence for thirty years, growing from a small, one-man operation to its present size. Company stock is still closely held by the officers of the company.

The product line consists of raw chemicals (acids, alkalies, solvents, and so forth), and a special line of industrial preparations. Raw chemicals are picked up from major chemical manufacturers. The special line is compounded by Choctaw. The special line includes cleaning compounds, boiler-treatment compounds, water-treatment formulations, and certain specialized mixtures. The products are well received by industrial users and wholesalers.

Dry raw chemicals are stocked inside a warehouse. They are stacked on pallets around the exterior walls. Shelves and pallets in the center of the warehouse hold the special preparations that come directly from the adjacent packaging room. One side of the warehouse opens on to a railroad siding for easy unloading of carload shipments. The opposite side of the warehouse opens on to a storage yard. Here, trucks load and unload shipments of chemicals.

Outside the warehouse, in the area not used for truck loading, are bulk storage facilities. These consist of above-ground and below-ground storage tanks containing the more volatile chemicals. Considerable care has been taken in planning the layout to insure maximum safety and efficiency.

The service buildings are strung out along the railroad tracks. First in line is the warehouse. This is connected to a sizeable packaging room. Next comes a fire-proof compounding shed which opens on to the storage yard. An array of mixers, vats, and blenders in this shed are used to put the formulations together. Quality control is practised religiously, although supervised on a part-time basis by a competent chemical engineer. Company products have gained a reputation for quality and consistency.

About eight months ago, one of the company sales engineers succeeded in having one of the company's products adopted for use by a large industrial chain. The product is an air-entraining agent called DisperAir. Since the adoption, sales of the product have climbed rapidly, as have the sales of two other air-entraining agents made by the company, D.A.–10 and D.A.–20.

Air-entraining agents are used in connection with cement mixes. The material, if correctly employed, gives the mixes a stronger structure and richer texture. Air bubbles are dispersed through the mix and allow the ingredients to combine more freely. The result is a more homogeneous blend of rock, sand, and cement.

Choctaw makes the three products in the air-entraining line so that it can satisfy a wider range of tastes and pocketbooks. The difference between these three products is basically in the degree of concentration possessed by each. These differences are reflected in the prices for each product.

	Ounces used per 100 pounds of cement	Price per gallon
DisperAir	3	$1.25
D.A.–10	2	$2.25
D.A.–.20	1	$3.25

Prices have been set after careful inspection of the direct costs involved in the manufacture of each of the products. As an example of this, because of their differing qualities, the products require differing amounts of mixing time. DisperAir can be thoroughly mixed in 10 minutes. D.A.–10 requires 15 minutes, while D.A.–20 needs 25 minutes of careful blending. The same is true of packaging. A drum of DisperAir can be filled and sealed in two minutes while D.A.–10 and D.A.–20 take four and five minutes, respectively.

All three products are sold and delivered in 55-gallon drums. For this reason, most of the estimates of time periods and costs are figured in these terms. For example, production is not continuous but is by the batch method. These batches may be of varying sizes, but they are generally in multiples of 55 gallons. Even the ordering of the basic materials that go into the mixtures is done with this unit in mind.

The three products employ the same material as a base. This material is a concentrated anionic wetting agent which possesses a high concentration of sudsing ability. DisperAir contains 30% by volume of the wetting agent. D.A.–10 contains 60%, and D.A.–20 contains 80%. This wetting agent is purchased from a major manufacturer of industrial detergents. It is delivered in tank truck lots.

The planning that went into the layout of production and storage facilities was performed meticulously to take advantage of every square foot of space. This was because the plant is located in a modern industrial park which has a relatively high cost per square foot of land area. Any changes or additions to the present plant would cause an upheaval and require major expenditures of time and money. The storage tank originally installed for storage of the wetting agent had a small capacity. This tank was supplemented by a tandem tank, which increased storage capacity to 6000 gallons. Since tank truck loads contain 5500 gallons of material, great care must be taken to keep a careful check on the contents of the storage tanks. As the inventory level approaches 500 gallons, a tank truck load must be ordered. On a few occasions in the past the inventory has been allowed to fall below the minimum level, and production has been stopped for lack of the material.

Since the three products contain the same basic material, their production runs are made concurrently. Blending is a matter of dilution, mixing of additives and stabilization. Changes in the batching require very few adjustments. Initial set-up and the clean-up times are somewhat costly. In order to make the most effective use of blending facilities and to satisfy present weekly requirements, a limit of eighteen hours per week has been placed on mixing time for the air-entraining agents. This includes both set-up and clean-up time.

Personnel in the packaging room also perform other duties in the warehouse. At almost any time they may be required to load a truck or unload a shipment or move warehouse stock to make room for expected shipments. This multiplicity of duties has required that a special time be set aside to perform packaging so that the men will be relatively uninterrupted. Based on past experience, the best time for this seems to be after the morning delivery trucks are loaded and before the long-haul transport shipments arrive. In the case of the air-entraining production, this has placed a limit on the packaging for these items of four hours.

In line with the previously mentioned practice of estimating all cost and time figures for these materials in terms of 55-gallon drum multiples, cost information for these three products is given in the following form:

	DisperAir	D.A.–10	D.A.–20
Selling price	$68.75	$123.75	$178.75
Minus direct costs:			
Raw materials	22.75	48.25	73.40
Manufacturing	11.00	25.50	47.35
Drum	2.00	2.00	3.00
Total direct cost	35.75	75.75	123.75
Contribution, per drum	$33.00	$48.00	$55.00

Company officers have asked for suggestions on how to organize production to maximize profitability on the operation.

THE PERSONNEL-TRAINING ASSOCIATES CASE

Personnel-Training Associates (PTA) offers three types of personnel services. During the past two years PTA has developed the reputation for having a high degree of professional competence. This reputation has brought the company many referrals of applicants and client companies. Activity has increased to the extent that PTA, working with its present staff, will soon be unable to provide all services effectively. The company prefers not to expand its facilities nor to add new employees. Consequently, a decision must be made as to the amount of time that will be devoted to each type of service offered.

The three services that PTA offers are (1) placement, (2) recruiting, and (3) consulting. In its placement activities, PTA operates as an employment agency. Individuals who are seeking employment register with the agency which, in turn, submits qualifications of the applicant to prospective employers and arranges for personal interviews. PTA works primarily with college graduates who are interested in salaried career opportunities. Several hours are spent with each applicant in counseling, testing, and referring. For this service, the applicant is obligated to pay a fee based upon his starting salary in accordance with the schedule of fees shown in Fig. 18–2. (Actually, the employer almost always agrees to pay this fee.)

Positions paying up to $5,999.99 –	6%
$6,000.00 to $6,999.99	– 7%
$7,000.00 to $7,999.99	– 8%
$8,000.00 to $8,999.99	– 9%
$9,000.00 to $9,999.99	–10%
$10,000.00 to $10,999.99	–11%
$11,000.00 to $11,999.99	–12%
$12,000.00 to $12,999.99	–13%
$13,000.00 to $13,999.99	–14%
$14,000.00 to $14,999.99	–15%
$20,000.00 and over	–20%

FIG. 18–2 Schedule of employment fees

PTA has several client employers who have a continuing need for recruiting service. These employers have found that their facilities are not adequate to allow them to search for and to find qualified employees to fill vacancies. By contractual arrangement PTA is paid $100 per day (for an eight-hour day) plus expenses to advertise job openings, interview and screen prospects, and recommend the most qualified candidates for employment. This activity generally requires some travel by one or more PTA staff members. Travel time, however, is considered to be working time and travel expenses are paid by the client.

It was just recently that PTA increased the recruiting fee from $75 a day to $100 and several client companies discontinued using PTA as their agent. For this reason, PTA believes that $100 a day is the absolute maximum that clients will allow them to charge. At this charge the demand for the service is greater than PTA can provide. Below this figure, at $75, there will be considerably more clients requesting the service. But the demand is such that at even a small increment above $100, recruiting requests from clients will be virtually nonexistent.

The consulting activities performed by PTA include development and implementation of training and management-development programs, design of employment and psychological testing, writing of job descriptions and evaluation of hourly jobs and salaried positions, organization of overall personnel-industrial relations programs including implementation when necessary. PTA charges $25 an hour plus expenses for this service. At this time, only two PTA people are qualified to perform this service and one of these is available only on a part-time basis.

A study of the journals and statements of PTA reveal the following monthly costs:

Rent	$ 474.00
Insurance	146.00
Accountant (retained)	40.00
Salaries	4300.00
Advertising	650.00 (Rate holder—annual contract)
Telephone	375.00
Postage	20.00
Office Supplies	10.00
Equipment	45.00
Entertainment	25.00
Total	$6085.00

Regardless of the amount of activity, these costs remain constant. Therefore, all the above costs are considered to be fixed costs.

As an incentive to increase placement activity, each employee is eligible for a quarterly bonus. A quarterly quota of ten times the monthly salary is the basis for the bonus. The employee receives a percentage of all fees above quota, with the amount being based on a sliding scale. Because no one has yet earned bonus, this factor is not considered to be pertinent for immediate planning purposes.

There are no variable costs, then, associated with the operation of this agency.

PTA employs four full-time employees and one part-time employee. Each full-time employee works eight hours, Monday through Friday, and four hours on Saturday for an average total of 180 hours each month. Due to other commitments, the one part-time employee can work only 100 hours per month. These hours are all that are available because the company does not wish to add to its workforce and the individuals wish to limit themselves to the hours shown. This is not only their personal preference but the nature of the personnel work makes it difficult or impractical to work beyond the normal work day of a client, which is generally of eight hours duration. Therefore, a maximum of 820 manhours is available monthly for all three services performed.

Because of a skills limitation, only the hours of the part-time staff member and one of the other employees are available for consulting. As a result, a maximum of 280 hours a month is available for this activity.

In order to maintain the goodwill of the agency, management has deemed it necessary to devote at least half the time in placement activity and, thereby, keep the office adequately staffed at all times.

Placement activities were studied for a three-month period that most nearly represented expected future activity. A total of $28,600 in fees were earned and 2,460 hours were devoted to the placement activity. The average hourly rate is, thus, about $11.00.

The recruiting rate is fixed by contract at $100 per day, net of expenses. Since expenses are paid immediately by the client, they represent neither an expense nor a revenue to PTA. A day is considered by PTA and the client to be an eight-hour period. Therefore, the hourly recruiting rate can be considered to be $12.50.

Consulting fees are charged at the rate of $25.00 per hour. This rate is also net of expenses.

PTA wishes to build a model, based on the assumptions listed below, that will aid it in finding an answer to its problem. The assumptions are:

1. Personnel-Training Associates is a going concern and will continue operations indefinitely.

2. There will continue to be only five employees, four will work 180 hours each month and one will work only 100 hours monthly.

3. It is necessary to spend half the available hours on placement activities to keep the office staffed and to maintain goodwill.

4. The demand for all of PTA's services exceeds its capacity to supply these services. This situation will continue.

5. Consulting activities require specialized skills and experience possessed by only two of PTA's employees.

6. All costs are and will continue to be fixed.

7. The objective to maximize revenue is proper.

8. Rates for the respective services will remain as presently stated.

THE LAGRANGE HOME PRODUCTS COMPANY CASE

The LaGrange Home Products Company is engaged in the manufacture of many products for the home. One of its departments, the rug-and-cloth department, is responsible for the manufacture of three products. The first product is a rug, designated Rug *A*. This is a high quality rug which has exceptionally even surface finish. The finish is obtained by passage through a special shearing machine during the manufacturing process.

The second product, Rug *B*, is manufactured in a process similar to that used for Rug *A* except that it does not receive the shearing treatment. Two other differences between Rug *B* and Rug *A*, although not as significant as the shearing process, are (1) the manner of spinning the wool thread and (2) the actual weaving of the rugs. The wool for Rug *B* is sent through the spinning machine at a slightly faster speed and the finished thread is not twisted quite as tightly as is the thread used in Rug *A*. A similar situation exists in the weaving process. Rug *B* is woven at a slightly faster speed than is Rug *A*; and although they each have the same specification as to threads per inch, the weave of Rug *B* is not as uniform as that of Rug *A*.

The thread for both Rug *A* and Rug *B* passes through a special washer that both washes and dyes the thread.

It should be pointed out that the shearing process used on Rug *A* does result in a quantity of wool waste. This waste cannot be used in spinning new thread. The amount of waste is relatively small and, in the past, it has simply been stored for several weeks until a quantity was accumulated sufficient to make feasible a sale to other wool processors. Data is not available that would permit the assignment of a return on a per-yard basis to Rug *A*.

The third product of the department is wool cloth. This cloth requires the use of a different type wool than that of Rug *A* and Rug *B*. The same spinner and washer used for the rugs are used in the manufacture of the cloth, but a special weaving machine is used.

Both the rugs and the cloth are made in solid colors only and have no pattern.

All of the output from the department is transferred to other departments of the company. The department is operated as a profit center but no selling costs are assigned to its operation.

All of the output of the department is easily sold, so the manager of the department is interested in two major questions:

1. What is the maximum profit that can be obtained with the present equipment and other resource limitations?

2. If management agreed to invest additional money in this department, how should the money be used?

The department has sufficient spinning machines to provide 200 hours of operation a day at a cost of $1.50 per hour. The washers cost $0.20 per hour and 50 hours a day are available. The weavers for rugs cost $3.20 an hour and 150 hours a day are available. The shearers cost $1.00 an hour and 24 hours a day are available. The weavers for cloth are available for 100 hours a day at a cost of $1.50 an hour.

Enough wool for one yard of Rug *A* or Rug *B* costs $0.80 and enough wool for one yard of cloth costs $0.90. These are total costs of the wool delivered to the department. Because of problems beyond the control of the department, only enough wool for 125 yards of rugs in any combination of Rug *A* or Rug *B* can be obtained each day.

The department has adequate storage facilities at each processing point in which to store material to insure a ready supply for the machine at all times. The manager wishes to establish a mix of output and a rate of production each day that will maintain these storage areas at their current level.

The manufacture of one yard of Rug *A* requires 1.1 hours on the spinner, 0.2 hours in the washer, 1 hour on the weaver, and 0.3 hours on the shearer.

Rug *B* requires 1 hour on the spinner, 0.2 hours on the washer, and 0.9 hours on the weaver.

Cloth requires 0.7 hours on the spinner, 0.1 hours in the washer, and 1.1 hours on the weaver.

Rug *A* sells for $7.50 per yard, Rug *B* for $6.00 per yard, and cloth at $4.70 per yard.

The operational costs indicated for each machine were reported by the company's cost analyst as including all costs associated with the machines.

THE CRESCENT CITY LUGGAGE COMPANY CASE

The Crescent City Luggage Company of Lawrenceville is one of three plants in the United States owned and operated by the firm, Crescent City Luggage, Inc. The home office of the firm is in a large northern city. The firm and each of its three plants manufactures the same types, styles, and colors of luggage, each plant servicing the area in which it is located. The firm manufactures and wholesale-jobs, through its own salesmen, these lines of luggage:

1. A low-priced line, called "end-bound", sold in sets of three pieces.
2. A medium-priced line, called "long-bound", sold in sets of three pieces.
3. A low-priced line of metal-wood footlockers, sold individually.

Crescent City Luggage Company of Lawrenceville is located in a small rural community near the city of Lawrenceville. The local plant is operated by two of the firm's shareholders, one of whom serves as plant supervisor and salesmanager and the other of whom serves as general production manager. This plant was opened eight years ago to supply the southeastern United States market for the three lines of luggage. Its operations have expanded each year since its opening. In general, the plant operations have been highly successful and highly profitable.

The Crescent City parent organization's principal owner developed an innovation in the manufacture of low-priced luggage several years ago which was found to be very competitive in terms of the advantages of ease and simplicity of fabrication and assembly, low assembly-line equipment costs, low labor-cost ratio, and minor advantages of other kinds. The firm has found that it could design, fabricate, assemble, package, and sell at a wholesale price about one-third the price of competing firms. The firm has elected to price its line of luggage slightly below the going market wholesale price so as to be quite price competitive and has realized a very considerable profit from the manufacture of this particular line of luggage. This low-priced line is sold principally through pawnshops and through the usual discount house and wholesaler-premium store outlets; it is sold also through numerous other retail outlets which cater to customers for this type of luggage product. Demand for this product has been quite good for the past few years, principally due to the market price position of the manufacturer and the annual demand for this product is expected to total between 200,000 and 250,000 sets of luggage during the next season. Last year, average demand for the line amounted to 4000 sets per week, except during the peaks of the season when as many as 5200 sets were demanded each week.

Crescent City also fabricates a medium-priced line of luggage which is marketed in the discount and wholesale outlets previously mentioned, but usually in smaller lot quantities than the low-priced line. The principal outlet for the medium-priced line is through national department store chains. These types of outlets account for approximately eighty percent of the total production during last year. Estimates of next season's demand for this line indicate that 100,000 to 120,000 units will be demanded during the year. Demand during last year averaged about 1800 sets per week but ran as high as 2400 sets per week during the peak of the season.

The third product Crescent City manufactures is a fairly commonly seen low-priced painted metal and wood footlocker. The principal reasons for manufacturing this line of luggage, which is the most difficult, troublesome, and most costly of the three lines produced, are these:

1. Many of the accounts which buy the low-priced line and/or the higher priced line also have a market for these low priced footlockers. The sales force has found that

these accounts will buy their low-cost luggage from a jobber who can also service their needs for the footlockers. Crescent City manufactures this line to service these accounts in an effort to retain them.

2. The footlockers are profitable and the manufacture of them adds to overall profits of the firm.

3. A third consideration is the fact that Crescent City is considering at present whether or not to bid on a government contract to supply 40,000 footlockers to the Army.

During the last year, the demand for footlockers has averaged a fairly steady 1200 units per week. Demand is expected to continue at this level, or slightly higher, during next season, not counting those which would be needed to fill the government order, if it is undertaken.

The firm operates three production lines. One line, hereafter designated production line "A" for clarity, is used exclusively for production of the low-prices end-bound line of luggage. The second line, hereafter designated production line "B", is ordinarily used to produce medium-priced long-bound luggage. However, by skipping two operations on line B, this line can be used for production of the low-priced line of luggage. There is only a slight increase in costs (associated with additional set-up costs), and there is no change in the average time required to produce low-price luggage on the B production line. Line A cannot be adapted easily to the production of the medium-priced line, however. The third line, hereafter designated production line "C", is used exclusively for the production of footlockers; it is not adaptable to the production of either of the other two lines of luggage.

Raw materials used to make the two luggage lines, such as plastic, masonite-hardboard, locks, hasps, hinges, and miscellaneous other hardware, are purchased on the open market. The raw materials requirements for both lines of suitcases are essentially the same in quantities, except that the higher-priced line uses a better grade of hardware and a more expensive wooden frame. Raw materials for the footlockers are also purchased on the open market; these materials cannot be used for the production of the two lines of luggage. The general availability of all of these raw materials is not considered to be a problem as all of them are in plentiful supply and are relatively inexpensive.

Employees must be individually trained to do each of the production line tasks. One group of employees has been rotation-trained to operate either of the two production lines for suitcase luggage and another group is trained to operate the footlocker production line. The two groups cannot, without extensive retraining, be transferred from the footlocker line to either of the other two lines nor can the employees from one of the A or B lines be transferred to the footlocker line.

A third and separate group of employees perform the finishing, inspection, and packaging operations. This group of employees can perform these functions for any and all of the three lines, even if all three lines are running simultaneously.

The plant operates on a five-day work week, eight hours per day. Because of the excessive extra costs, the firm does not put on overtime production runs unless it is absolutely necessary.

One of the principal problems this firm faces is that it is operating in a seasonal industry and does not have access to adequate warehouse facilities. It has space in the plant, on which it is paying the premium price, to store a total of 40,000 cubic feet of its products. After each set of luggage is produced and inspected, it is packed, a small piece in a larger piece, and sent to the shipping and receiving area where it is temporarily stored awaiting shipment to a customer. Shipments are made through local motor-freight lines and each week's production is shipped out during the following week. Maximum storage time usually does not exceed five working days.

Although all the lines of luggage manufactured and marketed by this firm are competitively priced, the plant manager is certain that a considerable amount of profit, not to mention customer goodwill, is being lost during the peak weeks of the season because they cannot fill many new and repeat orders which come in during the busy season. On occasion, weekly orders have exceeded production capacity by as much as 30% for three or more weeks at a time. The firm realizes that lack of adequate warehousing facilities is a severely limiting factor but the home office has not cleared the rental or construction of facilities for this purpose. The manager of the local plant finds himself strapped by this situation but realizes that he must make the best of it until it is resolved.

In this connection, the plant manager has asked for a review of the current situation to see if a more precise method can be found to schedule the use of present facilities and to determine the best product mix so that the maximum amount of profit can be attained, while not going into overtime production runs. This problem and the situation lends itself quite well to a determination of an appropriate product mix strategy and from that strategy a better method for scheduling production through linear programming.

The plant manager has stipulated that the plant must meet minimum weekly production quotas in order that average weekly demand requirements can be satisfied. The minimum requirements are these:

Product line	Minimum per week
End-bound luggage	4,200 sets
Long-bound luggage	1,800 sets
Footlockers	1,300 sets

Information relative to profits, production time requirements, inspection-finishing-packaging time requirements, and storage space requirements, for each of the three lines of luggage produces, is summarized in Fig. 18–3.

	Profit Production line			Production time required (in minutes)			Finishing, inspecting, packaging time	Storage space required (cubic feet)
	A	B	C	A	B	C		
End-bound (per set)	$5.35	$5.15	—	0.5	0.5	—	0.10	4.5
Long-bound (per set)	—	$10.85	—	—	1.2	—	0.15	4.75
Footlockers (per unit)	—	—	$3.45	—	—	1.4	0.25	6.75

FIG. 18–3 Production time, storage space, and profits, for three lines of luggage produced

THE KIMBRO INSURANCE AGENCY CASE

A few years ago the agency Vice President of a large life insurance company, Mr. Richard Kimbro, became quite concerned with the steadily increasing volume of term insurance that his agents were submitting for consideration. It is a generally held tenet that the sale of term insurance erodes the sale of permanent insurance and excessive amounts of term are detrimental to the estate of the insured. The insurance industry further held that mortality was significantly higher under term experience than under permanent, the extra cost being passed on to term policyholders.

With these thoughts in mind, Mr. Kimbro sought out various ideas to make the selling of permanent insurance more attractive. Various schemes were tried, from offering two-week, all-expense-paid vacations to limiting the amount of term one agent might submit. While a leveling in the sale of term was noticed, Mr. Kimbro wanted better results. He felt that if the appropriate variable or variables could be isolated, a graphic illustration of how term sales hurt the pocketbook of the agents themselves would tend to slow the unnecessary term sales.

Since the company had ample data processing equipment and regularly ran a market survey for the agents, most of the needed information was at hand. The problem was to isolate the relevant data and to put them into some meaningful model. The company sold no group insurance and they would only accept business on a non-brokerage basis, meaning that all insurance sold must come from an agent who works almost exclusively with the company and was trained by them. The agents they licensed were considered the best in the business and could generally sell any reasonable volume.

A questionnaire was mailed to all agents asking them to break their costs into three groups: amounts spent on the sale and servicing of the three main classes of business—(1) term, (2) whole-life and 65-life, and (3) limited-payment life. The surprising answer was that the costs to sell and service all three were practically equal on the basis of premium volume. One important fact did come to light, however. It took twice as long to sell and service the permanent forms of life insurance as it did for the term. The agents estimated that it took approximately five hours per $10,000 face amount of term and ten hours per $10,000 face amount of permanent. The agents also reported that out of a possible 3200 hours per year available to them, they were in the field selling only 2000 of those hours on the average.

From the market surveys, it was determined that the agents averaged 35% commission on premium volume of term, 50% on whole-life and 65-life, and 40% on the limited-payment plans. The survey also showed that a remarkably high percentage of the company's agents qualified for the Million Dollar Round Table. (MDRT membership consists, in part, of selling one million dollars in face amount of permanent, or equivalent, insurance.)

One other bit of data was considered to be significant to the case. The company, having placed limits on the amount of term it would accept from an agent, set its average limit per agent at one-half million face.

Before actually attempting to build a decision model, Mr. Kimbro tried to determine if he could be objective about the study or whether he simply had a prejudice against term insurance. From a profitability standpoint, the agency made considerably more money from its term business than it did from the permanent forms. The potential financial bias eliminated, Mr. Kimbro decided that he had no other biases against term except for the fact that he felt excessive amounts of term were detrimental to the company's image and against the policyholders' best interests.

THE TENABLE INTEGRATED CIRCUITS, INC., CASE

Tenable Integrated Circuits, Inc., has been offered a very lucrative subcontractor position as a supplier of integrated circuits on a major defense program. The price that has been offered for the integrated circuits is above the current market price, but the prime contractor wants an immediate committment on quantities to be delivered over the next year. The prime contractor will not commit to paying for the integrated circuits until six months after delivery. This delay in payment is required by the prime contractor because he will not get paid until he puts the integrated circuits together with other components and delivers the completed piece of electronic equipment.

In order to be able to participate in this contractual relationship, TIC must immediately commit themselves to the quantity and delivery schedule they can handle. The premium price makes the opportunity attractive, but they must be certain that they will not over-commit themselves because the six-month receivables will be a very heavy drain on their cash position. Their normal terms are 30-days and according to a very recent analysis of the receivables, accounts average being paid out by 45 days.

The present tight money situation makes the cash drain-off even more critical since getting additional loans or lines of credit is much more difficult now than normally. In addition to the limitations on cash, TIC also is concerned with maintaining a reasonable amount of business with their regular customers throughout the period of time the defense contract is being filled in the next year. After reviewing their backlog of orders and discussing anticipated needs with most of their regular customers, it appears that the customers will be depending on TIC to supply them at least an average of 10,000 integrated circuits per month for the next year. TIC would like to maintain their inventory balance at about its present level; therefore, they must produce the regular customer quantities plus whatever they can on the defense contract each month throughout the year.

The present uncommitted cash balance is $200,000. The present accounts receivable balance is $100,000. A line of credit is available for use with the bank in the amount of $300,000, none of which is now taken down. The bank usually requires that the balance of the line of credit loan be zero for at least one month out of the year. However, due to the circumstances of this defense contract, TIC believes that the bank would allow an outstanding balance beyond the normal eleven months if necessary because of the large, highly collectable accounts receivable they will have at that time. The current accounts payable balance is $90,000 and is practically all payable within 30 days. The terms on all raw material used by TIC is net 30-days. TIC tries to consistantly meet these terms in order to maintain good relationships with their suppliers.

Other fixed funds committments for the next year include the following:

1. Anticipated tax payments:

	July	$ 75,000	(1st quarter)
	October	$100,000	(2nd quarter)
	January	$125,000	(3rd quarter)
	April	$125,000	(4th quarter)

2. Each month the out-of-pocket type cash expenses such as overhead wages and salaries, utilities, and so forth, are expected to average about $30,000 per month for normal full production activities regardless of whether or not any committment is made for defense contract production.

3. On January 31st of next year a mortgage payment of $200,000 is due. (This is the 3rd quarter planning period.)

Based on the present facilities and equipment, the normal average maximum production capacity per month of integrated circuits is about 30,000 units. Because of the need of all available funds for working capital during the next year, it is not anticipated that productive capacity will be increased.

The current market price and the anticipated price for the next year is $10.00 each for the integrated circuits; this is the average price expected to be received from regular customers. However, the defense contractor is willing to pay $11.00 per unit for the integrated circuits, mostly because of the payment-terms requirement.

A review of labor standards and time studies made in the past indicates that the direct labor expense, which has to be paid within one week of incurrance, is expected to average about $3.00 per unit. The direct material costs, which must be paid within 30 days, is expected to average $2.00 per unit. The estimate of material costs is based on recent production data and anticipated stability of the market prices for these materials.

The managing officers of TIC wanted to develop a mathematical model that, hopefully, would be helpful in formulating a plan that would allow them to meet their objectives of optimizing their committment for the defense contract quantities and delivery schedule within the overall objectives of maintaining regular customer relationships and maximizing profit contribution to fixed charges and expenses anticipated within the situation constraints.

THE HARD ROCK FURNITURE COMPANY CASE

The Hard Rock Furniture Company manufactures several lines of medium-priced furniture in their home plant in Juniper, Virginia. Although Hard Rock seeks sales nationally, over 80% of actual sales are made east of the Mississippi. The company hopes to improve the sales picture by gaining identification with a portion of the total market; however, this has proved to be exceedingly difficult because of the great number of furniture manufacturers.

The top executives recently returned from the High Point Show where they were elated over the reaction to their new line. Hard Rock will introduce this line in the fall in an attempt to appeal to the younger portion of the market. The new furniture, called the Generation Gap Collection, catches the modern flavor by combining the richness of pecan wood with free-form designs in psychedelic patterns for the upholstery. The line was such a hit at the show that the marketing department has revised its original sales forecasts.

It is never easy to predict sales to consumers; however, experience has shown that the dealers who generally have a feel for the market can be relied upon as a barometer for short-term activity. Based upon this reaction, Generation Gap's sales potential forecast for the fall quarter has been increased to the following:

Living room group	2500 sets
Dining room group	2100 sets
Bedroom group	3000 sets

Hard Rock does not sell furniture in groups, but there is always a strong tendency for actual sales to stabilize into predictable "groups." Few consumers ever buy an entire collection, but they do often buy from more than one group. Dealers have long indicated the desirability of having available the complete line; however, the company officials have often been tempted to drop less profitable items. As a rule of thumb, Hard Rock makes sure that the production of no one group makes up less than 20% of the average of the other two groups.

When the plant manager, Richard Router, was informed of the revised sales forecast, he foresaw problems in changing the planned production. Based upon earlier projections he has anticipated production for the three groups of Generation Gap to be 1000, 800, and 1500 respectively. Regarding capacity, he was not immediately concerned for it would be no problem to phase out more or less of an older line of furniture. He immediately asked his industrial engineer, Jerry Joiner, to revise his takeoff of material required so that an analysis could be made of the situation.

Wood Requirements by Groups (Board Feet)

	No. 1 Pecan	No. 2 Pecan	Gum	Total
Living room group	10.8	3.6	21.6	36.0
Dining room group	38.4	19.2	6.4	64.0
Bedroom group	12.5	20.0	17.5	50.0

Wood requirements by group (percent)

	No. 1 Pecan	No. 2 Pecan	Gum
Living room group	30	10	60
Dining room group	60	30	10
Bedroom group	25	40	35

Cost of wood (per 1000 board feet)*

No. 1 Pecan	$390.00
No. 2 Pecan	303.00
Gum	242.00

*F.O.B. Juniper, Virginia

FIG. 18–4 Wood requirements and costs for the generation gap group

The design of Generation Gap incorporates three different types of wood important to the overall effect. It contains two grades of pecan wood, #1 and #2 furniture grade, and gum. The #1 pecan is slightly better than the #2 pecan. It is specified for the portions of the furniture pieces that are subject to the most critical inspection. The #2 pecan will be used in less important parts. Finally, gum is used where the wood is to be painted or where it will not be seen. There is no objection to using a higher grade than specified for any portion if it can be justified economically. Figure 18–4 gives information about wood requirements and costs.

The usage rate for the pecan wood as used in the furniture is 75% whereas the usage rate for gum is 90%. Based upon the original sales estimate, orders were placed for 80,360 BF for #1 pecan, 65,280 BF for #2 pecan and 58,800 BF for gum. After considering the revised sales estimate, Mr. Joiner increased the estimates for wood requirements to 193,520 BF for #1 pecan, 145,760 BF for #2 pecan, and 142,200 BF for gum.

To avoid any delays Mr. Joiner then informed Celia Couch, the purchasing agent, of the new requirements. Mrs. Couch, who has contacts throughout the industry, began an extensive search to satisfy the additional needs for woods; however, the best she could do was 75,000 BF of #1 pecan, 62,000 BF of #2 pecan, and 65,000 BF of gum. She placed tentative orders for all that was available with the understanding that the actual orders must be confirmed within two days.

It also became evident that a new constraint might be placed on production because of the quantity of fabric that was available. Hard Rock could get a commitment on 92,000 yards of fabric. An additional order could be placed for a minimum of 45,000 yards at a price premium of $1.50 a yard if this were necessary. The fabric requirements for each group are 36 yards for the living room group, 4 yards for the dining room group, and 2 yards for the bedroom group.

It was determined that capacity would be limited to 6600 groups due to prior commitments on older lines of furniture. Not being able to cut back other production beyond this point and expansion being impossible, a decision had to be reached regarding the most appropriate level for Generation Gap. Due to the urgency created by the requirement to place immediate orders for wood and the potential importance of the new line, Mr. Router referred the entire problem to the Executive Vice President, Ben Bench.

Mr. Bench felt that any decision on this level had to be based upon what was best for the company in the overall view. He, therefore, said to produce all of the Generation Gap possible, but to ensure that it was done in such a way that profits would be maximized.

Van Vanear, the young president of Hard Rock, heard that a decision was being developed in the matter of the Generation Gap group. Being very concerned about the situation, he called a meeting of the Executive Planning Committee to learn the status of the new line. Mr. Bench and Mr. Router summarized their reasoning in the situation and began explaining the strategy outlined by the linear programming model they had used.

Mr. Vanear listened patiently to their presentation and then replied, "Knatz, men, you still think like my father thought for the fifty years he ran the business. I don't give a flip about squeezing every dollar out of this one production run. We are sitting on a potential rocket to national prominence and you are fiddling with peanuts. Don't you realize that Generation Gap can literally take us out of a crowd and put us in with Frexel and Froeler?

Come on, men. Let's think big. Let's put out every piece of furniture we can sell, or at least all we can produce. I know labor presents no problem. There are enough furniture men available around here to produce ten times our present output.

I want Hard Rock to go public before long; but if we don't get with it, we can forget about attracting investors. Mr. Bench, I know you can take it from here. Therefore, I won't be further concerned with the problem. Let Sales know what to expect and be thinking about a really big expansion after Generation Gap gets on the market!"

THE FARRINGTON COMPANY CASE

The Farrington Company has decided to set up an employee pension fund. While some current income will be required to pay benefits, the primary objective of the fund will be overall return at minimum risk.

The ground rules under which the manager of the fund operates are fairly simple. At least one per cent of the fund's assets must be held as a cash reserve. At least 25% of the assets must be in senior securities or cash, including 10% in U.S. Treasury Bills. The remainder may be invested in common stock, but at least 10% of the assets must be invested in the stock of Farrington.

Another major restriction is that all securities (other than treasury bills) must be listed on the Consolidated Stock Exchange. This restriction is included because one of the more influential directors is a member of the Board of Governors of the Exchange. The ten stocks and two bonds which are listed on the Consolidated Exchange are shown in Fig. 18–5.

Security	Price	Growth rate	Confidence interval low	high	Dividend interest	Standard deviation
Mammoth Telephone	50	0.05	0.04	0.06	0.046	0.005
Lame Duck Airlines	30	0.30	−0.10	0.70	0.014	0.200
E–Z Load Camera	100	0.20	0.20	0.30	0.015	0.050
Diversified Electric	80	0.08	0.02	0.14	0.030	0.030
Farrington	70	0.10	0.16	0.14	0.035	0.020
H.A.L. Computer	300	0.15	0.11	0.19	0.009	0.020
Conglomerate Industries	80	0.25	0.05	0.45	0.000	0.100
Cosmic Electro-Technical	60	0.50	−0.50	1.50	0.000	0.500
Confederate Chemical	45	0.09	0.03	0.15	0.044	0.030
Northern Electric Utilities	25	0.08	0.06	0.10	0.039	0.010
Mammoth 4's 88	80	0.00	−0.002	0.002	0.059	0.001
Lame Duck 5's 77	85	0.00	−0.004	0.004	0.065	0.002
U.S. Treasury Bills	—	0.00	0.00	0.00	0.045	0.000
Cash	—	0.00	0.00	0.00	0.00	0.000

FIG. 18–5 Securities listed on the consolidated stock exchange

Assets of the fund will amount initially to $5 million. If a net return of six percent per year above current costs can be achieved, no additional funds will be required from the company. The goal of the fund manager, therefore, is to obtain enough current income to meet expenses (approximately $125,000 the first year) and a six percent return, with a minimum of risk. The profits of the fund are not taxable so that there is no relative advantage of capital gains over current income. All income not needed for current expenses will be reinvested. Short sales and buying on margin are not permitted.

Through the influence of another member of the board of directors, it will be possible to obtain analyses of the various companies on the Consolidated Exchange from a highly respected investment advisory firm.

In addition to determining the least risk portfolio with a six percent return, it would also be desirable to obtain comparable measures of risk for portfolios with returns of 7%, 8% ..., to determine the relationship between return and risk.

Problem Formulation

The investment advisory firm was asked to analyze all securities on the Consolidated Exchange and to provide the following information:

1. Expected growth rate in the per-share price of the security over the next year.

2. A range of growth rates within which the actual growth rate should fall 95% of the time (a 95% confidence interval for the expected growth rate).

3. The average dividend or interest return expected over the next year.

The results of the analysis are shown in Fig. 18–5 also.

If we make the assumption that the probability distributions of the expected growth rates are approximately normal, 95% of the values should lie within two standard deviations of the mean. From the 95% confidence interval, therefore, an approximation of the standard deviation of the distribution can be calculated. These standard deviations are shown in Fig. 18–5. They will be used as a measure of risk.

With current return, expected growth rate and risk expressed quantitively, it is possible to formulate this situation as a linear programming problem.

The controllable variables may be defined as:

X_1 = percent of portfolio invested in Mammoth Telephone and Telegraph.
X_2 = percent of portfolio invested in Lame Duck Airlines.
X_3 = percent of portfolio invested in E–Z Load Camera.
X_4 = percent of portfolio invested in Diversified Electric.
X_5 = percent of portfolio invested in Farrington.
X_6 = percent of portfolio invested in H.A.L. Computer.
X_7 = percent of portfolio invested in Conglomerate Industries.
X_8 = percent of portfolio invested in Cosmic Electro-Technical.
X_9 = percent of portfolio invested in Confederate Chemical.
X_{10} = percent of portfolio invested in Northern Electric Utilities.
X_{11} = percent of portfolio invested in Mammoth 4's 88.
X_{12} = percent of portfolio invested in Lame Duck 5's 77.
X_{13} = percent of portfolio invested in U.S. Treasury Bills.
X_{14} = percent of portfolio invested in Cash.

The objective is to minimize the weighted average risk which is given by:

$$0.005 X_1 + 0.2 X_2 + 0.05 X_3 + 0.03 X_4 + 0.02 X_5 + 0.02 X_6 + 0.1 X_7 + 0.5 X_8$$
$$+ 0.03 X_9 + 0.01 X_{10} + 0.001 X_{11} + 0.002 X_{12} + 0 X_{13} + 0 X_{14}.$$

The constraints are as follows:

1. At least one percent of assets in cash:

   $X_{14} \geqslant 0.01.$

2. At least 25% of assets in senior securities of cash:

   $X_{11} + X_{12} + X_{13} + X_{14} \geqslant 0.25.$

3. At least 10% of assets in U.S. Treasury Bills:

   $X_{13} \geqslant 0.10.$

4. At least 10% of assets in Farrington common:

   $X_5 \geqslant 0.10.$

5. Current income of at least $125,000:

   $125,000 \div 5,000,000 = 0.025$ return

   $0.046 X_1 + 0.014 X_2 + 0.015 X_3 + 0.030 X_4 + 0.035 X_5 + 0.009 X_6 + 0 X_7$
   $+ 0 X_8 + 0.044 X_9 + 0.039 X_{10} + 0.059 X_{11} + 0.065 X_{12} + 0.045 X_{13}$
   $+ 0 X_{14} \geqslant 0.025.$

6. Investments must total 100%:

   $X_1 + X_2 + X_3 + X_4 + X_5 + X_6 + X_7 + X_8 + X_9 + X_{10} + X_{11} + X_{12}$
   $+ X_{13} + X_{14} = 1.0.$

7. Six percent return above current costs:

   $0.096 X_1 + 0.314 X_2 + 0.215 X_3 + 0.110 X_4 + 0.135 X_5 + 0.159 X_6 + 0.25 X_7$
   $+ 0.5 X_8 + 0.134 X_9 + 0.119 X_{10} + 0.059 X_{11} + 0.065 X_{12} + 0.045 X_{13}$
   $+ 0 X_{14} \geqslant 0.085.$

Explicit Assumptions of the Model

1. A net return of six percent above current costs is the minimum acceptable return.

2. Current costs will be $125,000 per year.

3. A dollar of current income not needed for expenses will be invested proportionally in securities appearing in the minimum risk portfolio.

4. Brokerage commissions are ignored.

5. The fund may buy odd lots.

6. Purchases may be made at current prices.

7. The fund can take any size position without bidding up the price of a security.

8. The expected return and risk estimates of the investment advisory firm are the best available.

9. The distributions of expected growth rates are approximately normal (symmetrical).

10. The expected interest and dividend return projections are not subject to appreciable uncertainty.

11. The standard deviation of the expected growth rate distribution is a meaningful measure of risk.

12. Estimates for economic outlook of the economy as a whole are incorporated in the growth rate and current income estimates for individual securities.

13. Total assets are $5,000,000.

Assumptions Implicit in the Model

1. The risk factors remain constant throughout the period and at every price level.

2. There is no correlation between price movements of any of the securities.

3. A weighted average of the risk of individual securities is a meaningful measure of overall portfolio risk.

Problem Solution

The minimum risk portfolio for a 6% net return is outlined in Fig. 18–6.

Mammoth Telephone and Telegraph	0.551	or	$2,755,000
Mammoth 4's 88	0.239	or	1,195,000
Farrington	0.100	or	500,000
U.S. Treasury Bills	0.100	or	500,000
Cash	0.010	or	50,000
	1.000		$5,000,000

Risk = 0.005

Other Variables: $S_2 = 0.099$ $495,000 more invested in senior securities and cash than required.

$S_5 = 0.0224$ $112,235 more current income than required.

Returns

Mammoth Telephone and Telegraph	$126,730	$137,750	$264,480
Mammoth 4's 88	70,505	0	70,505
Farrington	17,500	50,000	67,500
Treasury Bills	22,500	0	22,500
Cash	0	0	0
	$237,235	$187,750	$424,985

FIG. 18–6 Minimum risk portfolio for six percent net return

Solution Interpretation, Six Percent Return

The information in Fig. 18-7 shows the effect of introducing an amount of the variables not in solution equal to one percent of total assets. The maximum amount that can be entered without changing the optimal solution is also shown. Lame Duck 5's can be entered without greatly increasing the total risk. Each $50,000 increases risk by only

$$0.000004/0.004994 = 0.08\%.$$

The total amount that could be invested in Lame Duck 5's in this way is $(0.285) (\$5,000,000) = \$1,425,000.$

Variable not in optimal solution	Increased risk if 0.01 forced into solution	Maximum amount that can be forced
Lame Duck Airlines	0.001714	0.080
E–Z Load Camera	0.000321	0.131
Diversified Electric	0.000235	0.400
H.A.L. Computer	0.000082	0.204
Conglomerate Industries	0.000784	0.107
Cosmic Electro-Technical	0.004513	0.046
Confederate Chemical	0.000209	0.272
Northern Electric Utilities	0.000025	0.340
Lame Duck 5's 77	0.000004	0.285
1% each	0.000054	0.062
10% Treasury Bills	0.000005	0.173
10% Farrington	0.000108	0.268
6% Net Return	0.001081	0.004

FIG. 18-7 *Increase in risk resulting from forcing nonoptimal portfolio*

At the other extreme, a $50,000 investment in Cosmic Electro-Technical increases risk by

$$0.004513/0.004994 = 90.4\%.$$

The total amount that could be invested is $(0.046) (\$5,000,000) = \$230,000.$

If any size position in any security can be taken without bidding up the price, substitutions should be made which increase overall risk the least.

Figure 18-8 outlines the effect on risk of a change of one percent in the right-hand-side values. If one percent additional net return is required, risk increases by

$$0.001081/0.004994 = 21.6\%.$$

Similarly, a decrease of one percent in the required net return, decreases risk by this same proportion.

	Original value	Change in risk for a 0.01 increase in R.H.S. value
1% Cash constraint (S_1)	0.010	0.000054
25% Senior Securities constraint (S_2)	0.250	None
10% Treasury Bills constraint (S_3)	0.100	0.000005
10% Farrington constraint (S_4)	0.100	0.000108
2.5% Current Income (S_5)	0.025	None
6% Net Return constraint (S_7)	0.085	0.001081

FIG. 18–8 *Effect on overall risk of a one percent increase in right-hand-side values*

A reduction of the required amount to be invested in Farrington by one percent of assets, lowers risk by

$$0.000108/0.004994 = 2.2\%.$$

A reduction in this requirement is particularly desirable.

Since more than the required amount of current income is being earned, changing this constraint has no effect. Similarly, changing the requirement on the amount invested in senior securities would have no effect.

The ranges over which the right-hand-side values of the constraints can be varied without changing the optimal solution are given in Fig. 18–9. This exhibit also gives the variable that leaves solution at the maximum and minimum points.

Constraint	Original value	Minimum value	Outgoing at minimum	Maximum value	Outgoing at maximum
1% Cash (S_1)	0.010	0	X_{14}	0.072	S_2
25% Senior securities (S_2)	0.250	Unbounded	—	0.349	S_2
10% Treasury bills (S_3)	0.100	0	X_{13}	0.273	X_{11}
10% Farrington (S_4)	0.100	0.0062	C_2	0.368	X_1
2.5% Current income (S_5)	0.025	Unbounded	—	0.047	C_5
6% Net return (S_7)	0.085	0.646	X_1	0.0887	C_2

FIG. 18–9 *Right-hand-side ranging, Farrington Company Case*

The most critical constraint is the 6% net return. If a net return of only 6.37% (as opposed to the current 6%) is required, the solution changes, and the variable leaving solution is the slack variable S_2, indicating that no extra investment in senior investments exists. At a required return of 2.96%, Mammoth Telephone and Telegraph leaves the solution.

The range of values which may be assumed by the objective function coefficients without changing the optimal solution is shown in Fig. 18–10.

Variable in solution	Original value	Lower limit	Variable incoming	Upper limit	Variable incoming
Mammoth Telephone and Telegraph (X_1)	0.005	0.0036	S_3	0.0066	X_{10}
Farrington (X_5)	0.0200	0.0092	S_4	Infin.	—
Mammoth 4's (X_{11})	0.0010	0.0000	—	0.0014	S_3
Treasury Bills (X_{13})	0	0	—	Infin.	—
Cash (X_{14})	0	0	—	Infin.	—

FIG. 18–10 *Objective-function-coefficient ranging, Farrington Company Case*

The importance of having a good measure of risk for Mammoth Telephone and Telegraph is evident. The solution changes at risks of 0.0036 and 0.0066, which are very close to the assumed risk of 0.005. At the lower limit, extra funds will be invested in Treasury Bills. At the upper limit, Northern Electric Utilities enters into the solution.

The upper limit on Mammoth 4's is also critical. At a risk of 0.0014, extra funds will be invested in Treasury Bills. Since 0.0014 is very close to the assumed value of 0.001, an error here would have important effects.

We have seen that the optimal solution for a 6% return changes when the required return is raised to 6.37%. The minimum risk portfolios for the required returns of 7, 8, ..., 11% have also been determined and are given in Figs 18–11 through 18–15.

Mammoth Telephone and Telegraph	0.411	or	$2,055,000
Farrington	0.100	or	500,000
Northern Electric Utilities	0.239	or	1,195,000
Lame Duck 5's 77	0.140	or	700,000
Treasury Bills	0.100	or	500,000
Cash	0.010	or	50,000
	1.000		$5,000,000

Risk = 0.0067
Slack Variables: S_5 = 0.0203 $101,635 more current income than required.

Returns

	Current income	Capital gain	Total
Mammoth Telephone and Telegraph	$94,530	$102,750	$197,280
Farrington	17,500	50,000	67,500
Northern Electric Utilities	46,605	95,600	142,205
Lame Duck 5's 77	45,500	0	45,500
Treasury Bills	22,500	0	22,500
Cash	0	0	0
	$226,635	$248,350	$474,985

FIG. 18–11 *Minimum risk portfolio for seven percent net return*

Farrington	0.100	or	$ 500,000
H.A.L. Computer	0.014	or	70,000
Northern Electric Utilities	0.636	or	3,180,000
Lame Duck 5's 77	0.140	or	700,000
Treasury Bills	0.100	or	500,000
Cash	0.010	or	50,000
	1.000		$5,000,000

Risk = 0.0089

Slack Variables: $S_5 = 0.017$ $85,150 more current income than required.

Returns

	Current income	Capital gain	Total
Farrington	$ 17,500	$ 50,000	$ 67,500
H.A.L. Computer	630	10,500	11,130
Northern Electric Utilities	124,020	254,400	378,420
Lame Duck 5's 77	45,500	0	45,500
Treasury Bills	22,500	0	22,500
Cash	0	0	0
	$210,150	$314,900	$525,050

FIG. 18–12   *Minimum risk portfolio for eight percent net return*

Farrington	0.100	or	$ 500,000
H.A.L. Computer	0.264	or	1,320,000
Northern Electric Utilities	0.386	or	1,930,000
Lame Duck 5's 77	0.140	or	700,000
Treasury Bills	0.100	or	500,000
Cash	0.010	or	50,000
	1.000		$5,000,000

Risk = 0.0114

Slack Variables: $S_5 = 0.0095$ $47,640 more current income than required.

Returns

	Current income	Capital gain	Total
Farrington	$ 17,500	$ 50,000	$ 67,500
H.A.L. Computer	11,800	198,000	209,880
Northern Electric Utilities	75,270	154,400	229,670
Lame Duck 5's 77	45,500	0	45,500
Treasury Bills	22,500	0	22,500
Cash	0	0	0
	$172,650	$402,400	$575,050

FIG. 18–13   *Minimum risk portfolio for nine percent net return*

Farrington	0.100 or	$ 500,000
H.A.L. Computer	0.514 or	2,570,000
Northern Electric Utilities	0.136 or	680,000
Lame Duck 5's 77	0.140 or	700,000
Treasury Bills	0.100 or	500,000
Cash	0.010 or	50,000
	1.000	$5,000,000

Risk = 0.0139
Slack Variables: S_s = 0.002 $10,150 more current income than required.

Returns

	Current income	Capital gains	Total
Farrington	$ 17,500	$ 50,000	$ 67,500
H.A.L. Computer	23,130	385,500	408,630
Northern Electric Utilities	26,520	54,400	80,920
Lame Duck 5's 77	45,500	0	45,500
Treasury Bills	22,500	0	22,500
Cash	0	0	0
	$135,150	$489,900	$625,050

FIG. 18–14 Minimum risk portfolio for 10 percent net return

E–Z Load Camera	0.114 or	$ 570,000
Farrington	0.100 or	500,000
H.A.L. Computer	0.491 or	2,455,000
Northern Electric Utilities	0.045 or	225,000
Lame Duck 5's 77	0.140 or	700,000
Treasury Bills	0.100 or	500,000
Cash	0.010 or	50,000
	1.000	$5,000,000

Risk = 0.0182

Returns

	Current income	Capital gain	Total
E–Z Load Camera	$ 8,550	$114,000	$122,550
Farrington	17.500	50,000	67,500
H.A.L. Computer	22,095	368,250	390,345
Northern Electric Utilities	8,775	18,000	26,775
Lame Duck 5's 77	45,500	0	45,500
Treasury Bills	22,500	0	22,500
Cash	0	0	0
	$124,920	$550,250	$675,170

FIG. 18–15 Minimum risk portfolio for 11 percent net return

The risk factors compared to the minimum required returns are as follows:

Required return	Risk factor
6%	0.0050
7%	0.0067
8%	0.0089
9%	0.0114
10%	0.0139
11%	0.0182

It can be seen that the risk rised rapidly as the required return is increased.

Evaluation of Model in Light of Assumptions

If the estimate of current costs is too low, the results are not serious since more current income than necessary is produced by the six percent minimum risk portfolio.

Brokerage commissions for bonds are generally lower than for stocks. Thus, bonds are slightly more desirable than indicated. It seems very doubtful that this would alter the optimal solution, however.

Even if the expected growth rates are not normal, 75% of the values should lie within two standard deviations of the mean by Tchebysheff's Theorem. Thus, by using a 75% confidence interval, an estimate of the standard deviation could be obtained.

Probably the most unrealistic assumption concerns the lack of correlation between price movements of the securities. Certainly the bonds and money rate stocks would move together in response to changes in the interest rate. Similarly, the companies connected with the electronics industry might move together. To avoid this difficulty, some measure of covariance between stocks should be developed and some method of placing a premium on portfolios with small covariances between securities would be desirable. This is merely another way of saying that portfolios should be diversified.

The estimated returns for the various securities are highly subjective and subject to error. Subjectively, however, in this area is unavoidable.

Conclusions

1. Since risk rises rapidly with required return, a six percent net return seems most desirable.

2. Lame Duck 5's and Northern Electric Utilities are the best alternatives to securities already in solution.

3. The requirement that 10% of assets be invested in Farrington significantly increases the risk of the portfolio. This requirement should be reduced or eliminated.

4. Because covariance has been ignored, the inclusion of both the stock and bonds of Mammoth Telephone and Telegraph is not as desirable as indicated by the model. Substitutions should be considered.

THE MID-REGIONAL COMPANY CASE

The Mid-Regional Company is an electric utility holding company with a service area of 120,000 square miles, located in central United States. It serves approximately two million customers through its four operating companies: Central Power Company, Mid-Central Power Company, Mid-South Power Company, and Mid-West Power Company. A service subsidiary, Mid-Regional Services, Inc., provides financial, administrative, and technical support to the operating companies. Assets of the Mid-Regional Company exceed $2.2 billion; annual revenues approach $5.45 million, and 1967 earnings per share of common stock were $1.56, up seven percent over the 1966 earnings.

The predecessor, Mid-South Company, was dissolved in 1945 under the Public Utility Holding Company Act of 1935. However, in 1947 the Securities and Exchange Commission permitted the Mid-Regional Company to form in its present dimensions. Decided economies are realized in the operating companies via collective financing and fuel purchasing and especially via joint use of generating capacity through power pooling and interconnected systems. These economies are reflected in the average price per kilowatt-hour paid by the customer being 20% below the national average and in the financial health of the Mid-Regional Company.

Electricity is a unique product in that it may not be stored. Its moment of production, delivery, and use coincide in the timespan of a fraction of a second. Furthermore, franchise for utility service carries the obligation to serve every customer with as much power as he requires, at the time he requires it. Unfortunately for the utility company, customer demands usually coincide, producing "peaks" in demand daily, weekly, and seasonally. Investment in generating equipment required to meet demand—including peaks—is usually expensive compared to investment in other industries. Rapidly expanding demand for electrical energy (in the United States, kilowatt-hour usage has been more than doubling each decade) and now rapidly rising interest rates (Mid-Regional system companies finance approximately 60% of new generating capacity from bond funds) have converged to make decisions about investment in generating equipment critical to the company's financial performance.

The procedure presently used by the Mid-Regional Company in analyzing the equipment investment required to meet projected demand is approximately as follows:

1. Based on historical data and sales expectations, demand for electrical energy is projected a minimum of five years into the future for generating capacity studies.

2. Based on (a) increased projected demand, (b) a knowledge of the existing generating capability, and (c) a knowledge of the operating and economic characteristics of various types of generating equipment available to meet the projected demand, a decision is reached to provide so many "standard size" units within the system of a certain type by a certain date.

This approach is highly oversimplified but economic analysis is limited to comparing standard generating units, predetermined to be applicable to certain areas of the demand curve. For instance, newer steam-electric generators are depended on for "base load" generation; purchased power and older, more expensive steam plants, for additional capacity; hydro-electric plants and the most costly steam plants for covering the top of the peak demand.

The application of linear programming to this problem situation may be far from ideal but, if interpreted correctly, it will be a valuable new tool in the generating equipment selection process.

These data seem to be significant to the study:

1. Time span of the study: 1967–1971.

2. Peak demand in megawatts (MW): 1967 (actual)   8,540 (June)
                                    1971 (projected) 12,370 (August)

3. Total annual power output in megawatt-hours (MWh):
                                    1967: 47,020,000
                                    1971 (projected): 67,700,000.

4. Equipment alternatives to meet projected demand:

a) Nuclear plant—none on system but 800 megawatt plant planned. High initial cost "base load" plant. Fuel costs not verified but preliminary indicators are lower than coal or gas. Will operate at full load 8000 hours per year.

b) Steam-electric—the backbone of the "base load" capability with 250 to 500 megawatt units common. High initial cost but low operating costs with newer units. Full load operation 6000 hours per year.

c) Hydro-electric—highest initial cost, lowest operating cost. Seasonal water flows limit most hydro plants to use as peak units (1000 hours per year). Sites for future hydro developments are limited in the Mid-Regional Company system. Size of units vary from 20 to 50 megawatts; average is 40.

d) Gas turbine generator—lowest initial cost, highest operating cost of new equipment. Used for handling peak demand. Operated approximately 1000 hours per year.

e) Purchased power—no investment, highest megawatt-hour cost.   Limited availability from neighboring systems.

5. Projected investment available for 1971 demand: $420 million.

Investment and variable operating cost data are shown below. Note the varying characteristics of the alternative choices and how they apply to the varying characteristics of the demand "pyramid" with its base load and peak characteristics.

Type	A^1 (per MW)	B^2 (per MW)	C^3 (per MW)	D^4 (per MW)
Nuclear	$130,000	$14,400	$143,600	$370,000
Steam	$110,000	$17,400	$126,400	$400,000
Hydro	$200,000	$ 2,500	$202,400	$241,600
Gas Turbine	$ 65,000	$ 3,500	$ 68,300	$123,400
Purchased	—	$20,000	$ 18,900	$333,300

1. This column is initial investment cost per megawatt. These costs vary linearly within the megawatt range of "standard" generating units described above.

2. This column is annual operating cost and includes those costs which vary directly with the additional of megawatt capacity, such as: fuel, direct labor, direct maintenance. Annual costs are derived by multiplying incremental costs per megawatt hour by annual operating hours normal to the type of equipment.

3. Investment cost (A) with the first year's operating costs discounted to present value for an interest rate of six percent are shown in this column.

4. Investment plus annual operating costs to perpetuity (that is, operating cost $\times$ $(1/6\%)$) are shown in this column.

The objective is to select the "blend" of generating possibilities which will meet the imposed constraints via the route of minimizing applicable costs.

THE AIRCRAFT MISSION ALLOCATION SCHEDULING CASE

A friendly government has requested a large airframe manufacturer to study their airlift capability in terms of estimated future military requirements. These requirements were estimated by the Air Force of the government in question. The present airlift fleet consists of twelve C–130A and twelve C–130E aircraft. The C–130A's were put into service approximately ten years ago and are becoming increasingly difficult to maintain. The C–130E's, on the other hand, are only one year old and are still in production.

The basic question is whether new aircraft are needed to perform the estimated missions and, if so, in what quantities. If additional aircraft are needed, the choice between new C–130E's and the all-jet C–141A must be made.

Airlift Requirements. Three separate sets of requirements were set forth. Two are annual resupply missions. The third is a 90-day deployment requirement. The deployment is based on a maximum allowable deployment time of 90 days with all items airlifted 1800 nautical miles. The quantities to be airlifted are as follows:

40,000 passengers,

16,600 short tons of equipment,

1,290 vehicles.

Previous Sales Study. A previous study, conducted by the airframe manufacturer, investigated all the various mission requirements and fleet combinations. The results of this study are summarized as follows:

1. Keeping C–130A's in the present fleet, the following quantities of new aricraft are necessary to meet the various requirements:

	C–130E	or	C–141A
Resupply mission A	2		1
Resupply mission B	93		41
90-day deployment	15		6

2. Retiring C–130A's from the present fleet, the following quantities are appropriate:

	C–130E	or	C–411A
Resupply mission A	11		5
Resupply mission B	102		45
90-day deployment	24		10

Discussions with the government involved, at the time the report was presented, revealed that their objective was to retire the twelve C–130A's in their present fleet. In addition, they felt that the first resupply requirement was unrealistically low while the second resupply requirement was impractically overestimated.   The 90-day deployment requirement seemed realistic in the sense that the required additional aircraft, either C–130E's or C–141A's, appeared to be in the correct magnitude and proportion.

Further analysis showed that the ten-year program cost for the C–141A fleet combined with the twelve C–130E's already being operated was substantially less than that for thirty-six C–130E's. At this point, the question became one of how to best utilize this mixed fleet to perform the deployment.

The marketing engineers for the airframe manufacturer must now tell the potential customer how to operate the new aircraft in conjunction with his present aircraft to do the most effective job.

Given a fleet of twelve C–141A's, the object was to determine the sortie utilization of each aircraft type in order to minimize direct operating cost of performing the deployment. A sortie, by definition, is one aircraft flight from point of departure with payload, to destination, offload and return empty. The end result of the present analysis should reveal the number of flights each type of aircraft will make with each variety of payload (passengers, stores, or vehicles).

There are certain basic assumptions which were made in order to determine the numbers of aircraft required.

1. The twelve C–130E's currently in the inventory will be utilized in conjunction with the ten new C–141A's.

2. Homogeneous payloads are carried on each sortie. In other words, on any one flight the payload is composed entirely of passengers, vehicles with one driver each, or palletized bulk cargo and equipment.

3. The equipment and bulk cargo (stores) density is adequate for attaining payload weight limits. This assumption is supported by historical data yielding an average density for military cargo of 25 pounds per cubic foot. On this basis, neither the C–130 nor the C–141 will be volume limited.

4. The aircraft utilization rate for a 90-day deployment can be maintained at ten hours per day. This is determined by dividing total flying hours for the period foe each aircraft by 90.

5. The deployment fleet availability is 75%. During any arbitrary 80-day period it is assumed that 25% of the total fleet will be unavailable because of maintenance or other requirements. Therefore, 75% of the fleet will be utilized for the deployment operation. This concept permits use of fractional numbers of aircraft since, for

example, one aircraft could be available for half the time period, thereby becoming one-half an aircraft for the purposes of the analysis.

6. Deployment must be completed in a total elapsed time of 90 days.

Aircraft Performance. The basic route over which the deployment sorties are flown is 1800 nautical miles with a refuelling stop available at the half-way point. It is assumed that no fuel is available at the delivery point. All enroute refuelling is done at the half-way point.

The following data summarizes the aircraft capability for each type payload.

	C–130E	*C–141A*
Stores (short tons)	21.5	51.0
Passengers	92	131
Vehicles	7	12
Flight time per sortie (hours)	13.6	9.8
Ground time per sortie (hours)	4.0	3.0
Cycle time (hours)	17.6*	11.9

Aircraft Operating Cost. The hourly direct operating costs used in this analysis are determined from Air Force planning data with appropriate adjustments for foreign fuel cost of $0.21 per imperial gallon.

	Direct operating cost in Dollars per hour per aircraft	
	C–130E	*C–141A*
Personnel	75	75
POL	145	335
Depot maintenance	136	204
Base maintenance material	20	53
Maintenance labor	114	218
Total	490	885

Fleet Sizing. In the deployment operation, the ground time is significant relative to the total deployment time. Hence, cycle time is shown by the relation:

$$T_c = \frac{\sum\limits_{\text{route}} T_g + T_b}{U},$$

where T_c = cycle time in days,

T_g = ground time over the route in hours,

T_b = block time over the route in hours,

U = aircraft utilization in hours per day.

---

* For vehicle and bulk stores sorties, a cycle time of 16.2 hours is applicable.

The fleet size is determined by the relation:

$$F = \frac{(T_c)(S)}{A[T_d + (T_c/2)]},$$

where F = fleet size in aircraft,

    T_c = cycle time per sortie in days,

    S = number of sorties required per deployment,

    A = aircraft availability in percent of fleet,

    T_d = deployment time in days.

These relationships were used to determine the numbers of additional aircraft needed.

THE TELEPHONE CABLE PLANT CASE

A telephone company has to make many choices involving economy in providing facilities to meet the needs of its subscribers. The rates for subscribers are normally based on the company's investment; that is, the company is allowed to earn some specific return on the investment in its plant. Consequently, the company must strive continuously to keep under control both the costs of any new plants and the operating costs in order to avoid being accused of imprudent management.

Since regulated industries operate with a predetermined "rate of profit", they are often more interested in the minimization of costs than the maximization of profits whenever a linear programming model is involved. One area in which linear programming can be easily utilized involves the placing of a cable plant to serve subscribers. The problem can become very complex for a number of reasons. Some of these reasons are as follows:

1. In order to signal a subscriber (that is, to ring a bell, light a light on a switchboard, or activate a relay), the electrical resistance of the cable plant must be below a specified level.

2. In order for the subscriber to be able to talk over the lines, the 1,000 cycle loss (transmission loss) expressed in decibels per kilofoot (kf) must be below a specified level.

3. Different types of services have different limitations.

4. There are four different types of cable available, each with its own set of electrical characteristics.

5. Additional increases in talking and signalling ability can be obtained through the application of relatively expensive equipment.

6. Any proposed additional plant must work with the existing plant.

7. The lower the resistance and transmission loss of a facility, the higher its cost.

Hence, quite a number of variable factors are involved in the successful design of a cable plant for a telephone company. With these facts in mind, we can approach a specific problem faced by a local telephone company.

The city of Sessums has a toll switchboard located in the telephone office building where the equipment for handling local calls is also housed. Any long distance calls from smaller nearby towns must come into the Sessums toll switchboard and then into the outside world.

The town of Billups Gate is located approximately 20 miles from Sessums. The existing trunks (circuits connecting the two towns) consist of 20 iron wire circuits on crossarms which follow the railroad. The iron wire is 40 years old, badly deteriorated, difficult to maintain, and has no room for growth circuits.

The Langford Manufacturing Company has a large plant located approximately nine miles outside of Sessums which is expected to expand in the coming years. This company has a local Sessums telephone number and is served by facilities on the same pole line as the trunks to Billups Gate.

Because of the age, the deterioration of the facilities, and the maintenance problems, it has been deemed necessary for the telephone company to replace the existing iron wire with cable. The size of the cable (number of wires inside the cable sheath) in the various sections should be large enough to provide for the ten-year forecasted demand.

After the appropriate size of the cable is determined, the gauge (diameter of each wire) must be selected. The four gauges available are: 26-gauge, 24-gauge, 22-gauge, and 19-gauge. The larger the gauge number, the smaller the diameter of the wire and the smaller the associated cost. The 26-gauge cable, consisting of very small wires, is used only for subscribers who are located near the central office and it is not considered appropriate for line to Billups Gate.

A word about "load coils" is probably appropriate. In order to reduce transmission loss and improve talking characteristics, H–88 type load coils are placed in runs of cable over 21 kilofeet and, hence, must be considered in determining cost. The load coils are placed at six kilofeet intervals along the cable. Their cost can be determined on a per kilofoot basis by dividing the cost per load coil by six.

Figure 18–16 is a graphic representation of the proposal. The route is divided into three sections. Section A requires a 100-pair cable, Section B, a 50-pair cable, and Section C a 25-pair cable. The 100-pair cable will tie into an existing 24-gauge cable at Sessums which has 100 spare pairs. The problem, then, is to determine what gauge or combination of gauges should make up the various cables in the three sections in order to minimize cost while still meeting the signalling and transmission requirements.

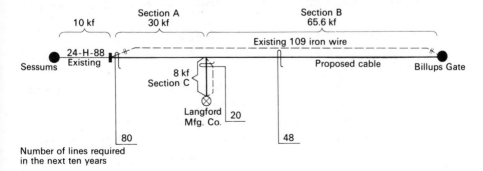

FIG. 18–16 Proposed replacement of existing iron wire with cable

The in-plant costs of the various sizes and gauges of cable under consideration are given in Table 18–1. Also shown are the resistance and transmission characteristics of these same cables.

TABLE 18–1 Specifications for cable plant

Resistance constants
(ohms per 1000 feet)

24 gauge cable   51.9

22 gauge cable   32.4

19 gauge cable   16.1

1000 cycle loss constants
(decibels per 1000 feet)

24 gauge cable   0.20

22 gauge cable   0.15

19 gauge cable   0.08

Cable costs
(dollars per 1000 feet)

100 pair	Non-loaded	Load coils	Total cost
24 gauge	$553	$48	$601
22 gauge	690	48	739
19 gauge	1091	48	1139
50 pair			
24 gauge	390	33	423
22 gauge	459	33	492
19 gauge	665	33	698
25 pair			
24 gauge	303	24	327
22 gauge	338	24	362
19 gauge	435	24	459

There are two limitations to be considered; these are signalling loss and transmission loss. The limitations between Sessums and Billups Gate are different from those between Sessums and the Langford Manufacturing Company. These limitations are as follows:

	Sessums-to-Billings	*Sessums-to-Langford*
Signalling loss	3500 ohms	1600 ohms
Transmission loss	15 decibels	7 decibels

Since ten kilofeet of existing 24-gauge cable is to be used, the limitations will be further decreased by 519 ohms for the signalling loss and 2 decibels for the transmission loss.

THE FICKELPICKEL COMPANY CASE

Plant No. 9 is one of a group of industries operated by R. J. Fickelpickel. The plant produces slate granules to be used in the production of asphalt base roofing.

The granules are produced in natural form, coated with a clear covering known as coder and with various colors such as yellow, green, brown, white, blue, and red.

Because of the quality of the product produced, the granules are in great demand by the producers of asphalt base roofing. The good quality is the result of the raw materials that come from the plant's mine and the quality control that is used in the refining process.

The market for the products of the plant are primarily producers of asphalt base roofing. Since the asphalt base roofing industry is an oligopoly, the number of customers is limited. Once a customer has started using the plant's products, they will mail in orders for additional quantities of the products as they are needed. As a result, the plant does not employ any salesmen. The home office sales force makes periodic calls on the customers to determine if the customer has any problems with the plant's products or is satisfied with the service received. These salesmen have reported that the only area of dissatisfaction is the result of the orders not being processed fast enough.

The plant is located in a rural area. As was the practice at the time the plant was constructed, a mill village was also constructed to house the working force of the plant. The firm furnishes the houses and utilities to the employees without charge. Thus the plant is able to maintain a labor force at a much lower wage rate than the average wage of the area.

The house and utilities represent a very low cost to the plant. The houses have been fully depreciated; painting and repairs are made by the occupants. The firm has its own water system. Electricity is purchased from the power company at reduced rates and then distributed via the plant's own lines and equipment.

Because of the low wages paid, the firm cannot find employees unless they can provide houses. Therefore, the labor force is limited to the number of houses they have. The firm considers it too expensive to construct additional housing at the present time. As a result of all this, the employees work approximately twelve hours a day, six days a week.

The company is not unionized and the work force is largely illiterate.

The location of the plant prohibits the firm using service companies to maintain their equipment. The firm has a group of carpenters, machinists, mechanics, and so forth, to provide service, preventive maintenance, and to install new equipment.

The raw material comes from the firm's mine. The mine is an open pit with tunnels running back into the mountain where the slate is mined. During the day, holes are drilled and explosives set to provide loose rock for the next day's work. The loose rock is loaded on trucks and hauled to a cable car in the open pit. The cable car transports the material to the coarse plant.

Storage for the product is provided at each processing center except the coarse plant. The coarse plant can only store three tons of slate. The cable car brings two tons of rock to the coarse plant. If the crusher operator doesn't have room for the rock, he will not signal the cable car operator to unload.

The mine and the processing plant are operated as separated departments. The cost of the slate to the processing plant was determined by averaging the cost per ton for the previous year and adjusting it for any known increases and decreases in cost. The cost of $5.00 per ton is fixed as far as the plant manager is concerned.

The cost of the raw material to the plant is the same even though the quality changes. Different rooms in the mine have more impurities in the slate than other rooms. The best grade is used for process route "*B*"; the next best grade for process route "*C*"; and the poorest grade for process route "*A*". The mine's lowest quality slate is considered to be equal to any competitor's best quality, however.

The controllable costs in the coarse plant include the cost of two men, one to operate the crusher and the other to keep the screens and elevators from overloading. This man also relieves the crusher operator. The other cost is the cost of electricity. The total controllable cost to operate the coarse plant is $2.00 per ton.

The controllable cost for each processing center was developed from the cost records, payroll records, discussions, and observations.

The coarse plant operates eight hours a day six days a week and can process 24 tons an hour. The capacity is, then, 1152 tons per week.

The shrinkage in the coarse plant is 90% for process *A* and 95% for process *B* and *C*. Shrinkage results from the elimination of impurities and dust that result from the crushing and screening processes.

When the slate leaves the coarse plant, it is about one inch in size. The refining plant continues the crushing process until the material will pass a #6 screen but not a #8 screen for processes *B* and *C*. Processes *B* and *C* require granules of #8 screen size; as a result, the shrinkage in these two processes is 30%. Process *A* uses the material on the #8 and the #10 screens, reducing the shrinkage to 20%.

The shrinkage in the coarse plant is caused by the dust created by crushing and screening processes and the material that passes the #10 screen.

A by-product, 50-Mesh, was developed and is sold to fertilizer companies to be used as filler in their products. Slate too fine for granules is processed by a ball mill until it passes a #50 mesh screen. Ten percent of process *A* and 20% of processes *B* and *C* is recovered in the by-product.

The refining plant is automated. It requires one person to check the elevators and screens and to oil and clean. The controllable cost in the refining plant is $3.00 per ton. The capacity of the refining plant is 1080 tons per week (15 tons per hour, 12 hours a day, 6 days a week). It is operated by two shifts. The first shift works for 40

hours and then the next shift comes on duty. Overtime was only paid on all time over
40 hours a week.

The by-product, 50-Mesh, is transferred to a storage tank in the 50-Mesh loading
plant by pipe. When enough has been accumulated to fill a freight car, it is loaded and
shipped. The 50-Mesh loading plant's controllable cost is $1.00 per ton. The plant's
capacity is ten times what is now being produced.

The material in process *A* goes from the refining plant to the coating plant where
the granules are coated with a mixture of "nubs and chips" and thinner. The controllable
cost is $2.00 per ton. This plant can process 5 tons per hour, six days a week, 16 hours
per day. The shifts are planned to eliminate overtime. There is a gain of four percent
in the coating plant.

Process *B* materials are moved by conveyor belt to the loading plant. The loading
plant has storage available for the materials from processes *A*, *B*, and *C*.

The materials in process *C* are moved from the refining plant to the coloring plant
by conveyors. The granules are colored. The plant has a capacity of 384 tons a week

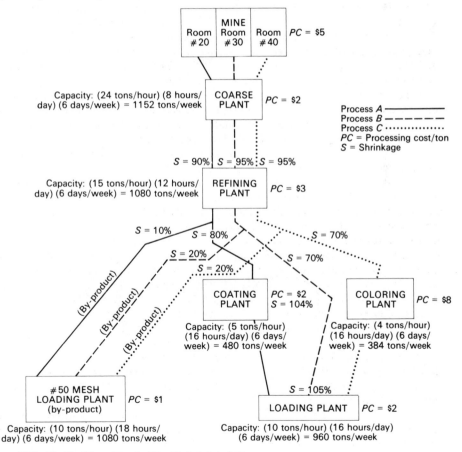

FIG. 18–17 Plant No. 9, The Fickelpickel Company

(16 hours a day, 4 tons an hour, and 6 days a week). The shifts are designed to prevent the payment of overtime. An analysis of the cost records establish a controllable cost of $8.00 a ton. The material increases in weight by five percent at the coloring plant. The material is then transferred to the loading plant by conveyors.

At the loading plant the material is loaded into freight cars for shipment to the customers. Before loading, the freight cars have to be cleaned.

Since the demand for their products is greater than the production of the plant, it was decided that the plant's objective should be to produce the mix of their products that would be the most profitable. To do this the number of tons needed each week from the various rooms of the mine would have to be determined and scheduled.

Since this was a problem of product mix, it was decided that linear programming would give an insight into the problem situation.

A flow chart of the processes *A*, *B*, and *C* was developed to assist in setting up the constraints and the objective function. (See Fig. 18–17.)

The selling price of the product produced by process *A* is $38.00 a ton, process *B* is $35.00 per ton, and process *C* is $42.00 a ton. The by-product sells for $10.00 per ton.

THE PULP PAPER COMPANY CASE

Paul Papyrus is the Risk Manager for the Pulp Paper Company, a paper manufacturing firm. Paul's job is to discover all of the static (that is, non-productive) risks faced by the firm and to propose to management suitable ways of dealing with them. The term non-productive risks is used to refer to those risks of loss which do not also pose a chance of gain. For example, fire could destroy some stock causing loss to the company but could not result in gain or profit to the firm.

In order to perform his job, Paul must be aware of all of the manufacturing processes carried on by the firm. Among other things, he must look for bottleneck situations that would be the most vulnerable points for critical losses to the firm. In the course of his surveys of the manufacturing processes, Paul has discovered a situation closely akin to a bottleneck. This situation came to light when Paul was analyzing the Wrapping Paper Division. This Division manufacturers three products:

1. Special paper, which is treated with a special chemical so that it is resistant to fungi. It is used for wrapping goods which will be in storage for some time.

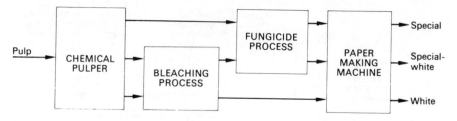

FIG. 18–18 Schematic diagram of processing in wrapping paper division, Pulp Paper Company

2. White paper, which is a bleached white paper such as is used in wrapping meats.

3. Special-white paper, which is white paper treated with the fungus resistant chemical.

A diagram of the Wrapping Paper Division process is shown in Fig. 18–18.

Paul discovered that all of the fungicide used by Pulp Paper Company in this processing comes from a single supplier. He would like to know how great a loss Pulp Paper would suffer if this supply were cut off by, for example, a fire in the supplier's plant. In other words, he needs to know the profit from this Division both with and without the fungicide-treated products.

In discussing this situation with the Division Manager, Paul finds that the Division is now operating at an optimal level based on the following data:

1. As the pulp wood goes through the chemical pulping process, there is a 50% loss in weight.

2. As the pulp moves through the bleaching operation, there is a five percent loss in weight.

3. As the pulp moves through the fungicide treatment operation, there is a 20% loss in weight.

4. The chemical pulping capacity is 200 unit weights of input per day.

5. The bleaching unit capacity is 50 unit weights of input per day.

6. The fungicide treatment unit capacity is 50 unit weights of input each day.

7. The paper machine capacity is 70 unit weights of input each day.

8. Enough fungicide chemical can be obtained to treat 35 unit weights each day.

9. Enough bleach chemical can be obtained to treat 100 unit weights each day.

10. The sale price, per output unit weight, is $500 for Special, $300 for White, and $700 for Special-white.

11. The input cost of pulpwood, for all products, is $50 per unit weight.

12. The cost of the chemical pulping process is $10 per unit weight for all three products.

13. The cost of the bleach process is $20 per unit weight.

14. The cost of the chemical bleach is $20 per unit weight.

15. The cost of the fungicide process is $20 per unit weight.

16. The cost of the fungicide chemical is $20 per unit weight.

17. Special paper requires 2 units of machine time per unit weight; White paper requires $1\frac{1}{2}$ units of machine time per unit weight; and Special-white paper requires 3 units of machine time per unit weight.

The gross earnings per unit weight of input for each product are computed based on the sales price less the variable cost. The sales price per input is the sales price per output adjusted for the wastage, or is as follows:

Product	Variable label	Sales price per output unit	Adjustment for wastage	Sales price per input unit
Special	X_1	$500 ×	(0.5) (0.8)	= $200
White	X_2	$300 ×	(0.5) (0.95)	= $142.50
Special-white	X_3	$700 ×	(0.5) (0.8) (0.95)	= $266.00

The gross earnings per unit weight for each product are then computed as:

	Special	White	Special-white
Sales price per input unit	$200.00	$142.50	$266.00
Less cost of:			
Pulp	50.00	50.00	50.00
Chemical process	10.00	10.00	10.00
Bleach	—	10.00	10.00
Bleach process	—	10.00	10.00
Fungicide	10.00	—	9.50
Fungicide process	10.00	—	9.50
Gross earnings per input unit	$120.00	$62.50	$167.00

Using this information, the Division Manager would like to set his daily production schedule so as to maximize gross earnings.

Paul has investigated the supplier of the fungicide and found that if the factory where the fungicide is manufactured were to be totally destroyed, it would take about six months for it to be rebuilt and back in production. Therefore, Paul needs to know how much the earnings of Pulp Paper would be reduced if the fungicide were not available for a six-month period of time. If no fungicide were available, the only product Pulp Paper could process would be the White paper. Because of the limitation on machine time, the gross earnings on the manufacture of this one product would be limited to $6125 a day. Pulp Paper operates on a 5-day week so in a six month period there are approximately $5 \times 26 = 130$ work days. The loss in gross earnings per day is $10,353 - $6125 = 4228. The six months loss would be $130 \times $4228 = $549,640$.

In considering the recommendations he should make to management concerning this potential loss, Paul finds that he can buy "Contingent Business Interruption Insurance" which will protect Pulp Paper if the supplier is shut down because of physical damage to its property arising out of fire, windstorm, and certain other perils. He also finds that this policy includes a provision which reads: "It is a condition of this insurance that if the insured could reduce the loss resulting from the interruption of business by making use of any other available source of materials, such reduction shall be taken into account in arriving at the amount of loss hereunder."

Thus, Paul investigated other sources of supply for the fungicide. According to the Division Manager, there is only one alternative supply of the fungicide. This supplier could provide only 15 units a day and at a price of $40 a unit. If this supplier were used, the unit earnings per input unit of Special paper would be reduced to $110 and for Special white to $157.50.

In presenting any proposal to management, Paul must consider any and all alternatives to protect the company against this potential loss. One possibility is for the company to maintain a six month supply of the fungicide in inventory. Since $700 worth of the fungicide is used each day, the value of a six-month inventory would be $130 \times $700 = $91,000$. If an internal rate of return of 10% per annum is assumed by the company, the cost of maintaining the inventory would be $9100.

THE GIANT TRANSISTOR, INC., CASE

Giant Transistor, Inc., has been in business for five years. Today they manufacture two products, regular transistors and the newer giant transistor. The plant has been operating at capacity (three shifts, five days a week) for the last fifteen months. The company's growth and profits have been most reassuring to both stockholders and officers.

One year ago the Vice President in Charge of Operations conducted a study that resulted in setting up an optimum operating point for the whole plant. Following are the highlights of that study.

GT employs 625 men per shift in the capacity of direct labor. The available labor per week was calculated as follows:

(625 men per shift) $\times$ (three shifts) = 1875 men,

(1,875 men) $\times$ (40 hours per week per man) = 75,000 hours per week,

(75,000 hours per week) $\times$ (60 minutes per hour) = 4,500,000 minutes per week.

The first shift receives an average wage of $2.00 an hour. The second shift receives the same wage as the first shift, $2.00 an hour. The third or graveyard shift receives a 15% pay incentive over and above the normal $2.00 an hour, for an average wage of $2.30 an hour.

Since all three shifts have the same number of men working and all three shifts produce the same quantity, the average wage for the entire plant would be $2.10 an hour.

Studies by the Industrial Engineering Department had shown that ten minutes of labor were required for each regular transistor produced. This figure was derived by dividing the total number of man-minutes allocated to the production of regular transistors by the number of regular transistors produced. By the same method, a figure of 20 minutes was derived for each giant transistor produced.

For regular transistors, the labor cost per unit would be:

(1/6 hour per unit) $\times$ ($2.10 an hour) = $0.35 per unit.

For the giant transistors, the labor cost per unit would be:

(1/3 hour per unit) $\times$ ($2.10 an hour) = $0.70 per unit.

Since raw materials for the two types of transistors is stocked separately for costing purposes, the calculation of the material cost per unit was a simple matter. They simply took the value of the beginning inventories, added purchases, and subtracted ending inventory values to arrive at the cost of the materials going into each type of transistor. This cost figure was divided by the number of units of the respective transistors produced during the period (in this case, a year) to arrive at the per unit material cost.

For regular transistors the average material cost per unit was $0.15. For giant transistors the average material cost per unit was $0.30.

The total decision cost per unit of regular transistors came out to be:

($0.35 for labor) + ($0.15 for material) = $0.50 per unit decision cost.

The total decision cost per unit of giant transistors came out to be:

($0.70 for labor) + ($0.30 for material) = $1.00 per unit decision cost.

Since GT sells regular transistors for $0.82 per unit, decision profit is:

$0.82 − $0.50 = $0.32 per unit.

Giant transistors are sold for $1.63 per unit; hence, decision profit is:

$1.63 − $1.00 = $0.63 per unit.

Other than the labor constraint of 4,500,000 minutes per week for the total three shifts, the only other critical areas are those of Soldering and Final Assembly.

GT has 84 electronic soldering machines that are capable of running 24 hours per day. The available soldering time was calculated as follows:

(60 minutes/hour) × (8 hours/shift) × (3 shifts/day) × (5 days/week) × (84 machines) = 604,800 minutes available Soldering time each week.

GT has 65 final assembly machines that are capable of running 24 hours per day.

The available final assembly time was calculated as:

(60 minutes/hour) × (8 hours/shift) × (3 shifts/day) × (5 days/week) × (65 machines) = 468,000 minutes available final assembly time each week.

Initial Tableau:

	X_1	X_2	S_1	S_2	S_3	
S_1	10	20	1	0	0	4,500,000
S_2	1	3	0	1	0	604,800
S_3	1.1	1.7	0	0	1	468,000
	−0.32	−0.63	0	0	0	0

Final Tableau:

	X_1	X_2	S_1	S_2	S_3	
X_1	1	0	−0.34	0	4	342,000
X_2	0	1	0.22	0	−2	54,000
S_2	0	0	−0.32	1	2	100,800
	0	0	0.0298	0	0.0199	143,460

FIG. 18–19 Tableaus for earlier study, Giant Transistors, Inc., Case

Regular transistors require one minute of soldering time per unit and 1.1 minutes of final assembly time per unit. Giant transistors require 3 minutes of soldering time per unit and 1.7 minutes of final assembly time per unit.

In the earlier study, the variables were defined as follows:

X_1 = number of regular transistors to produce each week.

X_2 = number of giant transistors to produce each week.

The constraints for the linear programming model were set up as follows:

Labor	$10X_1 + 20X_2 \leqslant$	4,500,000 minutes/week.
Soldering	$1X_1 + 3X_2 \leqslant$	604,800 minutes/week.
Final assembly	$1.1X_1 + 1.7X_2 \leqslant$	468,000 minutes/week.

The objective function for the model was

Maximize $0.32X_1 + 0.63X_2$.

The final tableau, showing the optimum operating levels, is shown in Fig. 18–19.

For the past year GT has followed the advice given in the model and has produced and sold 342,000 regular transistors per week and 54,000 giant transistors per week.

By following the model's advice, the weekly income for GT has been as follows:

Gross sales	$368,460
Less cost of goods sold (including manufacturing expenses)	225,000
Gross profit on sales	$1 43,460
Less selling and general expenses	100,000
Net profit before Federal Income Tax	$ 43,460
Less Federal Income Tax (at the rate of 50%)	21,730
Net profit after taxes	$ 21,730

GT has total assets of $12,000,000. The return on total assets, a ratio of great interest to the operating officers, is as follows:

$$\frac{\text{Income before interest and taxes}}{\text{Total assets}} = \frac{\$ 43,460}{\$230,770} = 18.6\%.$$

The above figures represent one week's income before interest and taxes; thus, total assets were divided by 52 in order to calculate the rate of return on a weekly basis.

The operating officers of GT had watched the Congressional hearings in the nation's capital on automotive safety with particular interest. Nolph Rader, the young crusader for the consumer, had succeeded in convincing Congress to make ejection seats mandatory equipment on all of the 1972 automobiles.

The automotive engineers had determined that only a giant transistor could meet the demands of multiple ejection seats from a single control panel. The representatives of a major automobile manufacturer had as much as guaranteed GT a contract for 150,000 giant transistors per week at the price of $1.63 per unit.

The operating officers of GT have to decide whether or not they want the automobile contract: and if they do want the contract, how they can best meet all of their commitments.

Pot Luk Electronics in Tokyo, Japan, offered to produce up to a limit of 300,000 regular transistors for GT on a subcontracting basis. The price to GT would be $0.75 per unit.

This offer looked rather attractive in light of the fact that GT has present sales contracts committing it to produce and sell a minimum of 300,000 regular transistors per week and a minimum of 50,000 giant transistors per week.

Only a handful of firms had the technology to produce the giant transistors, and they would be scrambling for their shares of the new automotive market. Subcontracting giant transistors out, then, was not possible.

GT, like most electronics firms, was a high-wage firm; and GT, like the others, stressed good labor relations. A poll of the workers' representatives showed that the workers would be willing, in fact they would look forward to, working 8 hours overtime on Saturdays on all three shifts. They would not consider working any overtime on Sundays. For this overtime, each worker would receive 1.5 times his normal hourly wage. The operating officers felt that a 48-hour week was the limit for a man. They felt that to exceed this limit would increase fatigue, increase rejects, increase accidents, and subsequently increase costs.

Working from these underlying assumptions, GT wished to determine whether or not they should opt for the auto contract.

THE SWANN COMPANY CASE

Management of the Swann Company is attempting to resolve several basic problems which confront them at present. These problems involve the conflicting goals of liquidity and profitability. The problem of liquidity involves several specific questions that must be answered regarding dividend policy, minimum cash balances, and additional borrowing. The company wishes to develop a dividend policy that will balance the need for additional cash against adverse shareholder reaction if dividends are insufficient. The problem of a minimum cash balance involves a trade-off between cash needs and the risk of unexpected cash drains. The company has already borrowed heavily to meet cash needs. A decision to borrow additional funds would have to be balanced against the explicit cost of higher interest, the implicit cost of a deterioration in credit rating, and the additional risk of default on the added commitment.

The desire for higher profits has to be balanced against the other goals of the company. In the case of liquidity, these goals may be in direct conflict with each other. In other words, additional profits may be obtained only if other goals are not achieved.

As a beginning point, the company has assembled the following information regarding the two products that are manufactured by the company.

Product W

Past experience has indicated that 75% of total sales of this product are on credit. The collections of accounts receivable are expected to be five percent in the month of the sale,

70% in the following month, and 25% in the third month. Purchases of raw materials are scheduled so that inventory balances remain unchanged. Raw material purchases are paid on delivery. Other variable costs are paid as incurred.

Product Z

Credit sales for product Z are expected to be 60% of total sales of product Z. The collections of receivables are expected to be 10% in the month of the sale, 75% in the following month, and 15% in the third month. Purchases of raw materials are paid in the month following the sale. Raw material inventory is to remain unchanged during the quarter. Other variable costs are paid as incurred.

Cost and revenue data are summarized as follows

	W (per unit)	Z (per unit)
Sales price	$5.00	$4.00
Variable costs:		
Raw materials	$1.75	$2.00
Labor	0.48	0.30
Other	0.27	0.70
Total variable costs	$2.50	$3.00
Contribution margin	$2.50	$1.00

Total fixed costs of $70,000 per month are paid as incurred. Non-cash expenses, such as depreciation, exactly equal month cash outlays on new fixed assets.

Selected Balance Sheet accounts appear as follows

March 31	
Cash	$10,000
Accounts receivable	65,000
Inventory	35,000
Accounts payable (raw materials)	50,000
Notes payable	80,000

Twenty thousand dollars of the accounts receivable balance will be collected in April and the remainder in May. The total balance of accounts payable is due in April. Notes payable are due in June.

The company's current policy is to maintain a minimum cash balance of $10,000. The quarterly dividend of $25,000 is tentatively scheduled for June.

The production characteristics are such that 0.4 man-hours is required to produce one unit of W and 0.25 man-hours is required to produce one unit of Z. The manufacturing facilities are adaptable to either type of product. Available man-hours are as follows:

April	48,000 man-hours
May	44,000 man-hours
June	40,000 man-hours

The decline is due to scheduled vacations during the second quarter. This data is based on one eight-hour shift each day. Labor supply is such that additional shifts cannot be added.

Capacity limitations can be surmounted to some extent with the use of overtime. All overtime would require a 50% wage premium.

Management of Swann Company has requested the following information to be presented at the next Board meeting:

1. The production mix between W and Z that will produce the most profit subject to the cash and capacity limitations.

2. Assuming this "maximum profit" is insufficient, what changes to the constraints can be made and at what "costs?"

THE FLASH GORDON AIRLINE CASE

Flash Gordon Airline is a small, scheduled carrier operating with a fleet of reciprocating-engine aircraft. mostly DC–3's DC–4's, and Convair 440's. In recent years business has been slipping badly, so that when the new president, Mr. A. C. Flyer, took over recently, he initiated a study to determine the source of the company's trouble.

The study disclosed that the obsolete equipment was at the heart of the trouble and also that there was considerable untouched market potential, both in cargo and in passengers, if modern, dependable equipment were employed. Thus, fleet modernization seemed to be the solution to the problem, but the poor earnings record in recent years limits the available credit to $95 million. About $5 million more will be realized from the sale of the existing fleet so the total funds available are limited to $100 million.

TABLE 18–2 Summary of costs, capacities, speeds, and utilization for available aircraft, Flash Gordon Airline Case

	Model 100	Model 984	Model 540
Price ($ million)	2.9	5.7	6.24
Cargo capacity (tons)	22.5	10.0	—
Passenger capacity	—	100	200
Average block speed (m.p.h.)	220	400	400
Utilization (hours per year)	3500	3000	3000

After examination of the aircraft available from the various manufacturers, the possible choices of new aircraft have been narrowed to three: the Century 100, and all-cargo propjet; the Walker 540, an all-passenger fanjet; and the Moody 984, a fanjet designed to carry a combination of passengers and cargo. The acquisition costs, capacities, speeds, and possible utilization are shown in Table 18-2, for each of the planes. Average block speeds account for all the time that the engines are running between two points and are shown here for the average stage lengths of the Flash Gordon system.

Annual utilization of the aircraft is limited by scheduling restrictions and maintenance requirements. Only about 10 hours service per day, seven days a week, can be scheduled for passenger planes, but cargo planes can schedule 14 hours per day, six days a week. After maintenance requirements are considered, revenue service time is limited to the hours shown above.

The company owns a four-plane maintenance hanger and will not consider expansion of these facilities. Presently, the maintenance crews work five days a week, but with additional men the shop could operate on Saturdays also. The maximum maintenance airplane-days, then, would be:

$$(6) (52) (4) = 1248.$$

Each aircraft will require a 100-hour periodic inspection, which will take one day each time. The propjet will also require an engine overhaul every 2400 hours which will take about four days, and the fanjets require a five-day overhaul every 1500 hours.

Only 200 people will be available for either pilot or copilot duty due to the shortage of qualified persons. This limit includes those people that can be hired and trained by the time the equipment can be delivered. Pilots are also limited to no more than 80 flying hours per month because of union contract.

The market study just completed indicated that Flash Gordon Airline's potential share of the market could be 325 million cargo ton-miles per year and 4 billion passenger-miles if the fleet is modernized.

Revenue rates are set by the Interstate Commerce Commission for commercial carriers at $0.20 per ton-mile for cargo and $0.03 for each passenger-mile. Although Payload is subject to variation, industry experience has shown that a load factor of 60% for passengers and 70% for cargo are appropriate for planning purposes. Full-capacity loads are seldom attained in practice because of volume limitations in the case of cargo, cancellation of passenger reservations, courtesy passes, and seasonal variation.

Crew requirements and salaries are shown in Table 18-3. Salaries include all direct fringe benefits and other direct payments to employees. They do not include administrative expenses or special concessions such as free travel.

The rate of consumption of fuel and oil is dependent on the weight of the aircraft, the altitude and the speed; and thus, the average rate of consumption will be different for each segment of a system. The average rate for the overall Flash Gordon system, however, has been determined for the aircraft under consideration and will result in a cost of $80 per hour for the propjet and $210 per hour for the fanjets.

Maintenance expenses can be predicted with reasonable accuracy when related to operational time. The engine maintenance estimate is particularly reliable since the frequency of inspection is dictated by FAA and the rate of wear is fairly constant because

TABLE 18–3   Crew requirements and salaries

	Model 100 No.	Model 100 Salary	Model 984 No.	Model 984 Salary	Model 540 No.	Model 540 Salary
Pilot	1	$21600	1	$30000	1	$ 33000
Copilot	1	16800	1	21600	1	23800
Flight engineer	1	14400	1	16800	1	18500
Stewardess	–	—	3	7500	5	8500
Total cost		$52800		$90900		$117800

of the precision of manufacture and the constant level of operation.   Airframe maintenance, on the other hand, will vary from airline to airline and will be influenced by factors peculiar to each operation. For Flash Gordon Airline, comparison of past maintenance costs with those of other airlines operating similar equipment will indicate their deviation from the "average". This average maintenance cost has been formulated by the Airline Transport Association and is expressed as a function of the weight and cost of the airframe and engines, the number of engines, and the engine rating. These equations, however, include provisions for maintenance "burden", or overhead, and so this quantity must be removed since it is a fixed cost and not pertinent to the decision at hand. The maintenance cost found by this procedure is $82 per utilization hour for the Model 100, $187 per hour for the Model 984, and $204 per hour for the Model 540.

Hull insurance is fixed at three percent of the initial cost of the unit. Liability insurance is required for all aircraft and is set at $2800 per ton of cargo capacity and $600 per seat of passenger capacity. These are annual rates.

THE SNEED TRANSFER COMPANY, INC., CASE

While the primary activity of this trucking firm is the transportation of asphalt, a secondary activity is the transportation of various rock products. The hauling of rock products is significantly different from the hauling of asphalt since the equipment requirements are almost totally different. In the former case, a tank trailer with tractor is used and the tractor required is more powerful because of the weight differences.

With the exception of managerial and other overhead items, the cost accounting for the rock hauling can be completely differentiated from the asphalt. This is true because of the isolated equipment and also because the drivers are (although interchangeable downward from asphalt tractors) in practice a distinct group.

With respect to the rock hauling, Sneed Transfer deals with three basic products.

1. *Feldspar sand*. This is a highly specialized product used by one customer. This customer is serviced on a contractual basis, the contract calling for Sneed to exclusively provide for his daily and weekly needs. Feldspar sand, because of its ensuing use, must

be hauled in a special truck body made of aluminium. Sneed Transfer, at present, has a has a dump truck (that is, a fixed-body truck) so equipped and has, in addition, an aluminium trailer body (that is, tandem dump trailer) which can be used for hauling this product.

The customer, Atwell-Otho, has a daily, six days a week, demand for this product of 80 tons. He has a stockpile capability of approximately 960 tons and desires to have a minimum stockpile of 160 tons. Sneed Transfer delivers this product at a delivered price, including the sand, of $16.00 a ton. The customer will accept up to 800 tons a week, limited by his storage. There is only one source (that is, one quarry) for this product and this is at Lewisville. The hauling distance is 30 miles. Drivers for this haul are paid on a per load basis of $8.00. The quarry charges $11.00 a ton, loaded. (See Fig. 18–20).

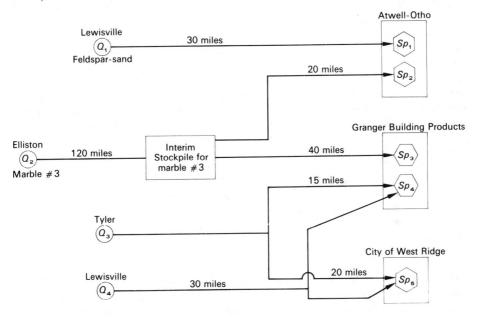

FIG. 18–20   Schematic of rock routes (hauls)

2. *Number 3 marble aggregate.* This product is crushed marble chips. The feasible original source is Elliston, which is 120 miles away. It is customary for the product to be stockpiled at a North Columbus facility by the producers, also.

With regard to Sneed Transfer, however, two distinct patterns of operation are available. The first is a hauling operation from the North Columbus stockpile to various metropolitan locations. Second, there is an opportunity to make the long haul down to Elliston to either the stockpile there, or, occasionally, to a specific customer. The producers generally move this product by rail but are indifferent to method if the cost is essentially the same. However, they will not accept weekly delivery in excess of 180 tons.

Sneed Transfer has commitments for delivery to two customers for this product. Atwell-Otho has a daily requirement, six days a week, for Number 3 Marble of 24 tons. It has stockpile capabilities of approximately 270 tons and prefers a minimum inventory of 54 tons. The hauling distance from the interim stockpile to their stockpile is 20 miles. This customer has a delivered price of $18.00 a ton. The price of the product from the North Columbus stockpile is $14.00 a ton, loaded. Drivers are paid for local hauls $8.00 per load. The price of the same product in Elliston is $8.00 per ton; thus, the hauling differential is $6.00 a ton. Drivers on the occasion of going to Elliston are paid $12.00, plus 10 cents a mile, or $24.00 a load.

The second commitment for this product is with the Granger Building Products Company. Granger makes building baceings, that is, precast blocks, and so forth. This company requires 108 tons per day, 5 days a week, and has virtually an unlimited stockpile capability. They do not, however, accept more than 900 tons in any one week and no more than 2700 tons per month. They, likewise, have determined that they want at least one week's supply on hand at all times. This haul is on a delivered price basis, and the price is $19.80 per ton. Drivers are paid $9.00 per load. The hauling distance is 40 miles.

3. *Granite aggregate #5.* The third rock product Sneed Transfer hauls is a rock commonly used as a foundation for concrete. It is locally sourced at either Lewisville or Tyler. It can be hauled in two ways, as far as the customer is concerned. First, on a delivered basis, and second, on a hauling only basis (that is, freight only). This product is not covered by a tariff and does not require Public Service Commission rights. Thus, it is highly competitive, and rates are negotiated. However, for delivered rock, the contract usually is annual and thus the price has been set.

Sneed Transfer has two annual contracts for hauling this product. First, the Granger Building Products has a contract calling for 48 tons a day, or 240 tons a week. Their primary source for this is via rail, and Sneed's service constitutes a filler plus a degree of flexibility for this company. As a result, they require at least 240 tons per week and will not allow more than 320 tons per week to be delivered by truck. The consistency derived from this contract seems very desirable to Sneed. As a result, the delivered price is $9.60 a ton. Drivers are paid $8.00 a load, and the quarry price is $5.00 a ton, loaded, at Lewisville, and $6.00 a ton at Tyler with drivers being paid $8.00 a load. For this particular type business, Sneed negotiates with the quarries predicated on delivery point and total volume and thus a differential is not uncommon. In Sneed Transfer's case, it was necessary to agree to haul at least an average of 40 tons a day out of Lewisville on a weekly basis. Based on six days a week, this is equal to 240 tons a week requirement for a $5.00 price.

The second contractual commitment is with the City of West Ridge, also on an annual basis. This contract calls for 128 tons per week, not to exceed 256 tons in any one week nor to exceed 480 tons in any one month. The City has sufficient stockpiling capability to handle a year's stockpiling. This is not unusual since there is a steady usage plus exceptional projects which require massive tonnage amounts. These projects are predictable by several months, at least, and Sneed has the opportunity to submit first bid. The delivered price to the City is $11.20 a ton. The same quarry price and driver expense as for Granger Building Products are applicable. Hauling distances are: from Lewisville to City stockpile, 30 miles; and from Tyler to City, 20 miles.

Sources and cost

Product:	Q_1, Q_4 Lewisville	Q_3 Tyler	Q_2 Elliston	Source Stockpile
Feldspar	$11/ton	—	—	—
Marble No. 3	—	—	$8/ton	$14/ton
Granite aggregate No. 5	$5/ton (240 ton minimum)	$6/ton	—	—

Commitments

Contractual commitments

Product:	Atwell-Otho	Granger Building	City of West Ridge	Pickup business
Feldspar	$16/ton usage weekly = 480 tons Max = 960 Min = 160	—	—	General
Marble No. 3	$18/ton usage weekly = 144 tons Max = 270 Min = 54	$19.80/ton usage weekly = 540 tons Max = 900 week Max = 2700 month	—	$14/ton delivered tonnage weekly <180 to interim stockpile
Granite aggregate No. 5	—	$9.60/ton Min = 240 week Max = 320 week	$11.20/ton Min = 128 week Max = 256 week Max = 480 month	Under 100 tons delivered at $14/ton or Freight at $8/ton

FIG. 18–21 Product costs, sources, and commitments

Haul Description	Distance in miles	Driver cost per load	Loading & unloading time	Average speed in transit	One-way running time	One-way total time	Turn around time	Operating cost per mile	One-way cost	Operating two-way cost
1 Feldspar Q_1 to Sp_1	30	$8.00	80	45	40	120	160	$0.20	$6.00	$12.00
2 Marble No. 3 Interim to Sp_2	20	$8.00	80	45	27	107	134	$0.20	$4.00	$8.00
3 Marble No. 3 Interim to Sp_3	40	$9.00	80	30	80	160	240	$0.20	$8.00	$16.00
4 Granite No. 5 Q_3 to Sp_4	15	$7.00	80	30	30	110	140	$0.20	$3.00	$6.00
5 Granite No. 5 Q_3 to Sp_5	20	$7.00	80	45	27	107	134	$0.20	$4.00	$8.00
6 Granite No. 5 Q_4 to Sp_4	30	$8.00	80	30	60	140	200	$0.20	$6.00	$12.00
7 Granite No. 5 Q_4 to Sp_5	30	$8.00	80	45	40	120	160	$0.20	$6.00	$12.00
8 Marble No. 3 Elliston to N. Columbus	120	$24.00	80	45	160	240	400	$0.15	$18.00	$36.00
	(a)	(b)	(c)	(d)	(e)	(f)	(g)	(h)	(i)	(j)

FIG. 18-22   Haul descriptions

This particular product is also widely used by both large and small users on a pickup basis. This type of business is usually accepted on a first-come, first-serve, as-available basis. But Sneed usually has at least seven day's notice. While price is negotiated on large orders (that is, orders over 100 tons), smaller orders are offered at approximately $14.00 a ton, in increments of 20 tons only, delivered, or $8.00 a ton for local hauling that is less than 30 miles distance.

Figure 18–21 gives the source of products and costs respectively, as well as the defined contractual commitments and the general price structure for non-contractual situations.

Figure 18–22 gives the various haul combinations. While trucks have different capacities for each product, as well as differences in basic cubic foot capacity, it has been determined that loading and unloading time is not appreciably affected by these considerations. Since the trucks are "belt" loaded and automatically dumped, it has been found that the major segments of time are related to two other areas which will soon be investigated. These two areas are: (1) queue time, waiting to be loaded; and (2) paperwork time. The latter is associated with authorization by the company (Sneed), the quarry, and, more significantly, the receiver.

Though the trucks differ in size, weight, and driver characteristics, it has been found that the highway route and time-of-day are the crucial factors in determining average miles per hour. Certain customers are hauled exclusively over four-lane highways. The estimated m.p.h. may reflect more accuracy than is merited but these have been observed transit times with a limited sample. It also appears, according to the company, that these may be conservative estimates if traffic tickets are any indication.

The one-way haul time is the sum of the loading and unloading time. This figure is defensible logically since the delivery of a product must of necessity incur both times. The turn-around time, however, is not so defensible since the reload point may not be the immediately previous loading point.

It is customary for the drivers, having been assigned their initial haul for the next day, to proceed to the appropriate load point prior to their normal business hours. They do this, in large part, because their pay is on a per-load basis and they want to get an early start. Thus, the initial transit time to a load point and the transit time after work are not considered in the available time per day. Essentially, deliveries are made from 7.00 a.m. to 6.00 p.m. or later. A quarry's open time, or to a lesser extent customers' open time, govern the time span for deliveries. In this case, all three source facilities start loading at 7.00 a.m. and will not load after 5.00 p.m.

With regard to the turn-around time, specifically that component involved on the return trip, it is assumed that the truck returns to the same load point. There is one clear exception to this and that would be the long haul to Elliston. The basic assumption supporting this approach is that since there are only three loading points, trucks hauling from any one of the three would continue to do so, at least for the remainder of that day. Additional support for this assumption is that the special-products customers (that is, those for feldspar and marble) are physically closer to a source of granite (Tyler) than to the source of their products. Thus, the return distance, if not the time, may, on the average, be less if a different reload point is required. This particular problem is to be investigated using simulation techniques.

Finally, in Fig. 18–22 an operating expense is indicated. This expense has been determined as relative to travel mileage. As previously noted, the costs for operating

| Unit | Load Capacity | | | Description | Relative load capacity | | | Available time | | |
	Product 1 feldspar	Product 2 marble	Product 3 granite		Product 1	Product 2	Product 3	Hours Daily	Hours Weekly	Minutes (weekly)
Truck 1	20	18	16	Aluminium body (fixed)	1	1	1	10	55	3300
Truck 2	0	22	20	Steel body (fixed)	0	$1\frac{2}{9}$	$1\frac{1}{4}$	10	55	3300
Truck 3	0	22	20	Steel body (fixed)	0	$1\frac{1}{9}$	$1\frac{1}{4}$	10	55	3300
Trailer 1	30	26	24	Aluminium body trailer	1.5	$1\frac{4}{9}$	$1\frac{1}{2}$	10	55	3300
Trailer 2	0	26	24	Steel body trailer	0	$1\frac{4}{9}$	$1\frac{1}{2}$	10	55	3300
Tractor 1	—	—	—	Pulls trailer 1 or trailer 2	—	—	—	10	55	3300
Tractor 2	—	—	—	Can be leased for $50 a day	—	—	—			

FIG. 18–23 Hauling capacities, Sneed Transfer Company

the trucks hauling rock are basically isolated, if one excludes management and certain overhead items. In this case, the costs considered determinable were gasoline, oil, tires, and minor repairs. Depreciation, and other expenses such as billing overhead, were excluded. Thus, the total cost figure will be incomplete. However, it was felt for purposes of this analysis, those costs are not fundamental to a decision since they will be incurred in any event; that is, they can be treated as fixed costs at least to the extent that they are incurred and unavoidable. For purposes of this analysis, the objective will be to maximize the profit which, as has been shown, is not profit in the accounting sense but rather revenues less appropriate cost elements. In this case, these cost elements will be: (1) driver cost, (2) materials cost, and (3) two-way operating costs. (From Fig. 18–22 these data are given in columns (b) and (j) and from Fig. 18–21 this is the source cost per ton times the number of tons per load.)

Sneed Transfer's hauling capacity is shown in Fig. 18–23. As previously noted, Truck #1 and Trailer #1 are the only units capable of carrying the feldspar sand. These same units can also carry the remaining products. The remainder of the units are restricted to the two aggregate products. Each of the two trailers can be pulled by Tractor #1, making at any one point in time a single unit. It is noted that, if necessary, a second tractor is available through a lease agreement at a cost of $50 a day.

In this analysis, it is clear that while any one load may be from zero to the maximum load, a load and its associated equipment are indivisible. That is, regardless of weight, a load requires one unit, either a truck or a tractor–trailer combination. Since the trucks or trailers have a different basic capacity, it seems necessary that capacity be expressed relative to some base. The logical base for each product is that unit which,

	Atwell-Otho Feldspar	Marble No. 3	Granger Products Marble	Granger Products Granite	City of West Ridge Granite
Minimum stockpile	8	3	6		NA
Maximum stockpile	48	15	NA	NA	NA
Daily usage	4	$1\frac{1}{3}$	6		
Weekly usage	24	8	30		
Weekly minimum				15	8
Weekly maximum			50	20	16
Monthly maximum			150		30
Starting inventory	12	5	30		

FIG. 18–24   *Requirements in load units, Sneed Transfer Company*

when fully loaded, has the minimum load (that is, the minimum maximum load). Figure 18–23 shows these relationships. It has been found, and generally agreed with these customers, that small variances in tonnage stockpiled are acceptable. More specifically a 12-ton variation from established limits is permissible. This particular fact is highly beneficial to Sneed Transfer since its effect is to allow full-load hauling. This allows the contractual requirements to be expressed in number of base loads per week, or day, or month, as appropriate. These are given in Fig. 18–24.

The information desired by Sneed is the optimal disposition of the various trucks throughout the week; that is, which truck should carry what product to which customer?

INDEX

INDEX